A Young Man *in the* Socialist Land

Growing Up in the USSR

Vladimir A. Tsesis

Palmetto Publishing Group
Charleston, SC

First Edition

Printed in the United States

ISBN-13: 978-1-64111-289-5
ISBN-10: 1-64111-289-1

Contents

There are two ways to live your life. One is as though nothing is a miracle. The other is as though everything is a miracle.

—Albert Einstein

Introduction

We live in the world of miracles. In our lives, miracles happen all the time: all that is needed is to bring them to our attention. Behind each significant event of our lives is hidden a chain of miracles—obvious and not so obvious. After all, the entire universe presents itself as an incomprehensible miracle. We know zillions of important scientific facts, but we still do not know who we are, where we're going, and where we came from.

CHAPTER 1

ESCAPE FROM DEATH

David Lamm, the second boy in the family, was born in the city of Beltsy in Moldova at the most unsuitable moment, on June 22, 1941, the day fascist Germany attacked the Soviet Union and initiated there a theater of World War II, a war that would take many millions of innocent human lives. David Lamm, as any newborn, belonged to the category of the most innocent human subjects of the war; the survival of children like him was nothing but a miracle.

His parents and their nine-year-old son, Victor—Vitya for short—were originally from Ukraine. Samuel Abramovich Lamm, Victor's thirty-five-year-old father, a regular officer of the Red Army, had participated in the annexation of the territory of Moldova on June 28, 1940. Subsequently, the Lamm family settled in city of Beltsy in Moldova, where they rented an apartment downtown. At the end of 1940, Ilana, who was two years older than her husband, became pregnant with her second child. A week prior to the beginning of World War II in Russia, the Lamms bought a house in the city of Beltsy and were ready to move in as soon as they repaired it.

Two movies produced in Russia in 1938, *Professor Mamlock* and *Swamp Soldiers*, informed Soviet Jews that Hitler's scumbags were bubbling with rage toward Jewish people and that the Jews could not expect any mercy from fascists. More than an ordinary citizen, as a Soviet officer, Samuel Abramovich realized that one of the most important objectives of fascist Germany was to clear Europe of the presence of Jews mercilessly, and he was convinced that Hitler would stop at nothing in achieving this goal.

On that day, the sounds of bomb explosions woke Samuel and Ilana at five o'clock in the morning. When they ran out on the balcony of their apartment, they saw a red haze on horizon from the unrelenting blasts and fires produced by German airplanes flying mostly over the city's airport. For the Lamms, the beginning of the war was not a surprise; nevertheless, they were terribly shocked by what they saw.

Amid the sounds of explosions of bombs and machine-gun bursts, Ilana Lvovna developed strong labor pains. For a moment, Samuel forgot about the war outside and concentrated on taking his wife to the city maternity unit of the First City Hospital, located two miles from the Lamms' house. Samuel's son was still asleep when Samuel, dressed in the uniform of a lieutenant of the Soviet army, ran out of his house to the nearby city square, where he hired a chaise, a predecessor of the taxi.

Back at the house, he woke up Victor and helped his wife get dressed, and then the family left the house at once. Under the explosions, smoke, and fires, the family reached the hospital in half an hour. Once Ilana was admitted to the hospital's maternity ward, a nurse on duty told the parents that, because of bombing, the hospital's patients were being relocated to an improvised bomb shelter in the basement of the building.

"We have a makeshift labor room in the basement, and Dr. Gandelman will take care of your wife there right away," the admissions nurse told Samuel.

"Dear Ilana, listen carefully to what I say, and do not forget a single instruction," Samuel told his wife before he and Victor left her, "First of all, I'm going to leave Victor in a safe place with the Pascals, our real estate agents who helped us to buy our new house. The Pascals own a second small house in Tsyganiya, in the south suburbs in the hills on the other side of the Kishinev Bridge. I'm sure the Germans won't bomb that area for now. Secondly, because I'm sure the war with Germany is in progress, I need to go to the *voenkomat* [military commissariat] to find out what military unit I'm assigned to. I'll do everything possible to visit you again. If I don't arrive, you have the keys to our both residences. If the military actions continue, return home with our newborn, pick up Victor from Pascals, pack up, and proceed to the railway station. At any cost, leave the city as soon as possible with our children and move as far east of here as possible. I'll try to see you again, but I can't guarantee it. Remember, that bloody monster Hitler transformed the Germans into merciless murderers. He's the greatest monster in the world; his scum will hunt every Jew they can put their hands on. I hope you have an easy labor, but after you deliver our child and recuperate, leave this city and move with our children far from the border as soon as you can."

From the hospital, Samuel Abramovich went to the home of the Pascals, with whom he left his older son. After that he headed to the military commissariat to find out about his military disposition.

Meanwhile in the basement maternity unit, Ilana's contractions were becoming stronger and more frequent, and soon an orderly brought her to the labor and delivery room. The delivery followed, and an hour later, Dr. Gandelman was holding in his hands a newborn, the first one born on the first day of the war. Immediately after the birth, the newborn at first refused to breathe, as if he hesitated to appear in a world filled with the winds of war. Dr. Gandelman did not share his hesitation. With a habitual motion, he slapped the newborn's buttocks. The piercing cry of a new life followed, overriding the sounds of the falling bombs and the airplanes' machine guns, as if they had forgotten about the war that was raging outside. For an instant, the medics who were present during the delivery exchanged the smiles that, from the time immemorial, accompanied the appearance of a new human life.

After the successful delivery, Ilana and her newborn were placed on an old iron bed in a damp and musty corner of the basement. After that, the tired "couple," mother and newborn, ignoring the new dramatic reality of a world suffused with hatred and killings, plunged into a deep sleep.

Samuel Abramovich had contacted the military commander three times since the war started, but each time, the decision about his military placement was delayed, which allowed him to visit his wife and his newborn son, who the couple named David in honor of his maternal grandfather.

On the morning after David's birth, Samuel ran to the Pascals' to take his son Victor to visit Ilana. Though the Pascals had taken good care of him, Victor, spoiled with parental love, had felt lonely and abandoned. At the sight of his father, he came to life and became himself. The Pascals' house was at least four kilometers from the hospital. As public transportation was not available, the father and son had to walk. There were no signs of war this morning; not a single bomb had exploded since they started their long walk. The city was peaceful, greeting the early pedestrians with tender rays of sun, the singing of birds, and tender touches of wind. This peace and quiet lasted until they reached the city park where at this early hour, many people were busy preparing for uncertain times. When Victor and his father got to the middle of the park, they heard the sounds of an airplane approaching.

"That's a German airplane," Victor's father said. "Don't worry, Vitya. Run with me to the bushes, sonny. Everything will be fine."

People fled for shelter in the scarce bushes, trees, and grassy ditches along both sides of the park alley. A minute passed; the German airplane flew in one direction and then returned along the park's main alley. The German pilot "entertained" himself by shooting random civilians of any age with a machine gun.

Victor, who was on the side of the road with his father, looked up at the sky and saw a sight he would never forget. The airplane flew above him at a low level; in the cabin, he could clearly see a German pilot on whose face was a broad smile of the satisfaction he derived from killing innocent people. At the sight of such inhumanity, Victor's hair stood on end, and he fainted. By the time he had regained consciousness, he was lying on the ground. Next to him were his father and adults who were unknown to him. They were trying to help him by holding his head up, fanning him with a newspaper, checking his pulse, and saying soothing words. The pilot who had derived pleasure from killing peaceful people had had enough "fun," and the airplane disappeared. The sadistic pilot who flew a technological miracle symbolized the evil that surrounded the actions of the fascist occupiers. Technology and morals are different things.

—

In times of peace, women who gave birth were supposed to spend seven days in the maternity unit with their newborn babies. During that time, other members of the family, including their husbands, were not allowed to visit them and their newborns in the hospital. However, during the war, many rules were temporary suspended, and Samuel and Victor were allowed to visit Ilana and David. Once again, Samuel reminded Ilana to flee the city with their children to the other side of the country as soon as possible. Ilana, who on the second day after the delivery was too tired to think about leaving the maternity unit, nevertheless assured him that as soon as she had restored her energy, she would do what he was suggesting.

—

Later in the morning, Samuel brought his older son back to the Pascals'. Solomon Pascal showered him with questions about the situation in the city and reassured him that he and his wife would take good care of Victor. Leaving his son with the Pascals, Samuel Abramovich hurried for another appointment with the military commander on Staro-Pochtovaya Street. He was on his way into the building, but a guard on the checkpoint at the gate of the metal fence told him that his visit had been postponed for an hour. To kill the time, he decided to have lunch. He hadn't passed one block when a new air attack began. Samuel was deafened and disoriented for a while from the violent bomb explosions. When he came to himself and looked in the direction of the military commissariat, he saw that the building he had left only minutes before, including the metal gates, had been entirely destroyed by a bomb. In the middle of the former building was a crater full of piles of bricks, debris, and glass.

Samuel ran back to the building and saw the dead body of the guard lying on the ground next to the former metal gates. If the guard had allowed Samuel to enter the building minutes before, he would not be alive now.

Deeply shaken up after this sad miracle of survival, Samuel headed to the other military commissariat building, located on Kanatnaya Street. On the way, another air attack took place. By midday, with his overcoat torn and dirty, Samuel finally reached his destination. This time he was lucky: the military commander, whom he knew well from the past, met him in the corridor and right away invited him into his office. The military commander, Major Anton Mironovich Mostovoi, had served with Samuel in the same infantry military unit in Taganrog, Ukraine.

Interviewing Samuel, Major Mostovoi asked him what his preference for military service was.

"It is entirely up to you, Comrade Mostovoi," Samuel answered. "I am an infantry officer, like you, so I suppose you will assign me to an infantry unit."

"Infantry is an easy choice, Samuel," Mostovoi answered, "but I remember you had some kind of education, didn't you?"

"Yes. I graduated merchandising school at Polonne in Ukraine. It was mentioned in my file in the military commissariat building to which I was assigned—the one that was just destroyed before my eyes."

"Forget about your file. I know you, and I believe you, officer. Listen, this morning I received a request for a quartermaster at a military engineers unit. I think with your education you ideally suit this position."

"Thank you, Comrade Major, but I know almost nothing about these kinds of responsibilities," Samuel objected. "I doubt I would be good in this position."

"Don't make me laugh, Samuel," the major protested. "Believe me; in the future you will thank me. There is nothing special in this new specialty. All that's necessary are dedication and creativity, and you have them both. As a fringe benefit, you will never be hungry; you will have alcohol and tobacco at your disposal. It appears to me that we're facing a long and bloody war, and you will be useful as a quartermaster at the military engineering unit.

"Take my assignment order: in two hours, you must appear at the unit I assigned you to. The four-two-oh-eighth bridge-engineering battalion is a specialized unit; they're now located near the airport. The Germans destroyed all the planes, so the airport practically doesn't exist. However, the engineering unit is intact. Go there right away."

"Comrade Major, I have a special situation: my wife just gave birth to our son. Allow me to visit her and to say goodbye to them."

"I'll give you two hours. That's plenty of time if you hurry," the commander responded and parted with Samuel.

The words of the military commander were prophetic: in the position of quartermaster during the war, Samuel Abramovich participated in many combat actions and received high military awards. He was also good at providing members of his unit with ammunition, living quarters, and nutrition. He was wounded twice, but four years later, at the end of the war, he was still alive and well.

Before joining the assigned military unit, Lamm had time to visit his wife; to see his older son he could not. In the hospital, he found Ilana and their son where he had left them: on a narrow bed in the labyrinth of the basement corridors. Holding David to her chest, she was breastfeeding him.

At the sight of the husband, she put their son aside and firmly embraced Samuel. When he told her that he was on the way to his military unit, she began to cry. Samuel comforted her, assuring her that eventually, everything would be fine.

"How is our son?" Samuel asked Ilana.

"He's fine, don't worry, but I'm very frightened. I'm worried about what will happen with you. I really don't know how we're going to survive with you at the front and me with two children, one of whom is just a newborn. I'm still weak, and I don't know when I'll be able to leave the maternity unit. How will we survive all these bombings?"

"We will survive. I guarantee you, my dear. The main thing is that, as soon as you perk up, do exactly what I told you before. I'm in a hurry to get to the military unit where I'll be a quartermaster. The Germans are continuing to bomb our city, and the city is still on fire, but the area of hills where the Pascals live looks as if the war hasn't started there yet. Vitya is waiting for you to pick him up. The sooner you can leave the city the better. The Germans or Rumanians could occupy city of Beltsy very soon. We are too close to the border.

"I heard on the radio that the state is going to organize a center to help people find each other. Hold these keys: they are to our residencies; and here are all the important documents I could find in our apartment. We don't have much money left after we bought our new house, so I can only give you two hundred and fifty rubles; I'm keeping only twenty-five rubles for myself. Keep the documents and money safe. I think the best choice for you will be to go to Dnepropetrovsk [now Dnepr, Dnipro], where my older brother Aron lives with his family. They'll help you. If by chance I happen to be in

Dnepropetrovsk, I'll meet you and our children there. Remember, I love you and our kids more than anything in the world. Be strong and believe me; everything is going to be all right. We are going to win. Our country is strong, and our army is the best. This war shouldn't last too long, and we're going to be together soon. Remember, you're a strong woman, and you're the one who's saving our family. And now I must run."

"Samuel, take good care of yourself and never forget us. Don't worry. I'll do my best to save our family. As soon as we settle, I'll try to find you. Come here and give our son and me a farewell kiss."

The spouses firmly embraced each other for a short time. Ilana was wiping away tears while her husband stepped resolutely toward the exit.

"Try to be safe, Samuel," Ilana said. "I'll take good care of our family. Be merciless toward our enemies; you are fighting for us."

Samuel nodded his head and left the room.

Unexpectedly, on the third day after delivery, Ilana miraculously felt a huge surge of energy when she woke up in the morning. She decided to leave the hospital immediately. After cleaning her newborn son and breastfeeding him, she had a breakfast consisting mostly of food that her husband had brought her yesterday. After that, she put all her modest possessions in a bundle and asked the nurse to return the clothes in which she arrived at the hospital.

The nurse responded that this was impossible as the clothes were locked up in the closet, and the housekeeper of the unit had the only key. Yesterday, a bomb had partially destroyed the housekeeper's home. They hoped that she would arrive in the afternoon.

"Besides that," continued the nurse, "your baby is too young to be signed out of the hospital. It's dangerous for you to leave the hospital for another four days."

"Dear nurse, thank you for your advice, but you forgot what's going on outside. My husband, an officer, is on his way to the front, and my nine-year-old son is living with strangers far from here. I am Jewish, and the Germans or Romanians will kill us right away. It's a question of life and death. Please don't fight my request."

"OK, OK, calm down, woman," the nurse answered in a conciliatorily tone. "I understand you; I am the mother of four children myself. Please don't be upset with me. I sympathize with you. Go ahead, leave the unit with your baby, but remember, I know nothing about your decision. I will give you an additional supply of medical necessities, my own kerchief, a spare pair of shoes, and one extra hospital gown. It's not too much; hopefully, you'll be able to get what you need soon. The world is not without good people. Take good care."

It was eight o'clock in the morning when, during a lull between bombing attacks, the young mother dressed in two hospital gowns and left the hospital to start the long trip to freedom from human cruelty. In her arms, she held her peacefully sleeping newborn son, born at an inopportune time, and a small bundle made of a handkerchief, which contained all her documents and money.

June 25 was a sunny and pleasant day. A nice breeze was blowing, birds were joyfully chirping, and only the destroyed houses on both sides of the road reminded a pedestrian about the current war. The powerful subconscious maternal instinct to protect the life of her family gave Ilana an unexhausted pool of energy; she felt that she could move mountains to achieve her goal. Her mind was clear and sober, and she realized that in order to reach the outskirts of the city, where her older son, Victor, was hiding, she needed help. Dressed in a hospital gown with a child in her arms, she presented a strange appearance, but there was a war going on, and during such horrible events, people's main objective is survival. On Leningradskaya Street, she asked a soldier where she could find the military commissariat office. He answered that it was on Kanatnaya Street and told her how to find it. Following his directions, dressed in hospital gowns, with her newborn son in her arms, she soon reached the office of military commander.

"Comrade Commander, my name is Ilana Lvovna Lamm," she said to the military commander." My husband is an officer. His name is Samuel Lamm. In my arms I'm holding our newborn son, who is only three days old. I don't know where my husband is now, in barracks or on the way to front. Please help me. I want to leave Beltsy immediately and travel as far from the border as possible. The problem is that while I was in the hospital, for safety, my husband placed our nine-year-old son, Victor, with people who are practically strangers on the outskirts of Beltsy, in the Tsyganiya suburb. I am a very exhausted, and every minute for me is now precious. Please, can you send your soldiers to find my older son, Victor, and bring him here? I delivered my son only three days ago, and I can't do it myself as I'm still bleeding. Please, help me Comrade Commander."

To her unfeigned surprise, the commander gave her a smile.

"Calm down, woman," he said. "I understand your problem. Don't worry. We'll help you; we'll do whatever is necessary to find your son. My name is Major Mostovoi. I'm smiling because just yesterday I spoke with your husband. I am the one who assigned him a quartermaster position. I know Samuel Abramovich well; he was under my command at the Taganrog military base."

The commander left the room and returned with three soldiers. Ilana, as best as she could, explained to them where they could find Victor. When the soldiers left, she found a secluded corner in the hall, where she fed and changed her younger son. Ilana was becoming more and more nervous: time passed, but the soldiers did not return. Another ten minutes passed, and she began to shake: what would happen if the soldiers were not able to find her son?

Luckily, she was wrong: after another twenty minutes, the door to the room swung open, and three soldiers entered with an expression of fulfilled duty on their faces. One of them was holding Victor by his hand.

"Here is your son, Mom," he said. "It was difficult to find him in that part of the city, but eventually we located him."

Victor ran toward his mother and tightly embraced her with tears in his eyes.

A load has been taken off Ilana's mind; her older son was found. Before leaving the military commissariat, she knocked on the door of Major Mostovoi's office. Receiving permission, she entered the office with both children and thanked him for his help.

"Never mind, Ilana Lvovna," the major answered. "I'm glad we found your son. What are you planning to do now?"

"I need to go to the railway station as soon as possible, and from there, I'll do my best to get out of the city on any available train. I'm afraid of the Germans, and I'm going straight to the railway station. I don't have time to visit the house. I must save my children. I know you understand me."

"You're doing the right thing, Ilana Lvovna. I will help you, as the railway station is located too far from here. You've already waited too long while we were looking for Victor. Lucky for you, one of my trucks will be running in your direction, so you'll get there much sooner. I'm sure you're hungry, so keep this package: it's one day's worth of officer food rations, and here are twenty rubles from my budget. Farewell!"

Ilana, who had eaten hardly anything that day, accepted the precious gift with gratitude. Before leaving the building, she took a piece of bread out of the package. She gave part of it to Victor and took another for herself. Both ate the food greedily, picking up the falling crumbs. Ilana carefully packed the rest of the food for later. Who could know what might happen next?

When the truck arrived, Ilana and the newborn sat in the cab, while Victor climbed up into the body of the truck.

—

An avalanche of civilians was fleeing from the troops of German aggressors. At the railway station, Ilana saw a mass evacuation of thousands and thousands of civilians, whose flow would multiply with every day. People with luggage, mostly sacks of all sizes, took each nook and cranny of the railway station, while Ilana was practically empty handed. All the ticket counters were closed.

"Where can I buy a ticket?" Ilana asked a railway agent, a man in a uniform she recognized by the red top of his hat.

"You don't need tickets, citizen," he answered. "It's wartime. Take any train that moves eastward. It's a first-come-first-serve situation, but I see you are with children. All the trains are overcrowded, but I'm sure in your particular case, with children, especially with your baby, people will let you in."

"Comrade agent, how can I get to the city of Proskurov [now Khmelnitski]? It's close to the town of Tcherny-Ostrov. My husband, an officer, recommended that I go to Dnepropetrovsk, but I think it's better for me to go to Tcherny-Ostrov, where my mother lives. I'll spend time there with her and my relatives, they will me, and then I will make a decision according to the circumstances. I think it's a good choice. Please tell me, what should I do?"

The agent on duty pulled a train schedule out of his pocket and told Ilana that there was a possibility that, at one o'clock in the morning, a passenger train would pass in the direction of Kotovsk station, where her family could transfer to a train that would take them to Proskurov.

In a month, Ilana would learn that it was another nine days before Romanian and German troops entered the city, but she never regretted leaving earlier because otherwise, she would have been among an enormous number of refugees, which could have prevented her successful exodus from the burning city. Later she found out that Romanian and German security forces had killed or deported most of the Jews in the city of Beltsy as well as the entirety of Bessarabia, a region in Eastern Europe, bounded by the Dniester River on the east and the Prut River on the west. Only about two hundred Jews remained in all of Bessarabia.

At the time when the train to Kotovsk was expected to arrive, a large crowd of refugees gathered on the platform. All of them had suitcases, bags, and sacks in their hands. Only Ilana, dressed in two hospital gowns, was practically empty handed. Holding David and the package in her arms and holding Victor by the hand, she approached the crowd when the train stopped. It was the first time she learned that people remain people in any circumstances. She did not say a single word, but a tight group of people parted in front of her, allowing her to reach the steps to the railway car.

Later, after almost five thousand kilometers of travel across the territory of the Soviet Union was over, Ilana, recollecting her numerous adventures during the long trip, never failed to mention that it was not she who saved her family, but her younger son, David. The newborn was an unwritten pass protecting the entire family. Whenever people saw a woman with a small baby, a creature with rosy cheeks and red lips peacefully settled in the package, they showed their best human qualities and allowed his mother to find a place in the security of the railway car.

"Citizens, allow the mother with the baby to pass." This phrase accompanied the Lamm family during the entire trip.

Even in such dramatic situations as Ilana was in with her children, an insightful observer could find an element of a miracle: after all, the hero of the story was born in the right place and at the right time. In the right place because David was born among people with good hearts and at the right time because, if not for him, it was unlikely that a young woman with her nine-year-old son could have safely completed her 4,500-kilometer run among the hordes of frightened people in the chaos of war to sunny Uzbekistan.

Thanks to being first to enter the railway cars, Ilana quickly managed to find relatively comfortable places for her family on a bench or on the floor. There she cleaned and fed her children, and the moment the overcrowded train departed, her family was in deep and refreshing sleep.

When Ilana woke up in the morning, she could see a beautiful and peaceful view through the window; the train had moved far away from the front line, producing an impression that the war had never started in the country.

The train reached the Kotovsk station on a glorious morning. The mother left the train with her children and headed to main railway building. She was pleasantly surprised to see tables and chairs on the platform; the country had reacted to the war with many compassionate actions. Plates of free hot food stood on the tables waiting for the refugees. Another feature simplified David's mother life tremendously. It was an important element of civilization that helped make traveling with a newborn baby much more comfortable: not only this station but all others—small or large—had *кипяток* (hot water) available, which, among other things, helped provide satisfactory hygiene for homeless people. Ilana Lvovna and Victor cheered up especially after they had a wonderful three-course hot meal for the first time in several days: borscht, cutlets with mashed potatoes, and compote.

At the Kotovsk station another event that could be interpreted as a miracle happened, which saved the lives of the Lamm family.

Finishing their food with a new supply of energy, Ilana and her children went to the information kiosk where an agent with a red-topped cap on his head was on duty. He opened the small window of the kiosk when she knocked on it. Briefly explaining her situation to him, Ilana asked him when she could take the train in direction of the city of Proskurov.

The railway agent belonged to a category of those who walk with God, those who have an inner drive to help people. He opened the window wider.

"Dear woman, think what you're doing," he said to her. "Obviously, you don't know what's happening. According to newspapers, radio, and other media sources, the Germans are advancing in the direction you want to travel. Forget about the city of Proskurov; the Germans will be there soon. Don't even think of going there, especially with your baby. Listen attentively: at noon, we expect a train to Dnepropetrovsk. Take it. I can't be with you at that time, but I will give you a special pass. It will allow your family to be among the first to board the train. It also entitles you to bread on board the railway car."

The railway agent's words were prophetic. If not for him, Ilana and her children would not be alive. Years after the war ended, in 1950, the Lamm family visited Tcherny-Ostrov. During the visit, Ilana was able to appreciate the value of her guardian angel's advice at the Kotovsk station. A terrible fate would have awaited her family if she had not listened to him. Indeed, during her visit, she learned that the Germans occupied Tcherny-Ostrov in early July of 1941. Very soon, along with local Ukrainian police, German special forces murdered, among other members of the Jewish population, about thirty members of Ilana's extended family. German soldiers raped her younger sister, Clara, a military nurse. Ilana's seventy-year-old mother, witnessing this horror done to her daughter, grabbed a knife and stabbed one of the rapists to death. For this heroic deed, a German officer sentenced the old woman to death by hanging. By the time the sentence was carried out, her daughter's defender had lost her mind, which did not prevent the punishment. The word *mercy* was absent from the dictionaries of German fascists, who belonged to the people who gave humanity Bach and Beethoven, Schiller and Goethe.

For Ilana and her children, boarding the train to Dnepropetrovsk was very easy thanks to the pass provided by the railway agent.

Moreover, during this leg of their travel, the Lamm family had an opportunity to sleep not on the floor but on the berths.

The train that the Lamms boarded was relatively comfortable, and according to Russian tradition—which continues to this day—the conductor provided the family with glasses of tea with a small piece of lemon. Enjoying a hot glass of tea and a piece of bread, Ilana remembered the nightmare of previous days and began to cry uncontrollably. Here she was: almost naked, without her husband, and with all her possession lost, but despite all of that, she was with her children on the moving island of civilization. She thought there was a chance that she and her children would survive the war and her family would return to normal life. She decided that nothing could stop her efforts to save the lives of her family.

The train reached Dnepropetrovsk in early morning. From the Inquiry Bureau kiosk at the railway station, Ilana learned that Aron Abramovich Lamm, her brother-in-law, lived about three kilometers from the railway station. After a long walk with children, a tired Ilana eventually reached the house of her close relative. It was one story, a typical not-large urban dwelling with a small garden in the back. Aron Abramovich's wife, Frieda Davidovna, opened the door of the house. Like Ilana, she was in her midthirties. She didn't recognize the woman with two children who stood before her in hospital gowns.

"Who are you?" she asked, "I already gave alms for refugees today. Go your way."

"Frieda, don't you recognize me?" Ilana asked in Yiddish, having difficulty holding back tears.

"Oh, Ilanochka, I'm so sorry. Indeed, I didn't recognize you. What happened to you? Are you a war refugee? I see you have a baby. Congratulations."

"Thank you, Frieda. This is my newborn son. His name is David. He was born on the first day of the war. As for Victor, you saw him two years ago. Frieda, we're running away from the German offensive. They're probably already in Beltsy," Ilana explained. "I left the hospital without waiting for discharge, and I was in such a hurry, I didn't have time to go home to change. That's why I'm wearing such strange clothing. I left Beltsy with the children, my documents, a piece of bread, and two potatoes. I have nothing with me. I was lucky that my Samuel at least provided me with important documents. "

The entrance door opened wider, and Ilana's brother-in-law Aron Abramovich Lamm appeared in the threshold. Aron was five years older than his wife. Holding his hand was their six-year-old son Michael, who was slightly shorter than midheight, with a serious expression on his handsome face. Ilana knew that Aron worked as a teacher at a chemical college. It was obvious that he had overheard part of the conversation.

"Ilanochka, dear, come in. Welcome. Congratulations on your new child! What a pity he was born at such a terrible time! Tell me, what's going on with my younger brother?"

"What else could happen to him? He went to the front. I suppose he might be somewhere on regrouping, but, actually, I have no idea where he is. I left Beltsy three days ago and came here by two trains. Your brother, when he saw me the last time, said I should come to Dnepropetrovsk to live with you, and here I am."

"Of course, of course," Aron answered. "Come in. Use my son's bedroom and make yourself at home."

Ilana was happy to reside with her close relatives. Frieda was about the same size as her uninvited guest, so, at last, Ilana could get rid of her hospital gowns and instead dress in regular civilian clothes.

A nice family meal followed after the guests washed up. After the meal, during which its participants exchanged what news they had about the war situation, both families went to sleep.

While Ilana was preparing to go to sleep with her children, through the thin partition of her room, she could hear sounds of a hot discussion between her brother-in-law and his spouse, but after the chaos of the last three days, she was tired and fell asleep right away. Her tired children were also quiet and content for the entire night.

In the morning, the family sat around a table covered with a white tablecloth. During the meal, the adults resumed their discussion of current events. At the end of the breakfast, Aron cleared his throat and told Ilana that he has something important to say to her.

"Do not be offended, dear Ilana," Aron started, "but you must understand that at this critical time, we have to think about not only the survival of your family but mine as well. Unfortunately, the morning news is not too good. The Germans are advancing on all fronts. Yesterday you told us yourself that according to my brother, Nazis are merciless killers and bloody monsters. Late last night, Frieda and I decided that we should think about evacuation. The college where I teach plans to move east from here, and as a teacher, they want me to follow them. Fortunately, relatively speaking, we have enough time. Please don't misunderstand me, Ilana, but Frieda and I have an obligation to our own family, and we sincerely wish you the best.

"Yesterday, Frieda and I thought you could stay with us as long as it is necessary, but today we think that staying with us will do you no good. We think that it will be much more beneficial for you to go with your children to a refugee center. One of these centers is located on Korolenko Street, not too far from where I once taught. There you'll be part of the state-supported refugee program, and without a doubt, with your newborn child, they will evacuate your family as soon as possible. You are in dire straits now, so here are thirty rubles for you. We don't think you need additional clothing because if they see you better dressed and with some luggage, they might not believe you are a true refugee. Don't tell them that you have relatives—they'll refuse to accept you and will send you to us. I know for a fact that in those refugee centers they provide the refugees all necessary help for evacuation."

"So you want me to leave your house. Is that what you want?" Ilana asked incredulously.

"Yes, Ilana, we want you to leave us as soon as possible. This morning, I went to the market near the refugee center, and an acquaintance of mine told me that it's not filled yet, so they'll provide you with all necessities there. It makes sense to go there with your children while the center is not yet overcrowded. You will be under state care there."

"Aron, for the sake of my newborn, can you allow us to spend another couple days in your house? I doubt the refugee center will have all the conveniences that you have in your house. Allow my family to be with you for a couple of days more," Ilana tried to plead.

"Forget about this house." Aron raised his voice. "We are on our way to leave the city ourselves, and you ought to clear the premises. In the remaining time before the evacuation, we need to sell our house and our furniture and do many other things. I'm sure you don't want my family to leave our home naked and barefoot as it happened to you. The way I recommend acting is in the best interests of both our families. Besides, before I leave Dnepropetrovsk with my college, the authorities might mobilize me for civil works. Let's not delay and depart right now, Ilana."

His sister-in-law was silent. Nothing she could say could change her relative's demand "to clear the premises." She felt betrayed.

In a short time, Ilana was on her way with David in her arm, holding Victor by the hand. Aron, who "graciously" offered to accompany her to the refugee center, carried her small sack of documents, money, and some clothing given to Ilana by Freda.

On this pleasant summer day, it was impossible to believe that only several hundred kilometers away, the war raged and thousands of people were killed. After a nice and refreshing rest at Aron and Freda's house, thirty-five-year-old Ilana was fast and resolute. Though she never forgave her brother-in-law's stance she experienced that day, she thought he might actually be right: it probably would be better for her to be among companions in misfortune. There, she would be better understood, and—being a part of an organized system of resettlement of the victims of the war—her family would be better taken care of.

The walk to the refugee center took thirty minutes. Before the group entered the building, Aron left them because, as he said, it would be better for Ilana's family if the center did not know that Ilana had local relatives.

Even before Ilana opened her mouth, refugee workers greeted her and her children with sincere enthusiasm.

"As you are the first here in our center with a very young child, we will provide you with a separate room on the first floor, dear," said a young worker with red cheeks.

Immediately after registration, the family was shown the assigned room, which was small but clean, with high ceiling. The only furniture in the room was a table, a chair, two beds, and a bedside cabinet. The washroom and the kitchen were in the corridor, not far from the room. After a short time, a nurse brought personal hygiene items for Ilana.

How lucky I am, Ilana thought while she was breastfeeding her little son. Only yesterday, in her wildest dreams she could not have imagined she might have a separate room and be surrounded with nice caring people. Now she was in a safe haven, not hungry, and far from mortal danger.

The next morning, Victor was playing in the corridor with his new friends and Ilana was breastfeeding little David, whose appetite was outstanding, when somebody knocked on the door. She opened the door and let in three unexpected visitors, who introduced themselves as the Zhukov family. The mother's name was Yulia, and her two daughters were Raisa and Zoya. They were volunteers who offered to take over patronage of the Lamm family. They brought clothes for Ilana's family, books for Victor, and the most precious thing: a small tub, where an hour later David had his first real bath. Subsequently, almost every day until the last day of the Lamms' stay in Dnepropetrovsk, the Zhukovs, more guardian angels along her way, did all they could to help Ilana.

One morning Ilana remembered that her younger son still did not have a birth certificate: in the nightmare of first days of war, there was no opportunity to obtain it. Accompanied by the Zhukovs family, she and the children went to the notary. Following the rules, the notary wrote on the David's birth certificate that he was born in Dnepropetrovsk, not in Beltsy. Thus, David became a legal citizen of Ukrainian Socialist Republic.

On the seventh day of the Lamm family's stay in the refugee center, the Zhukov family brought with them a used baby stroller, and both families went for a walk. When the group returned to the refugee center, Victor suddenly pointed in the direction of two men who were walking toward them. One of them was in an officer's uniform, and the other was in civilian clothes. Seeing them, the officer waved enthusiastically and began to run toward Ilana's group, something screaming as he ran.

The closer the officer got to the group, the more excited Ilana became: could it be her husband? Yes, it was he! With him was his older brother, Aron.

"Ilanochka, Ilanochka, it is me, your husband, Samuel!" She heard the familiar voice.

Yes, it was the one she had dreamed of seeing more than anybody in the world. Holding their newborn son with one hand, Ilana embraced father of her children. They kissed each other as if they hadn't seen each other for many years.

"Have you fallen from the sky, Samuel? How did you end up here? Look at your children!" Ilana almost yelled while her husband kissed their children.

"I can't believe it. Thank God, you're alive and well. I'm so happy," Samuel said. "My military unit is still in the process of regrouping. We were passing near Dnepropetrovsk, and the commander of my battalion allowed me to take twelve-hour leave to find you.

"First of all, I went to Aron, who told me that you decided that it would be better for you to stay in the refugee center. Don't worry about me; I'm all right. We were not involved in a single combat action yet. I hope that our superiors will send my unit to the front soon.

Let's go to your dormitory. I brought some good food for you and the children with me."

The unforgettable meeting lasted about two hours.

"If the Germans continue their offensive," Samuel said, "don't sit and wait. Throw all you have again and run to the east with the children as soon as you can. I don't have any idea what my address is for now. I won't have it until my unit settles down. The army told us that the government is organizing a state inquiry center, where family members will be able to find each other. Send letters there, and I'll do the same. Don't worry about me; I know that you and our children need me, so I'll stay alive. Trust me."

"Samuel, don't worry about Ilana and children. Frieda and I will do our best to make sure she has everything she needs," Aron, who had not visited Ilana once, interrupted.

"I'm sure you will," Samuel said, looking at him intently.

Ilana did not cry when she parted with her husband. She only wiped a tear or two when Samuel and his older brother left her. She knew she might never see Samuel again, but she had to concentrate now on her main responsibility, her children. The spouses parted outside the refugee center. Having no idea what the next day would bring, Ilana stood with both children in the middle of the street waving her hand to the gradually disappearing figure of her devoted friend, her husband, whom she might never see again. Victor stood next to his mother, wiping his eyes with his fists.

The next day the enemy's air raids became more frequent and longer; even without listening to the radio, it was clear that the enemy was advancing in the direction of Dnepropetrovsk. The refugee center employees assembled the residents in the main hall and told them to be ready to move on their own soon to the other side of the country. Three days later, the center informed the Lamm family and the most vulnerable refugees—the sick, the old, and women with children—that the next day they would be transported to the railway station, where each family or individual should choose their own evacuation route. The center promised to provide each of them with a certificate testifying that its owner was, indeed, a refugee who needed help in provisions of food, shelter, and transportation. The refugee center recommended that the refugees travel to the republic of Uzbekistan, where the climate was warm and conditions for resettlement promised to be the most favorable. The Zhukovs, who continued to visit the Lamms two or three times a week, approved such a recommendation.

"We can't accompany you, Ilana, as we must be at home tomorrow," Yulia Zhukov told her. "Write down our present address, and our neighbors will forward your letter to our new address," she said on departure.

Later, Ilana's letters never found the family that helped her so much in difficult times.

By now, thanks to the Zhukovs and the refugee center, Ilana had the necessary minimum of clothing for her children and herself. Though she was a rational woman, "for good luck" she took with her the hospital gown from the maternity ward where she gave birth to David. She decided to part with it only when she reached her final destination.

The next day, a truck brought the first group of refugees to the railway station. Formerly semioccupied, the station was now overflowing with a mob of people, most of whom carried luggage. The railway agent on duty told Ilana that in order to reach Andizhan, a large city in Uzbekistan, she should make her first transfer at the

Donetsk station. The first train to Donetsk was scheduled for afternoon, but because of the priority provided to military trains, the scheduled train to Donetsk direction was canceled. Later, air raids started, and the bombs were falling along the railway. All who were on the platform were looking for shelter. Fortunately, the air raid did not last long, and almost immediately, a multitude of people reappeared on the platform of the station.

Ilana had to wait in the main railway station hall until the next day for the train to Donetsk. At the end of the day, when Ilana heard the announcement of the train's arrival, she went to the platform with her children. People crowded together, trying to make sure they would be able to board the train. The majority of refugees on the platform had been waiting for a ride to Donetsk for two days. When Ilana approached the crowd with her two children, it didn't seem to her that she would be able to squeeze through the throng of closely pressed human bodies. However, here as well, before she said a word, she realized that people were parting before her like the sea parted before Moses and his people. In this challenging time, people continued the tradition of helping mothers with children. Hearing around her the familiar cries, "Let the woman with children pass," she soon found herself in the front of the crowd, on the edge of platform. The train to Donetsk arrived at 6:30 p.m. It consisted not only of regular passenger boxcars but a *teplushka* boxcar as well.

Boxcars as the main type of carriage on the Russian railways assumed a constructive possibility of its rapid conversion from a normal freight car to *teplushka* in 1917. (*Teplo* in Russian means "warmth" or "heat"). Since then, they were used for mass transportation of people, primarily troops and, if necessary, animals, up to 1953. *Teplushka* cars were equipped with two- or three-tier bunks. To insulate them from the outside, a layer of felt was used; the floor was made of two layers with the gap filled with sawdust. Doors and windows were also insulated, and a cast-iron stove stood in the center of the boxcar. One boxcar accommodated forty people, but during the war, the number of people in one car often exceeded sixty.

Its smokestack puffing and releasing steam, the train slowly approached the platform. In the expectation of the fight for embarkation, the crowd came as close to the edge of the platform as possible. The train stopped, and a conductor slowly opened the door of the car from inside while the railway agent on duty and a soldier with a rifle next to him squeezed their way toward the door of the *teplushka*.

The conductor of the railway car looked at a piece of paper he held in his hands and cried at the top of his lungs: "Comrades passengers, we are filled to capacity. Try other cars; we do not have a single opening here."

"You better tell me how many additional passengers you can accommodate." Having a soldier next to him, the agent on duty asked in a voice not expecting any objection, "Go and check. Quick."

The conductor disappeared and soon returned.

"We can accommodate no more than four people, and even this is too much for us."

"You will get five. Woman with two little children"—he addressed Ilana—"get in. And two more people, those who are pregnant, with children, or disabled, also get in."

Without objections from the passengers, Ilana and her children entered the *tepluschka*.

The appearance of a woman with two young children, one of whom was a little baby, could not be ignored by passengers of *tepluschka*, and very soon, a good soul invited the family to take a more or less comfortable position under the window of the car in the place that, in the freight car, was formerly boot side hatches.

After Ilana breastfed her baby, she and Victor ate the sandwiches she brought from Dnepropetrovsk, two slices of bread with a thin layer of margarine between them. In one of the corners of the car, Ilana found a luxury: a pile of straw. She scattered part of it on the floor of the car and covered it with all available shabby cloth for herself and her children. For a pillow, she used the hospital gown, her "security blanket."

In those days, priority in railway traffic belonged to trains with military personnel and military equipment, so the trip to Donetsk took much longer then it would have taken in peacetime, when the train could reach Donetsk in four hours. Now the train made long stops at big and small stations and, more frequently, just in the middle of the steppe. It took two days for the train to reach Donetsk. Passengers on train were not hungry: at any midsize and large railway station, tables with food were available on platforms. Mainly, the food for the transit passengers consisted of vegetable soups, though sometimes these soups contained pieces of meat, and a variety of porridges. Usual desserts consisted of *kissels*, fruit compote, and tea.

The flow of refugees was constantly increasing; when the family finally reached Donetsk, the entire platform of the station was full of so many people that it was impossible to find an empty space. The commandant of the Donetsk station told Ilana that, in order to reach Uzbekistan, she should first take a train to Volgograd (the former Stalingrad), which was expected to arrive at three o'clock in the morning.

"Don't worry about getting a seat in the train," he reassured Ilana. "People will always let women with young children into the car. I'm not just saying that; I see it daily."

Donetsk's railway station authority did everything possible to facilitate the large flow of refugees from the West. Operation Barbarossa, developed by Hitler and his henchmen, was similar to the plan Napoleon had designed before invading Russia in 1812. Both plans failed to take into account not only the heroism of the Soviet warriors but also Russian winters and the incredibly vast territory.

While fierce fighting was going on the Eastern Front, on the streets of Donetsk reigned peace and quiet. On arrival, Ilana and Victor had a three-course meal, simple but satisfying, served on the platform of the station. That was followed by a visit to the railway's showers. When Ilana and her family went outside, it was a pleasant warm day. After a short search, Ilana found a good place for rest: a shady grassy lawn in a small square next to the station. Lying on the warm and silky grass, the family had a refreshing rest.

Boarding the train to Stalingrad was uneventful except that by this time, railway military transport traffic had become much more intense, and Ilana's train made many more stops than during her previous trips. But with food and hot water available in railway stations, nobody was complaining.

—

Overall, the Lamm family's travel to Uzbekistan lasted more than a month. It was fortunate that the traveling took place during a warm season. If it had been winter, the trip would have been much more complicated. During the entire trip, Ilana observed that the majority of people she met spontaneously, without the intervention of the authorities, helped those who were weak and disabled to board the train and frequently shared their food and pieces of clothing with them. In the case of families like the Lamms, people universally demonstrated their human understanding of the plight of the young woman with little children. Ilana was satisfied that, though slowly, she was approaching her destination, which would allow her to save her children from the hands of Hitler's killers. The family slept in railway stations, on platforms, in freight cars, in *teplushka* and passenger cars, in the open air, and on the bare ground. Surprisingly, none of them, including the baby, ever got sick.

For Ilana, the time of the evacuation would be one of the most important events in her life. Many years later, when David was an adult, his mother never failed to tell him stories about the evacuation. Sometimes David would become bored with the repeated episodes. Only when he reached the age of his maturity was David able to understand the drama his mother had gone through when, without any special means except her will, she was able to conquer countless obstacles and save her children's lives. The thought of abandoning her children, as unfortunately happened with some women during the war, never entered her mind. The survival of her family would not have been possible without help of total strangers, who, performing obligations of their hearts, were able to rise above usual indifference and selfishness in those trying situations. The availability of free meals and hot water in stations allowed Ilana to save almost all the money she had when she left Dnepropetrovsk; she spent no more than fifty rubles, mostly for clothing and cloth diapers for her younger son. Cloth diapers were used, then washed and reused repeatedly many times until they were thrown away.

Ilana and the children traveled the last leg of the trip on a freight train. The family was fortunate that it wasn't raining; the sky was cloudless, and the days were dry and warm. The train arrived at its final destination, the Andizhan station, in the middle of night. Before Ilana left the car with her children, she made sure she had not forgotten anything onboard. The station was brightly lighted. While David and Victor were sleepy, Ilana was full of hope and high expectations. She easily found a clean and dry space on the floor of the railway station, and the family quickly fell asleep.

When Victor woke up, it was morning. He opened his eyes and looked at his mother. He could hardly recognize her. She was silent, but tears were running down her pale face. To his question about why she was crying, she answered that when she woke up, she had found that while they were sleeping, a thief had stolen all her money. In one moment, all Ilana's precious savings disappeared. Fortunately, the robber had not picked up the family's documents.

The railway agent Ilana complained to expressed his regret and told her that, at these difficult times, the station was full of pickpockets of all kinds. "Please be more careful in the future," he told. "Here, keep this." He removed his own wallet from his pocket, took out some money, and gave it to Ilana, who forgot her natural pride and accepted the gift so important for her.

"Bad things happen, woman, but everything will be OK. Welcome to Uzbekistan," said the agent before they parted. "Luckily for you, a group of refugees is gathered on the square in front of the station building right now. Go there with your children, and a special truck will take you to the local refugee center."

Indeed, an hour and a half later, a military truck arrived at the square. As had happened many times before, Ilana and the children were the first to be seated. Nobody protested when the driver offered to let Ilana and her children sit in the car's cab.

When the truck arrived at the refugee center, located in a former grammar school, the passengers sat on the benches outside and waited their turn. It was the end of an August day, when summer was still at its peak, which meant people didn't have to worry about outerwear—good news for those who were homeless and penniless. Ilana was able to forget about the recent loss of her livelihood; she was happy that she was now at a place where she would not be left without help. She was sitting on the bench with David on her lap, slightly tired and thin, but she was beautiful, with widely open brown eyes and her black hair waving in the wind. Hope for a good outcome of the tribulations of recent months returned to her. On her face was written the satisfied expression of a person who had achieved her goal. For the first time since the war began, she sang Russian and Ukrainian songs to her children.

It was three o'clock p.m. when the Lamm family was called for their interview. The refugee center's main hall reminded them of a disturbed noisy beehive; many people there had worried expressions on their faces. The future of many families and individuals was decided within the walls of this building.

The Lamms' caseworker was a middle-aged woman who performed her work with dedication and respect. She reacted with a genuine respect and sympathy to Ilana's story. All was smooth and promising until the caseworker asked Ilana to show her the document that would confirm that her husband was in the active military force. Ilana answered that she didn't have this document. The caseworker told her that until she received a document proving that she was the wife of the officer, she would not be entitled to enhanced food rations and financial help.

"Unfortunately, I can't help you now," she said. "But I heard on the radio yesterday that in Orenburg Province in Russia, in the city of Buguruslan, the state will soon open a central inquiry bureau that will help you find your husband. Meanwhile, don't be upset, everyone here respects a mother with an infant. Instead of putting you in the dormitory, as we do with many refugees' families, I can offer you a better opportunity. The room where you are going to live is small, but it is separate. You will have for your family a small but separate room. It will be your own place."

Another caseworker, a middle-aged woman, took the Lamm family to show Ilana where she was going to live with her children.

—

The promised dwelling was located several blocks from the refugee center on Trudovaya Street.

Ilana did not walk; she was flying. Finally, after more than two months of wandering in railway stations, freight boxcars, passenger cars, and *teplushka* cars, her family had the peace and quiet of a normal life in a world that had gone berserk.

The room Ilana's family was assigned to occupy had only yesterday served the owners of the apartment as a kitchen. The owner, the Gorbunovs, greeted Ilana with sincere hospitality. Thirty-seven years old and nice looking, Marya Petrovna Gorbunova was a remarkable woman who, in the ensuing years, would prove her natural kindness many times. Of average height and weight with pale skin, this woman had a tough feel about her. She had large, knowing blue eyes that radiated goodwill. Her straight black hair was pulled into a bun. Overall, she looked like an affable, kind, gentle, and affectionate woman.

Her husband, thirty-nine-year-old Anatoliy Petrovich Gorbunov, a qualified worker, had lost one of his eyes at the furniture factory where he had worked since he was young and was exempt from conscription. He also lost one of his fingers after a fall from a tree in his childhood. Anatoliy Petrovich was a tall, energetic, and athletically built man. People who did not know of his disabilities hinted to him that his place was not at the rear of the country but in the army. Both he and his wife did all they could to show their sympathy to those who suffered from the winds of war.

Marya Petrovna belonged to the category of people who are friends in need. During the times of national crises, such as revolution and war, it was a common practice in the Soviet Union to *уплотнять* ("make it more compact"): to transform large—in the eyes of authorities—private apartments into multiunit communal rooms. The original owners of the apartment, as a rule, were allowed to keep one or two rooms for themselves; new residents settled in the rest of the rooms of their residence. Communal apartments were nothing new in the Soviet Union. They were a norm before the war, and they still existed in many cities after the fall of the Soviet system in 1991. Many families could live in one former private apartment. Settling families of strangers in private apartments started in 1919, when the People's Commissariat of the RSFSR adopted health standards in housing. For example, housing in Moscow was divided into shares of ten square meters (for adults and children younger than two) and five "squares" per child from two to ten years. However, in

1924, regardless of age, a single rate of eight square meters (eighty-eight square feet) had been set.

In the first years of the Soviet rule and later, city councils were actively creating communal apartments, the primary motive being "to equalize the life of the workers and the bourgeoisie." Almost all male potential recruits in the big inner yard of the city block where the Lamms lived fought in the war. Marya Petrovna never complained about transforming her private spacious apartment to three communal rooms. She sincerely felt that it was her obligation to make a personal contribution during the war.

Ilana's family's room was very small, without any kinds of utilities, with one window that faced the terrace of the house. The room accommodated two metal narrow beds, a small table, one chair, and a small metal tub that served the bathing needs of all members of the family. The outside terrace, which encircled the back of the entire house, was a pleasant extension of the little room where the Lamms lived. For preparing meals, all the neighbors used wood-burning stoves. Each family was responsible for the procurement of their own precious wood. Water was available from a faucet in the middle of the courtyard. For lighting at night, everybody used *коптилка* (*koptilka*), a primitive oil lamp: a small jar with a wick in oil. This light, known from ancient times, was not bright enough for reading, so after dark people left their rooms, hot from the rays of the southern sun, and spent time outside, talking and drinking tea. Kerosene lamps were considered a luxury, and those few who could afford them brought them out on the terrace or into the yard where a primitive table stood for playing cards, dominoes, or chess. Nights on the latitude where the Lamms lived was pitch dark, with the vast sky lit by countless celestial bodies.

Marya Petrovna's tenants and neighbors had the opportunity to listen to her wonderful, intimate, and sweet voice. She was artistically talented, especially in performing old Russian romances and popular Russian songs, which she accompanied on her guitar. Ilana and Victor tried never to miss the chance to be present at her solo evening concerts. Under the influence of her voice, people temporarily forgot about war and all the adversities that had visited them in the recent months and years.

The small allowance that Ilana's family received from a governmental social agency was not enough for living needs. To provide for the family, Ilana began to work at a military factory where shells for the front were made. The family budget was miserable, and almost all their money was used for buying food. When Ilana went to work and Victor went to school, David was cared for on a voluntary basis by the neighbors, mainly by Marya Petrovna and her husband. In the afternoon, when ten-year-old Victor came home from school, he was David's main caregiver. In such an arrangement, little David learn how to be independent and to rely on his own mental and physical facilities. He was a contented child, and he was hardly ever sick; except for food, he did not ask for too much.

After returning from the factory, Ilana was always busy with household chores. Remembering the hell she had been able to escape from with her children and that her husband lived between life and death, she never complained. The short time left after household chores, Ilana spent with her children. The main staples of food for the family were different types of *kashas* (porridges). Nobody cared or worried about nutritional balance; the only objective for people during that period was simply to survive. In such circumstances, Ilana and her sons—especially the younger one—never suffered from a poor appetite and never refused from invitation to eat.

David spent most of his time outside. When he woke up, Ilana was already at work at the military factory. She worked long hours, and despite her efforts, she frequently did not have enough energy to spend quality time with her children. Before leaving for school, Victor fed David and then placed him in the shade of a tree in a small playpen, leaving him to be cared for by Marya Petrovna and other numerous residents of the big courtyard. With such a limited care, David's verbal communication was insufficient; for the first three years of life, he used words of his own invention. When he wanted to eat, he said "Me me"; for the word "ear," he used "leh"; for mouth, the word was "peh"; for nose, "su." The chronic hunger of the general population reflected particular badly on David's physical development.

During the war, *Narcompros* (the People's Education Commissariat) distributed food cards. These cards were important for survival, and people carefully protected them. Cards were issued for different food products, such as bread, cooking oil, potatoes, and sugar. Victor had an opportunity to receive additional small amount of food at school. Many years later, when the brothers became adults and were arguing, their mother never missed an opportunity to remind the younger brother that, during the war, his older brother had saved Russian-style pastry with jam, meat, or liverwurst from his school and shared it with David. Though David spent most of his time in the sunny outdoors, the lack of fat-soluble vitamins, specifically vitamin D, in his mostly carbohydrate nutrition resulted in his developing rickets. Because of this condition, he didn't begin to walk until he was three years old. Human beings, especially of young age, are flexible in their resourceful adaption to difficult life conditions; spending the first three years of his life crawling and communicating on his own language did not prevent David from having positive attitude toward life.

The local Muslim population liked both brothers. Following the Islamic variant of the biblical commandment "be fruitful and multiply," Muslim residents, men and women, suggested to Ilana on many occasions that for good money, they would adopt one or both of her sons, promising to make both of them good Muslims. Ilana refused to hear such offers, despite the family's miserable poverty and chronic hunger. She would not sell her children for any amount money in the world. After the war, when her children grew up and for some petty reason were giving her a hard time, she semi-jokingly reminded them to whom they should be grateful for their survival during the war.

—

In the middle of a hot Central Asian summer in Andizhan, two-year-old David was playing outside under the supervision of his older brother while Ilana was at work. Victor was involved in a lively conversation with his friend Aroshka. The conversation was so lively that Victor did not notice that his younger brother was energetically crawling on the grassy ground in search of adventure. While Victor's attention was distracted, David reached the *arik* (the irrigation canal), which in Central Asia is widely used for farming and landscaping. He did not pay any attention to the fact that he was on the edge of the *arik* and the next moment, fell in. The irrigation canal was not too deep, but it was deep enough for a small child to drown in it. Kicking his arms and legs and periodically producing loud noises,

David helplessly fought for his life. This story would have a sad ending if not for a local man, an Uzbek, a Muslim. Fortunately for David, his savior was passing by and saw a little child fighting for his life. He jumped into the *arik*, pulled the child from the water, took him in his arms, and—making sure the child was alive and well—yelled to Victor to take David back under his recently defective supervision. David never forgot that he owed his life to a Muslim savior.

—

Another bad accident happened to David on a warm and pleasant day. He was peacefully playing in a sandbox when he noticed an insect with eight legs and a tail curved over its back. The creature was crawling before him in the sand. David was too young to know that not all insects were funny and safe. Without hesitation, he extended his arm, picked up the insect, and began to examine it. The insect, which happened to be a scorpion, did not like such an impolite attitude and managed to bite the poor child's thumb with its strange-shaped tail. Soon David's thumb became red, swollen, and painful. He began to cry and crawled home, where he was taken care by Ilana. No other symptoms developed, but it was more than enough for David to limit his curiosity toward representatives of the insect world that were unknown to him. Fortunately, our hero had only localized signs and symptoms after the poisonous sting.

—

After the war, even young children spent their time outdoors unsupervised. Once, three-year-old David was playing with other children in a corner of the courtyard where his family lived, next to a place where neighbors threw away unwanted furniture. Squatting next to another child who was two years older than he was, David unexpectedly heard a loud cry—"Watch it!"—from the father of the child next to whom he sat.

This father had noticed that a large wardrobe standing in front of where the children were peacefully playing had lost its balance and slowly, as if it was hesitating, begun to tip forward. Then it collapsed and, with a deafening crash, fell down. The father of the child on whom the wardrobe fell and others who were around ran to lift up the heavy wardrobe. Expecting the worst, the father of the boy who was now under the wardrobe was shaking; his twisted face was as white as a sheet of paper. When the group successfully lifted the wardrobe, to their general relief instead of the expected horror, they saw unharmed children underneath it. Again, a miracle: the children were saved only because the old piece of furniture was without doors and without shelves. When it fell down, it covered children as if it was a big umbrella, not harming them at all.

—

All this time Ilana did not lose hope of finding her husband. The Central Information Bureau was officially opened in 1942, as was previously promised, far from the war zone in the Orenburg Province in the city of Buguruslan. Millions of Soviet citizens were sent to Komsomolskaya Street 6 with their passionate requests to find their close relatives. Ilana sent her requests to this organization five times a week. The future of the Lamms would have been completely different if not for existence of this unique organization. One day a very important person in a community where war refugees lived, the mail carrier, knocked at her door and handed her a gray envelope from the city of Buguruslan.

Shaking with excitement, Ilana opened the envelope, pulled the letter out of it, and learned from it not only that Samuel was alive and well, but also his field mail address. Victor had not seen such an incredible volcanic explosion of joy and happiness from his mother since the beginning of the war. The gray envelope that contained the letter became a keepsake in Ilana's family. In addition to her joy that her husband and the father of their children was alive, the Lamms now had the opportunity to receive additional rations for officers' families, which allowed the family to end their semi-hungry existence. Before long, all residents of the block knew the incredible news that Ilana's husband had been found. People came from all over the neighborhood to congratulate Ilana on the great news. Ilana and Victor's main hope now was that their husband and father would survive.

Early the next morning, Ilana and the children ran to the local agency and presented the letter she had received from Buguruslan. Thanks to the letter, the Lamm family became entitled to better financial and nutritional help. Finally, the semi-starvation period was over: even a modest addition to the family livelihood meant that the family would survive. In addition, officer Lamm had the right to send money to the family monthly, which meant that Ilana's family would definitely be able to survive during the war. Another major benefit was that from now on, Ilana could afford to take one day off from work a week to spend more time with her children.

A Nurse Tells David about Tcherny-Ostrov

The Second World War, as could be expected, rallied people, turning the society into one big family. The survival of Ilana and her family during her evacuation from Moldova to Uzbekistan had been possible thanks to numerous good deeds performed by many unknown people. However, as is well known, nothing in the world can be perfect.

Some unpleasant tendencies in the society could not be uprooted even in the time of historical events. Such was the persistent anti-Semitism in Eastern Europe. During the war, Victor attended a middle school for boys in Andizhan. Coeducation wasn't introduced in the Soviet Union until the 1950s. By Victor's appearance, it was impossible to determine to which ethnic group he belonged. Looking at him, it was impossible to see that he carried traits that anti-Semites ascribe to Jews. Furthermore, his status as the son of a military man made him more than equal among students, thanks to which his time at school was enjoyable and free of stress. This pleasant existence ended once and for all in September 1943, when he was a fifth-grade student.

In the Soviet educational system, it was a common practice to perform annual medical checkups in the pupils' classrooms. For this purpose, a medical commission consisting of physicians, nurses, and their assistants visited schools regularly. It was early November when such a commission came to Victor's class. The boys were called in alphabetic order, so Victor Lamm was among those who were examined in the middle of the checkup. In anticipation of the examination, which also included the inspection of intimate organs, the children of wartime stood in a row in front of the doctors and nurses.

Almost all of them were as thin as reeds with bones protruding from their skin and an angular configuration to their bodies.

The line moved slowly, but before long, it was Victor's time to be examined. The physical examination of each student was preceded by an interview with one of the two nurses, who were asking children questions about family history, allergies, and illnesses in the past. The nurse who was interviewing Victor was a woman in her fifties with black eyes, full lips, dark hair, and an expression of kindness on her face. When she learned from the list of the students Victor's first and last names, she opened her eyes wide and looked at him intently.

"So you are Victor or Vitya Lamm. Oh boy, oh boy! Tell me, Vitya, aren't your parents from a little town called Tcherny-Ostrov?" she asked, expressing a lively interest. When Vitya confirmed what she had just said, she brightened even more. The problem was that the nurse suffered from hearing loss, which made her speak unnaturally loudly, so loudly that anybody in the classroom could hear every word she said.

"Vitya, this is incredible," the nurse exclaimed, throwing up her arms. "You won't believe this, but I'm from the same town as your parents. You probably know that Tcherny-Ostrov is located next to the city of Proskurov. If you tell your mother my name, Shmushkevich Basya Israilevna, she will immediately recognize it. My family lived on the same street as your mother, Ilana Fikhman, and our families went to the same synagogue. I remember your grandfather Leo well. He was a ritual butcher, and he had a wonderful voice. He sang in the synagogue, and his Yiddish was beautiful! Would you believe, I was at your parents' wedding with my parents. Oh, what a wedding it was! Where is your dad now?"

"He's at the front. He fights Germans," Victor answered, blushing with embarrassment.

The unfortunate conversation was fateful for Victor. The class had not missed a single word of the conversation between Victor and the nurse, which allowed the of them to know "a terrible truth": that Victor or Vitya Lamm was a representative of the Jewish people.

"So you are Jewish," was the first thing that a student from Western Ukraine, who shared a desk with Victor, said to him when he returned to his seat.

"Come closer to me and show me your head," added a neighbor from the back with a malicious smile. "Let me take a good look at your little horns."

Some pupils of the class were laughing loudly with him.

Since then, whoever wanted to could taunt Victor without punishment, and until he left at the end of the war, his time at the school was poisoned by constant reminders of his belonging to an ethnic group ubiquitously abused in the Soviet Union. Victor was only one Jew in the class. Less than a quarter of the class was involved in the verbal abuse, but those who were actively involved did it on a daily basis, with gusto, and without consequences. For different reasons, schoolchildren hardly ever complain to their teachers; the idea of telling one of his teachers that he was being bullied never occurred to Victor. How could he know that the teacher he complained to didn't hide in himself a secret hostility toward the Jews? To physically fight his torturers, who by far outnumbered him, was also out of the question. The only strategy left for him was silence: the ability to show that the bullies did not affect him. Nobody knew what was happening in Victor's heart daily, how he suffered inside when derogatory words reminded him about his second-class citizen position as a child whose father fought at the front.

—

The countless mundane episodes of which our life consists, we gradually forget. Our long memories are like flashes that, like searchlights, highlight separate events that our minds forever imprint in our memory. These memories live and die with us. It is obvious that the episodes of our lives that we remember vividly have a special meaning for our psyches. They might appear sometimes to be nothing special on the outside, but there is in them, probably, something extraordinary if they become part of our permanent memory.

One such episode occurred with David when he was only three and a half years old. By then, he had learned how to walk and insisted on accompanying Victor wherever his brother planned to go. One night Victor decided to walk outside simply to breathe fresh air and yielded to David's insistence on accompanying him. It was a warm, mid-Asian, pitch-dark night when, holding his brother by the hand, Victor walked into the large courtyard to which their household belonged, following the light of a small bonfire in the distance. The moon had not yet risen, and the bottomless sky above their heads were strewn with innumerable stars. By the time they arrived, the bonfire was already gradually burning out. David had never seen a bonfire before, and standing around the dying fire with a small group of children, he was fascinated looking at glowing, slightly blinking flames and the smoldering pieces of wood. One of the boys picked up a dry twig from the ground and set it on fire from the bonfire's flickering flames. He held the twig in his hand while a thin tongue of flame flickered on the opposite end of it. This thin tongue of fire was gradually extinguishing, and all that was left was a glowing brilliant point. The same boy began to spin the twig. Thanks to the visual effect, the single moving spark transformed into magic kaleidoscopic figures of circles, ovals, figure eights, and ellipses. In contrast to the pitch-dark night around them, it appeared to David to be of incredible beauty. It took decades for David to understand why this became forever imprinted in the mind of little David. It was more than beauty that David experienced at this instant. It was more a feeling that here he was, a small child who, looking at the bright spark on the tip of the twig, could see its relation to the countless stars that shone at him from outer space. The world around him became united in one unit, and he was one who belonged to it. He yearned to share his discovery with Victor, but he was too young to be successful in expressing complex feelings; all he could say to Vitya were two words: "Great! True?"

—

All that is necessary to see amazing things around us is just to look for them. Sometimes a small event might appear to be a mundane experience, but on more careful contemplation, it could be something that has a deeper meaning.

Children who are lucky to live in well-to-do families receive toys from their parents or caregivers on the regular basis, while children who live in poverty frequently invent their own toys. One day Victor brought home from school such an improvised, self-made toy. It consisted of an empty Russian-style thread bobbin with a hole in the center of it. On one end of this bobbin was a rubber band secured by a string, which transformed it into a modified slingshot. Thanks to the rubber band, a pencil drawn back by the shooter, when released, could fly forward at a good speed.

One day, David was sick with flu. He was lying in a bed with metal boards on both ends, covered with a blanket. His older brother had just come from school with an improvised mini-slingshot. A "brilliant" idea arose in Victor's head: with a string, he attached a small vial to the rear board of the bed. The vial's opening was facing horizontally toward the head of the bed. Then he invited David to participate in a game with him, in which, taking turns, they would try to get a pencil into the vial's opening with the handmade slingshot. The winner would be the one who was able to hit the target. Taking into account that the "shooting device" was imperfect, that the bottle had a narrow opening, and that the distance to the shooter was five and a half feet, it was clear beforehand that this was an impossible task.

Victor was the first to shoot. As could easily have been predicted, he missed. David told his brother that it was impossible to get the pencil into the bottle, but Victor pretended not to hear his brother and continued to shoot without success until he became bored with what he was doing. Then he handed David the slingshot and offered to let him try his luck. Once again, the younger brother repeated that the goal was impossible, but Victor insisted. David put a pencil into the hole in the bobbin, pulled the rubber band with the pencil tip in it, and let the pencil go. Wow! The impossible happened: on his first attempt, the pencil was safely sitting inside the vial. Such a lucky shot could happen only once in a lifetime.

"Congratulations, David," Victor told him. "Never say never again. Always try again and again until you achieve your goal."

Besides his precious brother's advice, David gleaned another important life lesson: miracles do happen.

—

David's parents wrote to each other at least two or three times a week. Many years later, Ilana and Samuel's children placed their parents' correspondence in the archives of the Yiddish Scientific Institute (YIVO) in New York. This collection is interesting not only because of the content of the letters, but also because of the graphic design of the envelopes in which the letters were enclosed.

Samuel hardly saw his younger son after his birth, and lacking such parental bond, in his letters he mostly expressed concern about Victor, not David. Ilana expressed her disgust with such an attitude, and eventually Samuel apologized to her for ignoring the existence of his younger child. As for David, he intuitively had a very strong need for his father. That sometimes led to embarrassing episodes: in Andizhan, if any decent man happened to look at him, David immediately addressed him as "Papa." Later, when David noticed that his perspective dads were protesting such treatment, to be on the safe side, he began to call such candidates for paternity "Uncle-Papa."

A very important event happened in the Lamm family in the middle of 1944, when Samuel came from the front for a weeklong visit. At this time, Victor was twelve and David three. Ilana and Victor were overwhelmed with joy to see their husband and father, who was in a military uniform with orders and medals. David was also very happy to hear from his mother that, finally, his real father was before him, but that did not prevent him from calling Samuel "Uncle-Papa." Eventually, Samuel hotly protested such a strange title. David did his best to call Samuel "Father," but this did not always work.

—

Among other events associated with Samuel's visit to his family was an unforgettable one that transformed David from a crawler to a walker. To achieve such a result, Samuel used red cherries bought at a market. Before his arrival, the Lamm family could not afford this fruit: cherries were too expensive on their miserable budget. Samuel went to the market and used his officer allowance to buy a bag of cherries. Holding a plate full of the fruit, he showed it to David, who was on the other side of terrace. Before long, David began to crawl toward the lure and then, intuitively—maybe in order to increase the speed of his crawling—he stood up and, for the first time in his life, didn't just walk but ran toward his father. Everyone who was standing on the terrace applauded the great achievement in David's life: from a quadruped, he became a biped child.

On the third day of this marvelous transformation, the entire family was sitting on the terrace when David's father handed him some small change and asked him to go to fruit store nearby and fetch peaches. Peaches in Uzbekistan are not only delicious but they also have an unforgettable aroma. David obediently stomped into the store on his little legs, tightly holding the small change in his hand. He was nervous because he had never bought anything before, and at the same time, he was proud that his father entrusted him with an important mission. In the store, he could see the wonderful yellow-red peaches covered with gentle, fluffy, downy, yellowish-red skin. They were occupying a place of honor, lying on a counter in a small mound, radiating waves of fragrant aroma.

Being in the role of customer for the first time in life, David hesitantly approached the counter and asked the seller—a nice-looking Uzbek, a Muslim man—to sell him peaches for the coins, which he trustfully placed before him. He had not encountered a usual seller; it was a seller who truly liked children. David knew it right away when he felt on himself his adoring and full with affection warmth that was radiating from his big black eyes.

Nobody is perfect, especially not children. After Samuel's short visit ended and he left for the front, David began to forget about his real father. His thirst for a father in his life returned with a new force, and in a month or less, he resumed the search for a father, again awarding the "Uncle-Father" title to any man who appeared friendly.

CHAPTER 2

Immediate Postwar Years

Two years later, the war against Hitler's lunatics ended, and in October of 1945, Samuel was able to send his military orderly, whose name was Kuzma Pavlovich Frolov, to Andizhan to bring his family to the Karelo-Finskaya Autonomous Republic in the north of Russia, the place where he served,. Kuzma Pavlovich was a kind, simple, and unassuming man. Before he was drafted into the army, he lived with his wife, son, and a daughter of preschool age on the Volga River. Kuzma was very helpful, and for his natural kindness, he earned the appreciation and trust of Ilana and her children. During the trip across the country, which took a couple of weeks, Kuzma, in his military uniform, did not miss an opportunity to sit next to David, to whom he told countless stories.

The trip was long, interesting, and sad at the same time. It was fascinating to see the vast expanses and beauty of the country, and at the same time, it was sad and tragic to see the cities in ruins after the recent bombings. The railway cars were full of people, but people did not complain; after the recent victory, most of them were in an upbeat mood. The railway car windows were not closed tightly and could be opened. For Victor and David, a special pleasure was to stick their heads out the train's window, discovering the beauty of nature while the wind whistled in their ears.

On the last leg of the trip, at a small railway station, Kuzma temporarily left Ilana and the children. Before this, he introduced Ilana to a driver of a large Studebaker truck with two poles on either side of the hood—a gift of American lend-lease. This truck had been sent by Samuel to bring his family to the military unit where he served.

The place where Samuel was supposed to meet his family was thirty kilometers away. David sat in the truck between the driver and Ilana, while Victor sat next to the door. On this beautiful Karelian day, they drove on both sides of the road, on which tall evergreen trees stood in deep snow with large granite boulders among them. In an hour, the driver told Ilana that they were approaching the place where her husband would meet his family. The closer the car got to the meeting point, the more impatient David felt. At the next intersection, a large truck stood facing them, exactly the same as the one in which they were traveling. The door of that Studebaker truck opened, and Samuel jumped out in a warm half-length coat and military boots, waving his arms and laughing. When he approached the truck that had brought his family to him, Ilana opened the door. Four-year-old David was the first to jump out of the cab into the snow and run toward his father. The first one Samuel had intended to kiss was his wife, but when his younger son, whom he hardly knew, ran toward him first and hugged him, Samuel had no choice but to pick him up and kiss him. The next in the line were Ilana and Victor. For many years to come David's brother, the firstborn, could not forgive David for being the first to greet their father.

The Lamm family lived in a small military settlement, in a house that, before the war, had belonged to Finns. During the war, the original owners evacuated to Finland, and now the house stood empty. For Ilana and Victor, the change was amazing: from one tiny room, actually a kitchen, where they lived for four years, now they lived in a comfortable spacious house with conveniences they never dreamed of having. As for little David, this change did not make too much of a difference. All his daily needs had been adequately satisfied in both his old and his new homes. Most important was that he was loved and caressed as before, and now he also had the father he had been looking for since he was born. For four years prior, David had been playing outside on a terrace in sunny Uzbekistan. Now, in Kareliya, where the climate was different, most of the time he played inside his home, surrounded by the love of his parents and Kuzma, who continued to be a faithful ordinary for his father.

Samuel was a very natural man, who was open, sincere, and spontaneous. His paternal feelings he showed mostly to Victor. As for his younger son, who had grown up without him in the previous years, he hardly knew him and frequently ignored his presence. Ilana knew it and many times openly expressed her dissatisfaction with Samuel's lack of affection and emotion toward his younger son.

However, it was not his mother but David himself who forced his father to fall in love with him. David was not born to be a victim. Instead of feeling pain and sorrow at the rejection, he took matters into his own small hands. He did not need to read books on psychology; he was moved by a child's intuition. Formal acceptance was not enough for him. He wanted his father's genuine love.

Whenever Samuel was in his son's field of vision, David did not miss a chance to stage an improvised performance. Both brothers' favorite poet was Alexander Sergeyevich Pushkin, author of unforgettable tales. David knew many poems by heart, which Victor had learned in his presence for his school programs. As for songs, David had heard them from his mother and brother and every evening in the performances of Marya Petrovna, in whose prewar kitchen the Lamm family had lived.

In his father's presence, David recited poems, sang songs, and told stories, some of which he composed on the fly. Eventually, what he was trying to achieve subconsciously was fulfilled: his father began to pay attention to his younger son's talents, and little by little, he fell in irreversible love with David. After that, David became the recipient of many precious benefits: his father talked and joked with him as he did with Victor. Samuel invited David to climb on his back and took him for car rides to the woods, and to his military unit, making his son's life more interesting and filled with many events.

Sirkoyarvi, the small village where the family lived, was surrounded by spectacular dense forests in which tall coniferous and all kinds of evergreen trees grew. Besides that, there were countless large red-and-gray granite boulders and numerous scenic lakes around. Samuel liked to expose his children to unusual things, to surprise them. For this purpose, he used to bring rabbits, roosters, or squirrels home for household entertainment. Once he managed to bring home a goat, but Ilana hotly protested, asking him to take "the dirty animal" away, despite his children's pleas to let the creature stay. Another way Samuel entertained his children was by crawling into their bedroom in the morning on all fours, producing frightening sounds.

In the warm season, Officer Samuel once took his children on a trip in a truck, which he drove deep into the forest to practice shooting his gun. Besides this gun, at home he had a rifle with a bayonet, a saber, and a military dagger. In the forest, Samuel chose a more or less flat place, took several metal cans out of the truck, put them on a fallen dead tree, and began to shoot at them with his personal military pistol while Victor and David stood next to him, watching.

Samuel was good but not a perfect shooter, and when he was tired of shooting, he did something that his wife would never have allowed him to do. First he allowed Victor to shoot three or four times. Then, conveniently forgetting that his younger son was only five years old, it came David's turn. Naturally, David could not wait to pull the trigger on the gun. His father explained to him how to point and shoot. David followed his instructions and pulled the trigger, and the gun fired. The recoil of the gun after the shot, which his father had forgotten to warn him about, was so strong that the poor child fell to the ground. Since then, David had no desire to continue shooting. Nevertheless, he was proud of his first and last shot.

On the way back home, Samuel asked his children not to tell Ilana that they participated in the shooting practice. As could be expected, during supper, Victor forgot about his promise and asked Samuel if he was satisfied with the way he had shot. Ilana understood right away what had happened, which led to a big family scandal, at the conclusion of which Samuel gave his word that he would never again allow his children to have a gun in their hands.

The wooden Finnish house where the Lamms lived had many features that were surprising for the regular Soviet citizen. Of all the previously unknown luxuries, the children most of all loved the cozy and warm kitchen where they spent plenty of time. Victor used to do his homework there, and David read or drew. Both children adored the beautiful in-wall kitchen stove with white tiles that were smooth and warm to the touch, which David liked to stroke whenever he passed by.

Outside the Lamms' house was a ranch where many cows grazed. David was hypnotized by their large brown eyes focused on him and could not understand whether a cow liked or disliked him. Eventually, he decided that the big cows could easily harm him and stopped spending time in the pasture. A week later a cow, which had appeared to be quite peaceful, attacked his older brother when, returning home from school, he got too close to it. Victor was quick to run away from the cow.

—

Alcohol, especially in Russia and Ukraine, is an integral attribute of life. Before the war, David's father hardly ever drank. However, having been a quartermaster during the Second World War, Samuel had been in charge of the distribution of alcohol for soldiers and officers in the military unit where he served. His control of alcohol also made it necessary for him to participate in drinking parties with officers from his military unit, and—more inconvenient—with different bosses who came to his military unit for different inspections.

When the war was over, Samuel, instead of forgetting his bad habit of consuming alcohol, began to use vodka as a means of escaping the inevitable stresses of human life. Though he never became an alcoholic and though he drank alcohol in relatively small amounts, he consumed it almost daily. Samuel's involvement with alcohol affected his rich and interesting personality unpleasantly, ruined his health at a relatively young age, and eventually resulted in many years of intermittent marital discord.

After military service in the Karelo-Finn Autonomous Republic, Samuel was transferred to serve in Pontonnaya Station, which was located near a railroad. The Lamms lived not far from the military unit where Samuel was stationed.

It was Sunday morning in Pontonnaya Station when Ilana asked Samuel to come shopping with her at the Pontonnaya Station store. The shopping trip was successful except for one item: on this day, vodka was not available for sale and nowhere to be found. Samuel had gotten used to his routine: drinking one hundred grams of vodka (three and a half ounces) during dinner, and returning home, he came to "ingenious" solution to procure the alcohol he needed.

"Come here, David," he told his five-and-a-half-year-old son, who was reading a children's book. "Do me a favor, son? Do you remember the grocery store in the Martovo railway station, where I bought you candies a week ago? It's not far from here. Here's the money—a ruble and fifty kopecks. Run there, buy me some *четушку* (*tcheкushka*), and come back."

A *tchetushka*, or bottle of vodka, contained one quarter liter, or two hundred and fifty milliliters of alcohol.

David, who did not miss an opportunity to please his dad, immediately agreed.

With money tightly clenched in his fist, he soon reached the railway. First, he jumped between the rails, then he ran, then he walked briskly from one tie to the other on his way to the little store at Martovo station, which was located almost two kilometers from his home. David knew well about the danger of walking between rails and periodically looked forward and backward to make sure there was no train approaching.

Time was flying fast. Full of energy, David soon reached the grocery store. The seller, a tired middle-age woman with an apron over her satin dress, not asking him for whom he was buying alcohol—an unnecessary formality from her point of view—took the boy's money and handed him a *tchetushka* of alcohol.

When David was back on the railway, the sun was higher on the horizon, and it was becoming hot. David was a little hungry and tired after his run. Remembering to check for an approaching train, from time to time he took a short rest and then continued his brisk walk. During one such rest, he felt somebody touch him on his shoulder. When he raised his head, he saw before him a middle-aged man with regular facial features and brown hair parted on one side. The most remarkable element of his face was his sunken eyes: from them, David could discern invisible rays of warmth that unite people together.

At this time, people did not worry about children communicating with strangers. An adult could freely start a conversation with a child. Nobody would suspect that anything sinister was going on if an adult in the appropriate context embraced a child's back with his hand, or if he stroked the child's head. Moreover, it was considered then that children needed such emotional support provided by adults. David trusted people and did not hesitate to reciprocate if a man or woman unknown to him gave him a friendly smile.

"Hi, little boy. What are you doing here on the railway?" the stranger asked affably.

"I'm going home. I bought vodka for my father," David answered.

"I see," said the stranger. "Now I understand what's going on; I saw a bottle of vodka in your hand and thought to myself, 'Why is this little child carrying it?' My name is Uncle Vanya. What is your name?"

"I'm David."

"OK, David. If you rested enough, we can join forces. I'm going in the same direction as you, and we can talk along the way."

While they walked, David learned that Uncle Vanya was a professional fisherman and that he lived with his family—a wife and two children—in Pontonnaya Station. The younger of his children was the same age as David.

In the midst of the conversation, Uncle Vanya began to listen attentively to the sounds that were coming behind them.

"I think that the train is approaching, David. Let's leave the rails before it is too late," he said and, taking David by the hand, helped him climb down the steep embankment.

Soon David heard the noise of an approaching freight train. The train rushed by, banging with wheels and puffing with cylinders. The roar of the locomotive was so intense that it rang in David's ears. After the train passed, Uncle Vanya and David climbed up to the railway track and resumed their journey.

Uncle Vanya, who personified kindness, spoke to David as if he was his older brother, listening to him attentively and complimenting him from time to time.

"Listen, David, it looks as you're getting a little tired," remarked Uncle Vanya when David began to lag behind him. "Do you have any objection if I take you on my shoulders? That will allow us to move quicker."

What child can refuse the opportunity to have a free ride on an adult's shoulders?

Before David climbed up on Uncle Vanya's shoulders, Uncle Vanya asked him to give him the bottle with vodka, which David held tightly in his sweaty hand. "You better give it to me, kid. The bottle is made of glass, and if it falls, it will break in pieces."

Sitting on Uncle Vanya's shoulders, David fell as if he was a little prince. He felt so good that he began to sing, and his "older brother" eagerly sang along with him. The new friends had a great time until they came to the place of parting.

Uncle Vanya returned the bottle of vodka to David and asked him if he knew exactly how to find his home. David assured him that he knew well where his home was, and Uncle Vanya accompanied him until they reached the street where David lived.

"Listen, David. I had a great time walking with you. You're a great kid. I'm sure you have a wonderful father, but remember, you should have nothing to do with vodka. If your father ever asks you to buy him vodka again, tell him you are a little kid, and if he wants vodka, he should buy it by himself," Uncle Vanya said and stroked David's hair. "Go!"

David had probably been absent for a long time because his parents met him in front of the house. His father looked guilty, and Ilana began to cry when she saw little David with a small bottle of vodka in his hand. Shaking, she pounced on David with kisses.

"Don't you dare ever send David for your cursed vodka," she yelled at Samuel. "You should not do it to any child and especially to your son. You know how I hate your vodka, and now you involve your son in your shameful habit!"

Samuel did not say a word in his defense and listened to Ilana with a guiltily lowered head. After this episode, he continued his romance with alcohol, but he never involved his son in its procurement.

David, who never met Uncle Vanya again, recalled his companion's human kindness whenever he encountered people like him.

Children Alone in Vyborg

From Pontonnaya Station, the Lamms moved to the city of Vyborg, located in Leningradskaya Oblast. There they lived in a second-floor apartment in a brick building. Once, the children's parents needed to leave them for an important five-day meeting in the city of Leningrad. During this period, Victor temporarily became David's caregiver. On the third day of the children's life without their parents, a warm and sunny spring day, Victor rushed into apartment and told David to follow him to watch a house on fire on their block. David had never seen a house fire before. Curious, he quickly put on pants and a shirt and followed his brother.

The brothers joined a small crowd of people who stood behind a rope observing the flames of a fire that was devouring a two-story house. After they had spent enough time looking at the fire, the brothers went home. On the way there, they walked past a grocery store where they saw a line so long that it spilled out onto the street. The brothers got in the line first and only after that—as was the usual practice—asked people what product the line was for. For such an inquiry was a common question: "What do they give?"

It turned out that the queue was for watermelons, which, like other fruits at this time, were in permanent shortage for Vyborg's residents. As for the brothers, they had not seen watermelon since they left Andizhan. After half an hour in line, the brothers approached the counter and were happy to get a watermelon. With the watermelon in Victor's hands, they returned home and cut it into pieces right away. The watermelon festivity began. The brothers' initial exaltation changed to disappointment, though, when it turned out that the watermelon was not ripe, not crisp, and not sweet enough. But . . . who cared? Victor remained highly upbeat.

"Listen, David, we're going to save all the seeds," Victor said, "and we'll plant them in one of our flower pots. You'll see: in couple of months, we're going to have our own watermelons. When they're ripe, we're going to enjoy them with Mom and Dad."

To get ahead of the story, it needs to be said that Victor's idea was a complete failure. To Victor and David's enthusiastic satisfaction, sprouts grew from the soil, but that was all that the seeds could achieve.

—

Alcohol destroys human relations. One night when the Lamms lived in Vyborg, Victor was out: he had a sleepover with a friend. That night David woke up when his father returned home late. He was too young to understand the details of what was happening. He saw his mother and father standing opposite each other in the hallway, shouting offensive words. From his previous experience, David understood that his father was drunk: his speech was slurred, and his movements were not steady. Gradually the conflict became hotter, and Ilana yelled, "OK, Samuel, in this case I am leaving you!" walked to the closet, grabbed her coat, put it on, and resolutely went toward the exit.

If only David's parents had known what a dark abyss yawned in front of their young son and how his heart fell deep down in his chest when he saw his mother leaving, maybe they would have been able to settle their conflict, but Samuel and Ilana were too busy trying to prove their point to pay attention to their son. David, who never been parted from his mother since he was born, was panic-stricken that his mother would leave him. Seeing in his vivid imagination that his mother might abandon him and never return, like a flash he jumped out of bed. In one leap, he reached his mother, caught her coat, and yelled so loud that his voice became hoarse: "Mommy, Mommy, please, don't leave us. Please! Don't leave me." David wanted to express much, much more, but he was only a child and his vocabulary did not include even a small fraction of the words that he wanted to say. What a pity that adults do not pay attention to their children when they are in a middle of an argument. Nevertheless, with a maternal flair, Ilana was able to understand what was going on in David's heart. She changed her mind and, to David's unspeakable joy, slowly took off her coat.

Samuel took advantage of this moment to apologize to his wife, and after his generous promises, the conflict was settled. Unfortunately, David and his brother would witness many similar conflicts in the future, all of which related to their father's passion for alcohol. Somehow, Victor was able to ignore family trouble, but David always perceived it painfully. Unfortunately, he had a good memory and never could forget that his father, whom he always loved, sometimes behaved as an irresponsible adult.

CHAPTER 3

Home, Sweet Home

After serving many years in the army, Samuel was demobilized in May of 1947, and he and his wife decided to return to the city of Beltsy in sunny Moldova. They hoped that the house they bought there six year ago had survived the challenges of the war and they would be able to take possession of it.

After a few weeks of preparation, the day of departure finally came. Kuzma Pavlovich Frolov, the old family friend and Samuel's former military orderly, helped them with preparation for the road. When the time came, the family, accompanied by Kuzma, left the apartment for the railway station. In the vestibule of the building, David met his good friend Kostya, who lived in apartment next to his and with whom he played. Seeing him, David began to talk about recent events, but he was interrupted by Ilana, who said something that, for the first time in his life, awakened in him philosophical thinking.

"Shake hands, Kostya and David, before we leave. This is the last time you'll see each other."

The perception that this simple sentence awoke affected David for the rest of his life.

For the first time in his life, he understood that life moves not in circles but in a forward direction, and that world in which he lived was so vast that people dissolved in space and lost each other forever. He understood that nothing in this world is permanent.

The Lamm Family Arrives in Beltsy

The Lamms' trip to the city of Beltsy in Moldova lasted half of a week and was uneventful. They arrived in the city late at night, and in the dim light of streetlights, Samuel and a man previously unknown to him were looking for a place where their families could spend the rest of the night. Eventually, they found an open door in a building on the station's square. In the vestibule, there was a space between the door and the stairs leading up. They decided the families would settle in this space for the night. They spread soft pieces of luggage on the floor and fell asleep in this improvised lodging.

The Lamm family woke up early in the morning, picked up their luggage, and with pounding hearts went to Svoboda Street to see if the house they had bought had survived the war. The day was pleasant, the city was peaceful, a cool breeze blew, and the streets were clean, but the sight of many destroyed houses on both sides of the road made both parents more and more apprehensive. In half an hour, the family reached the city park, the same city park where, on the second day of the war, Samuel and Victor hid in the bushes under bombardment by a German airplane. Surprisingly, the musical shell and a food stall on the southwest corner of the park had survived the war. The family took a rest, enjoying the calm and tranquility of the still-sleeping city.

Another twenty minutes and the Lamms were close to the place where their house had stood before the war. The faces of the parents and fifteen-year-old Victor betrayed their inner tension: Had their home survived the war? And if it did survive, was it occupied or not? Finally, the family reached the city block in the middle of which their house stood. They walked a hundred yards, and from the distance, to their indescribable joy, they saw that their prewar family house had, indeed, withstood the war! As if they were possessed, Samuel and Ilana dropped their suitcases and began to sing and dance. Hooray, hooray! The majority of the houses on the block had been destroyed, but the Lamms' and five others houses stood as if nothing happened. The main reason for the survival of the Lamms' house was its construction: the walls of this cheap dwelling were made of twigs smeared with clay. The twigs provided a springlike action, which allowed the walls of the house to withstand bombardments during the war.

The parents and Victor picked up their suitcases and soon were near their house. Now the main question was whether anybody lived there. The door facing the street was closed, and the family went to the back of the house. That door was closed as well, and the newcomers began to knock on it. It was several minutes before a tall woman in her forties with attractive face opened the door. She was dressed in a satin gown and had a red kerchief around her neck.

"What do you want?" she asked, not hiding her annoyance.

"Good day, citizen," Samuel answered. "Please forgive me, but this house belongs to us. We bought it a week before the war began. When the war started, as an officer, I immediately went to the front, while my wife ran away from the city with our kids. Today we returned to Beltsy, and, sorry, but according to the law, this house belongs to us. This is our property."

"I don't believe a single word you said," the woman reacted. Now she was outraged. "Show me the title that proves your ownership. If you don't have it, there's nothing for us to talk about."

"As I said, we left Beltsy in the first days of the war," Samuel objected. "I went to front to fight the Germans, and my wife ran with our children on the third day. She did it straight out of the maternity ward of the First City Hospital where our son David was born. You can see him with your own eyes. It was war, and we didn't have an opportunity to take the title because it was still with the house authority—"

"I'm not a bit interested in your story, man," the mistress of the house protested loudly. "You can prove nothing. My husband, Captain Kravchenko, our son, and I have lived in this house several months. My husband is a KGB captain; the KGB gave this house to us for permanent occupancy. Is that clear to you? Get out of here immediately! Should I repeat that my husband is a KGB captain?"

The woman turned around, entered the house, and slammed the door in the Lamms' faces. There was nothing left for them to do but look for a place to live. On the way to the city street, Samuel slapped his forehead and said that he had an idea.

"Don't be upset. Do you see that house in the back of the yard?" he asked. "Before the war started, I clearly recall that a Jewish couple, Yankel and Manya Melman, lived there. Remember, Ilana, before we bought our house, we met them couple of times? They were very happy that we were buying our house. If they successfully survived the war and have returned from the evacuation, they might help us with our predicament."

Carrying their luggage, the family went to the house in the back of the yard. Coming to the door, Samuel knocked on it several times.

Oh, wonder of wonders! Samuel's wish came true! Yankel Melman, who was four years older than Samuel, opened the door. He was of average height, thin, with curly salt-and-pepper hair. His oblong facial features were typical for a Bessarabian Jew. Unable to recognize the strangers at his door, he looked at the Lamms with curiosity and then asked them who they were.

"Yankel Melman, don't you recognize us? It's me, Samuel Lamm, my wife Ilana, and my children, Victor and David. Remember how before the war, you and your wife, Manya, supported our decision to buy the house in the front of your backyard? Unfortunately, the war prevented us from being your neighbors," Samuel said in Yiddish.

"Oh my God! Oh my God! It's you! The Lamms! Right? Of course, I remember you! Four years of war changed you and your wife, but now I can recognize you easily. Manya! Manya!" Yankel yelled. "Look who's here. Come quick!"

Aunt Manya, a woman the same age as her husband, slightly more than moderately overweight with rosy cheeks, beautiful graying hair, and a face shining with goodwill, ran out of the house to the door where the uninvited guests stood.

"*Gottenyu! Gottenyu!* Oh my God, Oh my God! Yankel, I cannot believe this," she yelled. "Yankel, of course, these are the Lamms. I remember them. Look, they have an addition to their family. A son! Such a pretty boy. Ilanochka, I remember like it was yesterday that you were pregnant before this cursed war started. How wonderful that you all survived the nightmare of the last four years. We also survived by a miracle, but it's a long story. Let me embrace you all."

While the Lamms and the Melmans were embracing each other, the Melmans' son Arkady, whose household name was Eka, came out of the house.

"Eka, Ekale, sonny! Look who came to us. This is the Lamm family. They bought the house in front of ours right before the war," Aunt Manya exclaimed.

Arkady was Victor's age, a nice-looking boy. He looked at the newcomers with curiosity. Meanwhile, Aunt Manya addressed the youngest member of the Lamm family. She asked David what his name was, and when he answered, she embraced him and covered his face with kisses.

"Samuel, tell me, where are you going to live?" Yankel asked. "You know that the Kravchenko family lives in your house now, and the head of that family works for the KGB. What are you going to do about it?"

Samuel answered that he was well aware of the challenging circumstances that he faced. Aunt Manya interrupted.

"Stop worrying, Samuel. The most important thing is that our families have survived this horrible war. The law is on your side. Justice will prevail, and one way or the other, the house will be yours. Meanwhile, you all need a place to stay. You are welcome to stay in our house until you have your house back. What do you say, Yankel?"

"I wanted to offer the same," Yankel responded.

"We are Jewish, we went through hell during the war, and we have to help each other," Aunt Manya continued, "Besides our kitchen, we have two rooms: you can live in one of them as long as necessary."

The Melmans allowed the Lamm family to stay with them for more than a year until they finally were able to prove in court that they were the legitimate owners of the house. While living in Melmans' house, Ilana and Samuel shared all household expenses with them.

The Lamms did not want to hire a lawyer; they thought that his officer's uniform was enough to prove the veracity of their claim. Besides that, the couple hoped that their ownership could be proven with partially preserved official archives and witness testimony. There were three of them: Yankel; a Russian woman whom the Lamms hired to paint their house when they bought it; and none other than Solomon Pascal, the broker who had sold the house to the Lamms before the war and in whose suburban house Victor hid from German bombardment at the beginning of the war.

The Pascal family had survived in Kazakhstan. They partially owed their lives to Victor's father. Based on the experience of the First World War, the Pascal family had believed that the German occupation of Moldova would be nothing dramatic, and, therefore, they did not worry too much about the future. However, during conversations at the beginning of the war, Samuel Lamm was able to convince Solomon Pascal that the Nazi troops would be merciless toward the Jews. Samuel was wrong only in the sense that not only German but also Romanian troops were cruel toward the Jews. When the Pascal family finally decided to leave the city, there was no way for them to go but by horse-driven cart. They chose to move east in direction of the city of Ribnitza. While the family, which included Solomon Pascal, his wife, their son, and his father, slowly traveled around the countryside in their horse-driven cart, they never ceased to be surprised how peaceful and quiet everything around them was. It seemed to them that the war had stopped and peacetime had come back. They returned to reality when, on one of the roads, several military cars overtook them. An officer came out of the front car. He approached the Pascals, and in a pure German, asked them for direction to Dubossary. Fortunately, Pascal's father knew German from the First World War, when he fought in the tsarist army. He explained to the officer where the city of Dubossary was and, satisfied, the German officer disappeared into the car's cab. The Pascals' cart continued its path East. In another several days, the Pascals safely reached Ukraine, where Soviet power still reigned.

—

During the litigation, Samuel tried to persuade the KGB captain to move out of his house, offering him all kind of incentives, such as paying for moving expense or giving the captain a requested sum of money. This did not persuade the captain to abandon the house. One day Samuel, along with David, was on the way out from the backyard where they lived, when he saw the captain at the gate. Judging by Captain Kravchenko's appearance, he was drunk.

"Come here, Lamm," he told Samuel, who was not expecting anything dramatic to happen.

When Samuel approached, the captain suddenly caught him by his arm and twisted it. Samuel screamed in pain.

"Stop doing that," he yelled.

"Why should I? Let me show what else I am going to do to you," the drunken KGB man said and with these words pulled his gun out of its holster. "I will kill you if you don't stop your harassment. I know you Jews. You must have been sitting somewhere deep behind in the rear when I fought on the front line, and now you came here to take advantage of me, of the Russian officer."

The captain let Samuel's hand loose, cocked his gun, and in a threatening manner put the gun barrel to Samuel's temple.

"Are you going to leave my family alone?" he demanded with a dark menace in his voice.

"OK, shoot me, Captain. Go ahead, shoot me in front of my son," Samuel said quietly, pale and motionless. "Tell your own son how you killed an officer who went through the war, faced death daily, and was awarded orders and medals. Go ahead. Shoot. I'm not afraid of you."

While David looked at both men in a state of a sheer panic, Samuel's words somehow produced a sobering effect on the captain. He pulled the gun away from Samuel's temple and put it back in the holster.

"All right, this time I will let you go. However, don't forget where I serve; one day, you might see me there. Remember, the house is mine, and you will never have it. Understood?"

David's father, still pale and shaken, took his son's hand, and they were on their way.

Many years later, Samuel told David that that was not the first time he'd felt a cold touch of steel at his temple. During the war, when he was a quartermaster and in charge of food and alcohol, he also was responsible for parties for his unit officers and for treating different military inspectors who were coming to oversee how the battalion followed rules and regulations. Once a major general came to Samuel's military unit headquarters for an inspection. In the evening, during the party, the officers of the unit were celebrating another victory over the Germans. Everything was going according to plan. There was enough food and alcohol on the table where the officers drank and ate, according to the wartime standards.

Late that at night, when all the vodka had been consumed, the major general's thirst was still not satisfied, and he asked Samuel to bring him more vodka. At this relatively late hour, all junior military staff had gone to their beds, so Samuel himself went to the warehouse to bring the requested alcohol. The warehouse was dark, and for speed, Samuel decided not to light the kerosene light. In the dark, he grabbed the presumed bottle with vodka and ran back to the party with it, to help to the major general have a good time. Indeed, at the sight of the quartermaster, the major general showed his impatience by raising his faceted glass.

Samuel removed the cork from the bottle and poured vodka for the high authority. The high authority brought the glass to his mouth, began to drink, choked on it, and in disgust spit the liquid straight on the floor. "What did you try to do to me, officer?" he yelled at Samuel. "You are not a quartermaster; you're a German traitor. Did you want to poison me? Drink yourself what you just gave to me!"

Samuel took the glass from general's hand and drank it.

"I am very sorry, Comrade Major General," he said, spitting out what he just consumed. "Please forgive me. In the darkness I confused the bottles and gave you a bottle of vinegar instead of vodka."

"Aha, you got confused." The major general imitated Samuel. "I'll show you how to confuse. You tried to poison me, and you will pay for it. Follow me!"

Samuel, with the major general in front of him, left the room and went outside.

"Stand at the fence facing me," the major general ordered sternly, and when Samuel obeyed his order, he took his gun out of his holster and began to take aim. Samuel's life would have tragically ended and the Lamm family would not have had their husband and father if not for the intervention of Samuel's military commander, who fortunately appeared at the place of the impending execution.

"Comrade Major General, I ask you to stop immediately," he interrupted, while the major general was taking aim at Samuel. "My quartermaster is an exemplary officer. We went with him through fire and water, and he is one of my best officers. He participated in many combat operations. I can guarantee you that he confused alcohol with vinegar. I checked out the vinegar he poured in your glass. It's diluted vinegar, and it's totally harmless, Comrade Major General. I don't have anybody to replace Officer Lamm if you kill him!"

"All right, if you say he is irreplaceable, I will spare the life of your quartermaster," Major General said, returning his gun to its holster. "But remember, Lamm, next time I will not spare you. Bring me more real vodka."

It took a long time for David to forget the traumatic episode with the KGB captain that he witnessed, but every cloud has an unseen benefit. The episode remarkably shortened the amount of time it took to return the Lamm family's legitimate property. On the day after the incident, Samuel Lamm put in his officer's uniform, attached to it all the military decorations that had been awarded to him during the war, took his younger son with him as a witness, and went first to the militia station and then to the local military commissariat. Veterans were highly respected after the end of World War II, and the KGB captain was reprimanded after he promised never again to be aggressive and use his gun for intimidation.

—

Meanwhile, expecting a trial, the Lamms continued to live at the Melmans' house. Both families enjoyed each other's company: the

Lamm family helped ensure that there was an abundance of food, and the Melmans continued to express their hospitality. The four members of the Lamm family lived in a small crowded room but "the more the merrier." A house pet—a little dog called Touzik (which translates to *little ace*) entertained both families, especially the children. Victor was busy preparing to start his new school while David began to attend a kindergarten that was located relatively close, so he frequently walked there by himself.

There was one little problem. If Aunt Manya was the embodiment of kindness, Uncle Yankel, with all his proven kindness, had an obsession focused mostly on little David. Either he decided that the obedient and cooperative David had "destructive tendencies," or maybe it was the adult's desire to dominate a young creature, but this man was watching every step David made on his property. When David was reading kid's books or coloring books, Uncle Yankel sat next to him, silent, staring at him, as if he was expecting that any minute, the child would change from peaceful behavior to a destructive activity. When David was in motion and spontaneously touched any objects in the room or was trying to play with little dog, Touzik, Uncle Yankel immediately uttered a word hateful to David: "Neh!" which meant no. Uncle Yankel never explained what specifically his strong "Neh!" meant, but his constant "Neh, neh!" was gradually paralyzing the little child. David was doing his best to avoid touching anything, but "Neh!" did not stop.

It is easy to recognize child abuse when a physical trauma is inflicted, but how much more traumatic, sometimes, is verbal abuse, which—as a rule—goes unpunished.

—

One evening, Ilana and her children sat in their hosts' room. Ilana was mending clothing, Victor was doing his homework, and David was looking at the pictures in Kornei Tchukovsky's popular children book. Suddenly the door was flung open, and Samuel and the Melmans burst through it with happy faces.

"We won, we won! Hooray!" Samuel shouted loudly. "In three weeks, we're going to live in our own house. I learned about it in the court. Yankel, Manya, Pascal, and two more people witnessed that house was ours before the war. However, most important was that there was clear confirmation of our previous ownership in the surviving archives. So the judge decided that we are the legitimate owners. Thank you, our hosts, for all you did for us."

In the due time, the KGB captain and his wife vacated the property, and the Lamms' dream came true. The house was theirs.

CHAPTER 4

KINDERGARTEN

The kindergarten David attended was located in a one-story building. David liked his kindergarten because of all activities there but even more so because of the good food. As a child of the war, he never refused a second serving, and if one of the children in his group offered him food he or she did not want to eat, he rarely refused.

—

David belonged to category of people who had an inherent sense of personal guilt. That led sometimes to undesirable results.

One summer afternoon, David returned home from kindergarten and played in the backyard. Then he noticed that the teacher's aide from his kindergarten enter the backyard. When she saw David, she asked him to call his mother.

"Take your son and bring him back to the kindergarten," the woman said to David's mother politely when she came out of the house.

"Why?" Ilana asked.

"Somebody took another child's hat, and now the teachers are trying to find out who did it."

"But I didn't take anybody's hat," David interjected.

"OK, you can tell them that when we get to the kindergarten," responded the teacher's aide.

Ilana put on her jacket, and the group left the house.

Naturally, David had no idea who might have taken the cap and what this cap looked like; however, on the way to the kindergarten, he kept repeating that he did not take anybody's hat. To prove his innocence, he pointed on his own cap and added that one cap was enough for him. Eventually, the teacher's aide, a simple woman, told Ilana that her son indeed probably had stolen the cap, if he could not stop denying it.

By the time David arrived at the kindergarten, the lost cap was already found.

After many similar cases in his life, David deliberately restrained himself from denying his nonexistent guilt.

—

It was at the kindergarten where David encountered death for the first time in his life.

Not far from the kindergarten in the city park was a snowy hill, and in the winter, the teachers took the children there to sled.

On the way to the hill, the children were walking and holding hands. David's partner was Tanya, a girl who always sat next to him at dinnertime. This cheerful girl amused everybody around her. Relations between David and her were special because she did not like Russian-style fruit compote and would always share it with him. After experiencing hunger during the war, David was left with a healthy appetite for the rest of his life.

The snowy hill was not too far from the kindergarten. On the way there, Tanya and David were laughing and talking so loudly that their teacher asked them several times to be quiet. When the group arrived at the hill, the shouts and loud laughter of many kids resonated in the air. The children were sledding down the relatively narrow passage between chain fences attached to metal poles.

Tanya and David shared a ride: David in front and she behind him. During the ride, other sleds were pushing from both sides. Each time they wanted to slip away from the next push or pull, sleds from the opposite side would hit them again. After one especially strong strike, their slide sped toward the metal post of the fence. David managed to roll off the sled, but Tanya, tightly clutching to the edges, remained sitting until the sled reached the fence at high speed and loudly crashed against it.

The crash was strong: Tania fell off the sled; her forehead rammed straight into the metal pole. Hitting her head hard, she let out a desperate shrill scream. The teacher was already there by the time children ran up to her. Embracing her, she threw herself on Tanya's body and screamed loudly, desperately begged the girl to answer her. Each moment becoming more and more pale and lifeless, Tanya did not react. She, who had been so happy only seconds ago, with her eyes sparkling and a snow-white smile, was now motionless with her head thrown back, deprived of life. Something invisible left her face, which had been excited a moment ago; that "something" was replaced by what is called the mask of death. The teacher, with Tanya in her arms, surrounded by the group of adults and children, ran down to the road at the bottom of the hill.

The next day, David's teacher told the children that Tanya had died of a skull fracture. Observing the close and dramatic death of a human being for the first time in his life shocked and frightened him. It was difficult for him to recover after the indescribable transformation he had recently observed: the girl who only a minute ago was so full of life and laughter suddenly ceased to belong to the world of the living.

Fortunately, time erases tragic episodes from our memory, and soon David resumed enjoying his carefree life. The episode occupied its invisible place in his subconscious.

—

After four years of chronic malnutrition during his early childhood, it was not surprising that David's favorite time at kindergarten was during meals, when, along with other the children, he sat at the low square table and with gusto ate whatever was offered to him. He never criticized food and ate whatever was offered with appetite: soup, cereal, potatoes, sometimes meat, bread, and for desert kissel or compote served with cookies.

In movies young children are portrayed as if they are involved in meaningful conversation for a significant amount of time. In the real life, the communicative skills of young children are still limited. During meals, charming, beautiful, smart children talked without stopping, each of them expressing whatever was on their mind and answering their own questions. In order to function as social, communicating beings, children must go through the further stages of their nervous system maturation.

On a hot and humid summer day, David's group went for a long walk to a close suburb. While the children held each other's hands, three teachers walked along with them on both sides of the line.

The group was ready to return from the walk when David felt sick. Besides being very tired, he had a severe pain in his stomach, probably because of some kind of food poisoning. By nature, David took pain well and hardly ever complained, but this time he was forced to tell one of teachers he was not doing well. The teacher patted his back and encouraged him to keep walking: "Everything will be OK."

In another five minutes, David lost consciousness. Later he found out that while he was unconscious, somebody had carried him in the kindergarten.

When he woke up in the nursery's bedroom where children slept in the midday, he had no idea how he got there; consciousness having returned to him, he felt strong and healthy. In a T-shirt and briefs that did not belong to him, he ran out into the kindergarten's backyard and met the teacher to whom he had complained about his stomach pain during the walk there.

"Oh, David, you look so good," she said with a wide smile on her kind face. "Why didn't you tell me that you were really sick?"

How could I, thought David. I am only a young child, and I cannot yet find all the adult words to express myself. For this, I need more time.

"I washed your T-shirt and your briefs. They will be dry soon," the teacher continued. "Good boy!"

David understood that while being unconscious, he had also soiled himself and that his teacher was good enough to clean and wash him. Besides feeling ashamed, despite his young age, David felt gratitude toward those who took care of him while he was unconscious, a sign of a healthy psyche.

David's young organism was able to withstand a real shock. He felt ashamed for not controlling himself, but soon—this happens easily at a young age—he was able to distract himself from embarrassing thoughts.

—

At the time when David attended kindergarten, in the after-war environment, the education of young children was not a high priority. The main purpose of the preschool was taking care of children's well-being. One of pedagogical myths the educators believed was that children should not be taught how to read and write until they started grammar school. One of the peculiar explanations of this doctrine stated that in order for kids to learn to read and write, they must reach the age when their brain is ready for "concrete operations." The widely established opinion was that educating a child in the basic disciplines should begin later after the child was seven years of age.

However, David was not a complete illiterate. Thanks to his mother and brother, who read him children books almost daily before he entered grammar school, David loved books and dreamed of the time when he would not need to bother Ilana with a request to read him another book. He wanted to read by himself.

Once, a month before David was to finish attending kindergarten and enter a school, his kindergarten group was taken for a walk in the city park. While he was playing with children from his group, he noticed that the teachers of the group were gathered around a child who attended the same group as he did and whose mother was a teacher. To show his knowledge, the mother was asking him different questions. The boy, Igorek, demonstrated to the rest of the group his wide knowledge on many subjects. David felt very upset that, unlike him, the boy knew difference between the left and right. Listening to

Igorek's answers, David understood how little he knew. At his young age, he felt an urge to learn as much as he could in the future.

CHAPTER 5

School Years

On September 1 of 1948, Victor and David were supposed to go to school. Victor went to the tenth grade, the last one, and David to the first one. Until the early 1960s, schools in the Soviet Union were separate for boys and for girls, so, naturally, their school was for boys only.

Victor and David's school was located in one and a half kilometers from the Lamms' home. For his first day at school, David was dressed in new clothes and shoes. Ilana handed him his vinyl school bag, in which he carried his primer, notebooks, pencil case, and eraser. In the other hand, David carried a bouquet of flowers. Later, when Samuel held his younger son by his hand on the way to school, he gave the bouquet to his father. There were many other pupils with their parents in the little square in the front of the school when Samuel and David arrived there. Obviously, David's father did not share the solemnity of the moment, because after telling David that he had urgent business to take care of, he left right away.

The "A" and "B" first-grade classes were located in a small building that, before the October Revolution, had accommodated Cheder, a Jewish school. David's teacher of the first class A was a remarkable woman named Zoya Kondratevna Osintseva, who played an important role in the shaping of David's character. The other teacher was Valentina Petrovna Kazantseva, an elegant, tall, and slim woman with a beautiful face and an elegant stature. Her dog, a large German shepherd, obediently sat next to her at the head of the class.

Valentina Petrovna introduced herself to the schoolchildren of both classes, which were in the same classroom, and began her introductory speech. The theme of her speech was unexpected: she spoke about the plight of people in America. To first graders who, from the official propaganda, already knew that they lived in the best country in the world, Valentina Petrovna said that each student should double his gratitude to the Motherland because in such capitalist countries as America, people with dark skin were discriminated against and suffered on a daily basis. According to Valentina Petrovna, in America, innocent people, mostly with dark skin, were regularly lynched without trial or investigation. The class listened with open mouths, and three students began to cry in compassion with the victims of the capitalist system.

The first day lasted for three hours, after which the parents arrived to take their dear children home. The only exceptions were David and a boy who lived across the street from the school. Either David had so impressed his parents with his independence that they decided he could easily return home by himself, or his father simply forgot about necessity of bringing his son home. When the last child left the school, David realized that there was nothing for him to do but to return home by himself. The problem was that he had never gone from the school to his house alone, and he was not quite sure how he was going to find the way. His heart beating with excitement, he left the schoolyard and tried to remember how he came to the school with his father in the morning. He clearly remembered that he walked with his father to the school straight, making no turns, and now decided to do the same. His heart continued to beat like a bird in the cage when he began his long walk. When he was finally home, he was inexpressibly happy. David's appearance did not produce any surprise in his mother, who was sure that her son was so smart that he would never be lost. Another example of a wishful feeling.

—

The next month of study at the school was uneventful. Students studied six days a week, Saturdays included, so six days a week, with a small briefcase in his hand, alone or with other students from his class, David went to school and returned home five hours later.

After a month of study, his teacher, Zoya Kondratevna, began to give her students homework. David was good in all subjects except calligraphy. Despite his best efforts, handwriting was his weak point. There are people whose writing is nice and those whose writing is ugly—the main reason is different brain wiring. Ilana did her best to help him with the subject, but her contribution did not help, and all that was left for her was to sigh deeply at the sight of her favorite student's ugly doodles.

After the first month of study, David was returning home from the school. He had just received his notebook with the last homework from his teacher and now was very curious to learn what grade—the first in his life—he had received for it. Passing the alley in the city park, he took a seat on a vacant bench, opened his briefcase, and pulled out his notebook.

The Soviet school system had adopted a five-grade system for students' evaluation; the highest achievement was graded a 5 and the worst a 1. David eagerly opened his homework on calligraphy and to his great displeasure found that he received grade 3, written in red, for his work. From his brother, Victor, David knew too well that 3 was a bad grade, and therefore, his parents would be unhappy with him when they saw his low academic achievement. Shame on me, he thought to himself. Not to be a disgraced by his parents and brother, something had to be done.

Looking with regret at his bad evaluation—not just a three, but a three with a minus—David suddenly came up to a brilliant solution: he would erase the grade, and nobody would knew what had happened. Inserting his hand into the bottom of his briefcase, he pulled out an eraser. Looking around, he saw too many adults who could see him during his questionable action. To avoid undue interference, with a rapid movement, David put the notebook back into his briefcase and hid himself securely behind a large bush at the edge of the alley. Realizing that he was doing something inappropriate, David pulled his notebook out of the briefcase and began to erase the 3-minus grade from the page. Initially, he was happy that the grade written with the red ink was gradually disappearing from the page, but in a moment his success turned to disaster. In the place of the grade, there appeared a hole through which David could see the sheet underneath.

With the expectation of a punishment for his cowardly action, David dragged himself home. When he appeared before his mother, she met him with affectionate smile and a delicious dinner on the table. She asked her son many questions about his school day, but—what a relief—she never asked him to show her the notebook with its testimony of his inappropriate action.

During his school years, David's parents relied on his consciousness, and only on rare occasions did they asked him to show them his *дневник* (report card) that until the present time is the main way of communication between the teacher and parents.

The next day, David told his teacher, Zoya Kondratevna, that to his great regret (tears appeared in his eyes) he could not find his notebook. The teacher was so impressed with his trick that she tried to console the "poor" child.

When he returned home, following the conspiracy rules, David buried the notebook in his backyard.

Everyone draws conclusions in their own way. Instead of failure, the episode with the hole in the page had a positive effect on him: after that, he applied more effort to his homework and achieved better academic results.

—

Only a small number of buildings on the block where David lived had survived the war, and as a result, there were not too many children in his neighborhood. For a while, the only friend he had was a boy his age named Sashika. As his friend's father was in jail for theft, his mother and grandmother brought Sashika up. Overall, Sashika, with whom David spent plenty of time, was a peaceful kid. Among the many facets of street life, Sashika taught his friend about such details of human body anatomy that David's parents would not approve of.

When David was about to finish his first year at school, he shared with Sashika the news that he now knew numerals.

"Oh, numerals. I know them well," Sashika said with an air of superiority, but David did not believe him.

"OK, Sashika." David pointed to a large double-digit number depicted on a metal plate on top of the façade of his house, the house number. "In that case, tell me what number is written there."

"I can't say what's written there," Sashika responded after focusing intently on the number. "The digit on the plate is too small for me to see."

From time to time, "just for fun," Sashika took David with him to the city flea market. There the sellers of the secondhand goods easily recognized him; in low voices, they asked him about the whereabouts of his imprisoned father.

Once Sashika asked David to accompany him to meet his friend several blocks from the place where they lived. There, his friend introduced David to a gang of children. At his young age, David did not have any idea what this group of urchins between seven and twelve years old was doing and perceived the actions of the gang as fun. To his surprise, David heard the boys discussing with ardor how to steal a bicycle that somebody had left in the backyard of a printing company secured by a chain. Seven-year-old David, a child from a law-abiding family, heard about stealing first time in his life. Though he did not have any desire to participate in stealing, on the other hand, he did not want to end his connection with so many "interesting" friends with whom he himself he felt much older. Fortunately, during this episode, his new "friends" did not go any further than a theoretical discussion in their plans to steal.

It is hard to understand why David's very loving parents were not interested in learning more about their son's friends. Most probably, after the bloody war was over, they were under the impression that the peace reigned all over, or maybe they thought that they still lived in the little town where they grew up and where everyone knew each other. Another possibility was that they thought that their seven-year-old "smart kid" was always able to make perfect decisions. As for David, he was too young to tell his parents with whom he spent time and what he was doing with the young children's gang. For him to be a member of it meant fun and excitement in the otherwise boring routine of everyday life.

David had just started the second when, in at beginning of a hot October day, the leaders of the juvenile gang decided that the group would go to the city food market. As the youngest member of the gang, David did not have any right to ask what they were going to do at the market; he was not even interested in "why" and "how." He was pleased that he was treated as a full-fledged member of the gang where interesting things happened all the time, but most of all, he was interested in entertainment.

In the morning, under leadership of his friend and neighbor Sashika, the six-urchin band gathered at the city food market. In the market, all its members, except the youngest, David, who could not understand what was going on, began running back and forth around large piles of watermelons, looking at them as if they were on an exploration mission. Periodically, they gathered in a group and discussed something in muffled voices. Eventually, David got bored and went home.

—

Not a week had passed since the David's gang's visit to the market when a big, tall boy, two years older than David, approached him during a break at school. David knew that he was a student in his class, Lazar Schmerlehes, but he had never spoke with him before. Due to a miserable academic performance, he was taking the class for the third or fourth time. Lazar had swarthy skin, dark eyes, fat lips, and protruding black hair on his head. Hardly anybody talked to him; he was too old for his classmates. As for David, he hardly ever noticed this pupil in his class.

"Give me your lunch," Lazar said to David without introduction.

"Why should I? I'm hungry myself," David answered, surprised and indignant.

"Because this Sunday, I saw you with your friends at the market."

"So what?"

"You and your friends were stealing watermelons."

Only then did David understand the intentions of his gang when they were running around the piles of watermelons. What the result of their "operation" was, David did not know, but having an innate sense of guilt, he suddenly realized that regardless of the gang's success, he had indirectly participated in the act of stealing. That upset him very much because he knew well that thievery was not good at all.

"But I didn't do anything bad there." David tried to protest.

"I don't care. If you don't give me your sandwich, I'll tell your parents and the teacher that you are a thief."

David was too young to know how to deal with extortion. He did not know what might happen if his teacher and his trusting parents learned that he belonged to a gang of thieves. All his short life, he had tried to be a good boy, and he did not want to lose trust of his parents, who were generous in praising and expressing their love for him. He felt extremely ashamed about the possibility of appearing before his parents and his teacher, especially, for such an embarrassing issue. The sense of nonexistent guilt was burning in his young heart.

He had no choice but to give his sandwich to this Lazar. For his inexperience in dealing with extortion, he paid dearly: for the next three years, until Lazar was expelled for poor academic performance, each morning at school David handed Lazar his sandwich, which his caring mother never forgot to prepare for him. His extortionist never forgot to demand David's lunch. David was unable to avoid the bullying, but he decided that he was not going to be affected by extortion. He did not want to be a victim, so he ordered himself not to pay attention to the problem and allowed the situation to resolve itself. He never complained to his parents because he did not like to complain and because he was afraid that his parents might believe that he really was involved in theft. Besides that, it was his inborn philosophy that it was his own responsibility to deal with his problems.

Five years later, David's patience was rewarded. A ninth-grade student on his way home, he was passing the backyard of a furniture store. Unexpectedly, he heard behind the fence the loud, hoarse voice of his longtime extortionist, so familiar to him. David looked in the direction the voice came from: for sure, it was the extortionist of his young years, Lazar Schmerlehes. Dressed in sloppy, dirty clothes, he had become big, fat, ugly, and rough. Obviously, he worked as a loader in a furniture store. David felt more than avenged: he was receiving an education and had plans for the future, while his former bully was now overweight (probably because of his habit of eating other people's snacks) and worked as a luckless laborer, and his destiny most probably was to live in misery and poverty the rest of his life.

—

School Number 6, which David attended, consisted of two buildings. David's grammar school was located on the other street block from the one where his brother, Victor, studied. Victor's class was located on the highest floor of a three-story building.

One day, when David was in the first grade, after his school day was over, he decided to pay an unexpected visit to his brother. He climbed on foot to the third floor and found the class in which his brother was a student. The tenth graders were on a break, and David, who could not see his brother in the classroom, asked one of the students where he could find him.

The student to whom David had turned became excited.

"Are you asking for Victor Lamm? Follow me, kid. I'll show you where your brother is," the student said with a sly smile. He took David by the hand and dragged him toward one of the windows in the classroom. Three more students joined him. Jumping and whistling on the move, they surrounded David. When the group reached the window, David understood that something bad was going to happen and tried to get away. This was impossible: the students held him tight. The student whom he addressed opened the window wide while three others grabbed David by his hands and with joyful laughter pushed him toward the window. Then they took him by his legs, pushed him out, and let him dangle as if he were a pendulum. Afraid that his torturers would let him loose, in which case he would fall to the ground head first, David was silent. Several infinite minutes passed until the young sadists decided that they'd had enough of the entertainment. They pulled David inside the classroom and. not stopping to laugh at their victim's panicky appearance, let him go.

Later David learned that Victor had skipped school that day. He did not say anything to anybody about his frightening experience.

For better or for worse, he followed his principle that each person is responsible for solving his own problems. From this, it follows that if parents want to know what is happening to their children, they should speak with their children and not withhold important questions.

—

In the years following the Second World War, children were not spoiled with entertainment. Therefore, when the students at David's school learned that a troupe of young artists would perform a marionette play, they were very excited. The performance took place in the wide corridor of the second floor of the school. The students settled down on the floor and the Theater of Marionettes was placed in the center of the corridor. David, who was eleven years old at that time, had seen puppet shows in the past, but he had never seen the Theater of Marionettes, where puppets were controlled with wires or strings attached to the artists' fingers.

Impatiently and with great curiosity, David and the other children watched how, initiating the observers into the secrets of their trade, the artists installed their equipment. In the first row at one side of the corridor not far from David sat Leonid Zacharovich Spravtsev, head teacher of the school, a man in his early forties, strong, tall, handsome, and a little plump. His face was round and regular, and his hair was dark and straight. He was a good speaker, and his speeches were clear, logical, and understandable to children. He appeared as a man of authority on whose word people—children and adults—could rely.

After a short preparation, the performance started. Maybe because the marionette show's crew was talented or because David was seeing this kind of a show for the first time in his life, he was truly enchanted with the presentation. An unusual feature of the performance was that the artists who controlled the dolls were not hidden by the curtain but worked openly. However, this did not distract attention from the dolls at all. David was not the only one who enjoyed the show. Other children in the audience reacted to the extraordinary performance enthusiastically. It was enchanting to see how the lifeless dolls suddenly revived and how they became a part of an interesting and fascinating story that was filled with motion, passion, and emotion. Puppet masters pulling the appropriate strings were transforming inanimate dolls into images filled with a full-blooded life and unforgettable identity, transforming immovable objects into vivid characters.

Children were laughing, applauding, and singing with the puppets when all of sudden, like thunder from the clear sky, the audience heard head teacher's loud cry: "Stop the show immediately!" Nobody could understand the real reason for stopping of the production: the audience was well behaved, and the performers were on a high professional level. The actors looked at the head teacher questioningly, not knowing what was going on.

Despite children's polite protests, the head teacher was relentless.

David could never understand why an adult, especially a teacher, could spoil the children's pure joy. Like other children, David felt as if somebody had taken his favorite toy away from him without any reason. Is it possible for teachers, especially the experienced ones, to behave this way?

—

David was twelve years old when he started middle school. Aside from the unhappy episodes that might happen to any child, David was a cheerful boy overall. He belonged to a category of people who had the ability to forget the misfortunes they came across in their lives quickly and to hold much longer in their memory kind words of support and human warmth they encountered in life. One of David's main tools against bad moods was interesting books; with them, he was magically transferred to the world of their heroes. In grammar school, he was lucky to have a teacher named Zoya Kondratevna, a woman who, for reasons that were unknown to him, liked him so obviously that jealous students in his class called him "a teacher's favorite." David decided to take this nickname not as an offence but as a badge of honor. Zoya Kondratevna evaluated his academic achievements with the same strictness as of the rest of the students, but at the same time, she did not hide her respect for his personality. She was able to instill in David a respect toward his personality and a feeling that he must take himself seriously—qualities that David retained for the rest of his life. In the pedagogical approach, that is called "disciplining with love"; praise, spoken or implied, helps a child much more than criticism. The desire to be loved and respected is universal, and expressing love or respect to deserving children serves as a powerful positive stimulator to them. Besides that, children and adults behave much better if they are presumed to be innocent rather than when they are suspected of bad intentions.

Since David attended the middle school, instead of one teacher, he had different teachers for different academic subjects. Meanwhile, his classroom teacher was Elizabeth Alexandrovna Zek. This began a completely new era for David: he lost the sweet status of the teacher's favorite that he had enjoyed at the grammar school with his teacher, Zoya Kondratevna, and now he was an ordinary student.

Moreover, at the beginning of the school year, his reputation suffered irreversible damage in the eyes of his classroom teacher. This happened when his mother had to visit a sick relative in another city. She left David and his father alone two days before David started middle school. To entertain his son, who was temporarily without his mother, his father couldn't find anything better to give him as a gift than a toy gun that shot *pistons* (paper-roll caps).

"You see, David, I realize that you're not a small child," he said, handing David the gun. "I couldn't resist buying this toy gun. It looks very much like the one I had in the army.

David enjoyed the present and played with it at home, shooting the paper-rolls caps. Then he made a big mistake by bringing the toy gun to his new school in his pocket to boast about the toy.

Andrei Vachrushev was one of many new students David never met before. During a long break, he noticed something sticking out of David's pants pocket and asked what it was.

"A toy gun. It shoots paper-roll caps," David answered with pride, and pulling out his toy gun, demonstrated what it could do.

Andrei Vachrushev did not deign to comment. Using the ancient rule "the stronger rules," he quickly snatched the gun and a long tape of caps out of David's hands. At least he was noble enough to promise David that he would return the toy at the end of the day.

After the long break was over, all students returned to class for a math lesson. Suddenly, in the middle of the lesson, the sounds of gunfire were heard in the classroom. After a superficial observation, the teacher easily determined that they were produced by Andrei Vachrushev. The boy was entertaining himself by tearing separated caps from the paper roll and then rubbing them under his shoe, resulting in a bang. The teacher sent Andrei to the principal's office where, under a light interrogation, Andrei eagerly and willingly named David Lamm as the culprit who had given him the paper-roll caps. To protect himself further, he said that David had not only supplied him with the toy gun, but had also taught him how to make the paper-roll caps explode under his shoe during the lesson, which was a lie.

The next day, David and his father had a conference with classroom teacher Elizabeth Alexandrovna Zek. David's teacher decided that David would be the class troublemaker. She was outraged and ordered David not to attend school for the next three days. His long honeymoon with his previous classroom teacher at the grammar school, Zoya Kondratevna, was over, and from now on, teachers treated David as an equal among equals.

—

Starting in the sixth grade, David's classroom teacher was Raisa Chaimovna Yusim, a fair, slightly overweight woman in her late thirties. Raisa Chaimovna had a plain face with freckles, and her hair was fire red. She had an agreeable character but—nobody is perfect—on rare occasions, she exhibited an ability to be strong and inflexible in her decisions. That same year, a new history teacher, Kira Ivanovna, came to his school. She was in her midthirties, nice looking, tall, slender, and blonde. Her face was long, her eyes blue and deep set, her teeth even. She was a good teacher, and David liked it when, with a pointer in her hand, she guided the class through the tortuous course of history. She was very accurately dressed, usually wearing the same beige business suit, which was nothing unusual. In Russia, where people, especially teachers, earned a pittance, female professionals who belonged to the middle class often wore the same nice clothing, which they accurately maintained and carefully protected from damage for a long time.

Though Kira Ivanovna was not the students' favorite teacher, she was respected, and class discipline during history lessons was on quite a good level.

During a long break between classes, Raisa Chaimovna asked David to follow her to an unoccupied classroom, where Kira Ivanovna already sat. With a solemn expression on her long face, looking forward, her arms folded and knees tightly squeezed together, she sat at a student's desk. Raisa Chaimovna sat next to her, and they both stared at David, who stood before them not understanding what was going on.

"Student Lamm, we called you here so you could apologize to Kira Ivanovna for your bad behavior during her class," Raisa Chaimovna said in soft but resolute tone. The history teacher did not take her eyes off David.

David was a good student, loved to enrich his mind with knowledge, was interested in history, and hardly ever really misbehaved. He thought that Raisa Chaimovna, who had been his classroom teacher for the last two years, knew him well enough not to suspect him of significant mischief. With this in mind, he thought that there was some mistake and calmly assured both teachers that he never misbehaved and would not do so in the future, but the teachers were not satisfied. While Kira Ivanovna continued to stare silently at him, Raisa Chaimovna continued to demand the apology. Sounding now like a broken record, she repeated her unproven accusation, to which

David, also like a broken record, answered that that he would apologize if one of the teachers told him what he was to blame for.

"You know what you did wrong, student Lamm. You're mature enough to know that what you did requires an apology. Kira Ivanovna does not expect anything from you but a simple apology."

Again and again, David asked what he was accused of, but his inquisitors were not going to enlighten him on it. As a heavy loaded train, they could not stop demanding that David apologize. It was important for them to succeed in breaking the student's will to resist their demand for an apology for a misdeed unknown to him.

There was no end to the mini-torture and eventually—sick and tired of the absurdity of what was happening—David said, "OK, I apologize to Kira Ivanovna for something I don't have any idea that I did."

Strange as it may seem, his inquisitors were satisfied with the strange apology, ignoring or not even understanding how absurd it was. All they wanted to hear from David were two words of apology; the rest of the "apology" they either didn't hear or just didn't care about.

"Well done, David. If you had said this from the very beginning, then it would not have been necessary to lose valuable time for the whole conversation. You were supposed to admit your guilt from the very beginning and not waste our time. And now you can go."

This episode undermined David's faith in his teachers. How could he take them seriously after what happened? He did not doubt that Raisa Chaimovna and Kira Ivanovna were decent people. Unfortunately, their desire to prove a personal principle was above decency.

—

At the time that David went to school, children graduated after the tenth grade. Though the Soviet Union let the whole world know, day in and day out, that it stood for peace in the world, that rhetoric did not prevent it from military education of the population from a young age. Starting in seventh grade, during lessons in military education, students learned how to read maps and navigate in unfamiliar terrain, how to shoot a gun, how to throw grenades, and other related things.

Until children mature, they perceive life as a chain of adventures that revolve around them, each day expecting something new and intriguing to happen to them. David was an eighth-grade student when, during a long school break, a classroom teacher handed him a big anonymous envelope stamped "Personal and Confidential." At the sight of the letter, David became excited, and his chest filled with a pride. He thought the correspondence must contain something very special, and it might be related to an important mission unknown to him.

Unfortunately, the classroom teacher handed the letter to David in the corridor, where excited and curious fellow students surrounded him. They demanded that he show them what was in the letter. With difficulty, David escaped his schoolmates in the corridor and ran away from his friends down to the first floor, where he found an empty classroom. There, first making sure that the door was closed, with impressionable heart and shaking hands, he opened the envelope and pulled from it an accurately folded standard-size piece of paper. The anonymous author wrote in that he was sending this correspondence to David because he was the class's Komsomol leader. The author of the letter ordered David to keep the correspondence secret and not to share it with a single human being—his parents included.

In order to strengthen the defense of the country, the author of the letter stated, Komsomol leader David Lamm was responsible for the physical endurance of the students in his class. The author promised to inform him in the next letter how this was going to be implemented. Meanwhile, David was supposed to be ready for all kinds of contingences.

The letter excited David. In his young imagination, he saw himself at the vanguard of the defenders of the country. Only yesterday, he was just a regular student, and today he was on a special mission. That meant that he and his class would be able to make their own contribution to the task of defending their country from the imperialist sharks of the capitalism who, day and night, dreamed of occupying his country. David was not troubled that he was a general without army; his vivid imagination allowed him to see himself sitting on a white horse with the baton of a commander.

Having finished reading the letter, David carefully put it in his pocket and returned to the classroom, where the curious glances of his classmates were focused on him. He tried not to pay attention to the students and was as silent as a fish. His best friend, Yulius, with whom he was sharing a desk, called on David time after time to find out about the contents of the letter, but David ignored him as well.

During the school break, David, who suffered with the desire to share his news and forgetting all the warnings set forth in the letter, invited his friend Yulius Berkovich to the far corner of the classroom and laid out to him all the secrets in the letter. Yulius promised to keep the secrets like a spy. When they returned to the classroom, their classmates' glances were focused on both David and Yakov, but accomplices keep secrets tight.

Returning home, David assumed that his parents would be intrigued with the news as he was. To induce their interest, he put the letter on the dining table demonstratively, but neither of his parents expressed an interest in what was written there.

The next day, more classmates than before demanded that David and Yulius let them know what was written in the recent letter, but the friends were mum. During the next break, David signaled Yulius that he wanted to speak with him by pulling the letter from his pocket and waving it at him. Before he could put the letter back to his pocket, a student, Stepan Ribalko, seized it from his hand and disappeared with it in an unknown direction.

David realized that he had compromised the secret letter. What to do? What punishment awaited him? With Yulius he ran through the school floors in the search of the thief. Finally, they found Ribalko in the school latrine, where he was reading the stolen to his friend. They were having a great time: for some reason, they laughed loudly, as if the contents of the letter amused them. David and Yakov attacked them, and after minutes of fighting, David was able to get back only a part of his letter. Even this was torn into many pieces, as if it had gone through a meat grinder. The other part of the letter found its place at the bottom of the school latrine.

Now David was seriously worried what the letter's author would say if he saw the lamentable appearance of the secret document.

After two weeks of excitement and uncertainty, David's classroom teacher handed him another anonymous letter addressed to him. This time David hid the letter deep in his jacket pocket and opened it only at home, making sure that no one was watching him.

Finally, part of the puzzle was resolved: the letter said that David should come to the city military commander's office for a private meeting.

At the appointed time, not notifying his parents and not knowing what might happen, David arrived at the city military commandant and presented his invitation to visit to the officer on duty. The officer took him to a door at the end of corridor and, entering into the office, introduced David to the military commander, Colonel Grechkovsky.

Behind a big table sat a man in his forties with a stern expression on his manly face. Three stars on his shoulder straps confirmed that he was a colonel in the Soviet army.

"Hello, Komsomol member David Lamm," he said, shaking hands with the visitor. "Sit down. We're going to have an important conversation."

Sitting opposite a military commandant, David felt glowing excitement, a sense of his own worth increased to cosmic proportions. Who could doubt his importance when the military commander himself had had an adult conversation with him?

"As you know, David Lamm," the commandant began, intently looking at his face, "our country is surrounded by enemies on all sides. American and European imperialists are dreaming of destroying our country. That's why you're being taught military arts in school. Additionally, our Ministry of Defense wants to further improve the level of military teaching in schools. Specifically, your class had been chosen to make some of your students the future officers of the Soviet army. We want your class to be reliable defenders of our socialist Motherland."

"I agree," the visitor confirmed.

"In your class, David Lamm, you'll be the leader. We'll provide your class with the necessary knowledge, materiel, and practical training. You should keep this visit secret and be prepared for all kind of contingencies. Before you leave, we'll give you special literature about military service. Distribute it to your schoolmates and wait for further directives.

After the visit to the commandant, David had a secret meeting with the boys in his class. He distributed the literature given to him at the commander's office and hinted about the future advanced military training. The attitude of the students toward the upcoming advanced military training was mixed: on the one hand, they were reluctant to get involved in the extra work, and on the other hand, they wanted something unusual to happen, instead of the routine boredom.

Be that as it may, time passed and nothing happened. Eventually, when some pupils stated that they want to begin the advanced military training, David decided to write a letter to the commander. He wanted to know what was happening with the great idea, but instead of an answer, he met the commander, who was there in his military uniform, at the city cinema.

"Good day, Comrade Colonel. Remember me? I'm David Lamm, a student from School Number 6."

"Yes, I remember you. What do you want?"

"Comrade Colonel, I didn't receive any new instructions from you regarding the project that we discussed. Should I wait?"

"Student Lamm, the Ministry of Defense temporarily stopped the project. The plans changed; we are targeting a group of children younger than you."

"So we are no longer chosen?"

"Your class is not chosen right now, but please, tell the students of your class that we might introduce the course we discussed in the future. Do you understand?"

"Will be done," David replied, putting his hand to an imaginary visor.

—

Using citizens for social purposes was a usual practice in the Soviet Union, and students of all ages were an integral part of this movement. All over the country, it was popular to arrange periodic so-called Subbotniks, the full translation of which is "socially useful activities performed on Saturday." Subbotniks arose in the spring of 1919, during the Civil War and military intervention, in response to Lenin's appeal to improve the work of the railways. In 1920, Lenin himself participated in the Subbotnik, and his participation in cleaning a territory and carrying a log on his shoulder with three other workers (who were significantly taller that he was) became fodder for Soviet propaganda.

As with many other voluntary activities, in many ways Subbotniks were nothing more than an imitation of activity. Results were fragmentary and temporary, and subsequent benefit did not follow.

One of the socially useful activities in which students were obliged to participate was recycling, the collection of *Утильсырье*, paper and metal, raw materials for reutilization.

At the time of one of David's class's recycling drives, the most conscientious student was Pavel Maslov, who grew up in a family where he was encouraged to perform good deeds. David liked Vitya but instinctively kept a distance from him after Pavel unintentionally almost killed him. This happened when their physical education teacher persuaded the boys to extend their achievements in physical fitness. In order to pump up their young muscles, among other activities, he recommended that students work with weights. The most popular weight was a *poodovic*, which weighed sixteen kilograms, or thirty-five pounds. In the class, there were three such weights, and during the break, the boys took turns lifting them.

One day, David and his schoolmates were lifting such a *poodovic* next to the blackboard at the front of the class. His *poodovic* was at eye level when another thirty-five-pound *poodovic* passed within an inch of his head at a high speed. Speaking of miracles: if this weight had been only one inch closer to David's head, his skull would have been shattered into small pieces.

David recoiled and realized that the student who had almost deprived him of his life was none other than Pavel Maslov who, instead of apologizing, made a loud, reproachful remark advising David to stay away from him. After that, Pavel resumed working out with the weights as if nothing had happened while David stood next to him with his eyes bulging, unable to utter a single word.

The recycling campaign at David's eighth grade started at the beginning of the school year. The school coachman, who periodically swore in the presence of students without hesitation, was sitting on the crossbar of the school-owned, horse-drawn cart that provided transportation for students and now was used for hauling the collected paper and metal products.

The modus operandi was that the recognized leader of the students, Abram Levin, who did not suffer psychological inhibitions, visited any new office that was on the way. In the office, he asked for the administrator. During the short meeting with the administrator, he made a win-win offer: the administrator could clean unnecessary paper products out of the office while the schoolchildren got credit for procuring this stuff for recycling. Of all the calls, the most successful was the one made to the sanitary-epidemiological station. The administrators were happy to get rid of deposits of paper products that had accumulated there for many years. In response to Abram's eloquent appeal, the happy administrator and the office workers themselves helped remove the piles of paper, dropping them on the curbside. The students picked up the heaps of papers, roughly sorted them out, and put them in the cart.

Only Pavel Maslin, the pioneer of recycling, looked carefully through what was on the ground. At the moment the cart was almost full, Pavel found nice clean notebooks and several convenient folders for storage of documents and posters in good condition. Children can be charming, and they can be cruel. Instead of praising Vitya for reusing valuable paper products, many of his schoolmates began to give him different offensive names, ignoring the truth that he was more conscientious than they were. One of nicknames Pavel was "awarded" was Plyushkin, the character from book *Dead Souls* by the famous Russian author Nikolai Gogol who collected and amassed useless things.

He laughs best who laughs last. Nowadays a huge industry around the world confirms Pavel's foreknowledge regarding a rational approach to recycling.

In October 1957, when a scrap-collecting campaign was conducted in the country, the school principal, Michail Michailovich Mamaichuk, mobilized students to collect metal. Following the old national tradition, the girls were excused: they were probably considered too delicate for such a mission.

After hours spent in search of material to recycle, the students found a treasure in the fenced territory of a large yard that belonged to the local semi-military volunteer organization, the Society for Assistance to the Army, Aviation, and Fleet (DOSAAF). Through the top of the six-foot-high fence, the students of the ninth class carefully explored the yard and saw not just one or two metal objects, but piles of rusty metal of consisting of old beds, automobile parts, sheet metal, and household objects. All this was there for the taking. The students were excited in anticipation of the major success. It didn't seem that there was anybody on the horizon to prevent the students from becoming the school winners in the collection of metal junk.

David was among "the magnificent seven" who climbed and jumped down the fence. Trying not to attract attention (after all, the junk was the property of the state), the team rushed to the desired wealth. The students operated quickly and effectively, hauling heavy, rusty items and throwing them over the stony fence. Such inexhaustible enthusiasm was impressive.

It might have been a major victory on the front of the collection of recyclables if not for the appearance of a group four men from the building. They ran in the direction of the students to prevent them from stealing the rusty state junk. All the students except David noticed them right away and rushed toward the fence. David noticed what was happening only when his schoolmates where already behind the fence. Understanding the situation, he threw a deformed metal bed base on the ground and began to run toward the fence. He had almost thrown his body over the fence when the DOSAAF activists caught up with him and pulled him down to the ground by his shirt. Holding David by his arms as if he was a state criminal, the DOSAAF activists solemnly led him to the organization's main building.

The leader of the group, dressed in a business suit with a blue-and-white tie, was a short man with rosy, dimply, and shaven cheeks, who looked like a young revolutionary.

"Comrade Chief, allow me to report that we caught this young man on our organization's property," the leader of the pursuers reported to his superior when the group entered the office. "He and some other juveniles were stealing socialist property."

The superior was a mature man in whose eyes could be clearly seen sparkles of normalcy.

"What kind of socialist property did this guy tried to steal?" he asked.

"He and his friends were stealing metal scrap from the backyard of our building."

"Well, young man, this kid was actually involved in a useful deed."

"How come?"

"How come? Very simple! These guys were doing what we were supposed to do a long time ago. They were helping us clean up our territory, which we were supposed to do ourselves."

"But they were stealing from our organization, Comrade," the young leader protested.

"They were not stealing," his superior answered. "They were collecting scrap metal for recycling. They did it for our Motherland, respectably. Let this kid go."

The disappointed leader let the culprit's arm go, and David ran away from the building like a wild horse.

Eventually, David's group won anyway, because the other school group could find nothing else for scrap metal but sewer covers that were lying on the sidewalk. City workers had removed the covers a week ago when they were fixing the sewage line. The students were ready to haul two brand-new forty-pounds cast-iron covers to the school, which would have provided them the coveted victory, if not for a female supervisor of the public work, who caught them.

"Aren't you ashamed to steal? Shame on you, Komsomol members! Drag the sewer covers back right away; otherwise, I'll call the police," she yelled at them.

"But Comrade Supervisor, we're serving our Fatherland," the smartest student, who wore silver-framed glasses and whose father was a city lawyer, objected. "We're gathering scrap metal for our socialist motherhood. We were told that it will be used to defend our country from enemies."

"Smart aleck," commented the supervisor. "Yesterday, two people broke their heads because the hatches to the sewers were open."

For recycling enthusiasts from the other group there was nothing else to do as to return to school with empty hands. David's group won.

—

David's classmate Abram Levin was a colorful character in his school years. There was no end to his shenanigans in school and out of it. On many occasions, David could not understand when Abram was serious and when he was joking. To be with him was always fun, and David felt proud to see in Abram a Don Quixote figure while he was Sancho Panza.

At school, Abram was considered a pranks champion. His jokes and tricks were never wicked; almost all of them were self-deprecating. This did not prevent teachers and especially the school principal, Michail Michailovich Mamaichuk, from punishing Abram periodically for his lack of serious attitude toward the learning process. Different teachers ordered Abram to leave class on a regular basis and not to come back without bringing his parents to school for a conference regarding their son's behavior.

For unknown reasons, a bad relationship arose between Levin and the mathematics teacher, Khariton Maximovich Konischev. According to Levin, Konischev intentionally gave him mathematics quizzes that were difficult to solve. When Levin did not know how to solve such a problem, Khariton Maximovich, with his face in an impenetrable expression and refusing to provide any explanation, gave Levin bad grades.

Before becoming a pedagogue, Konischev had been an army officer. At forty years of age, he was well groomed and fit. His only problem was his passion for alcohol. He never came to class blatantly drunk, but when he addressed class, the alcohol vapors from his mouth sometimes could be smelled up to the third row of student desks.

Somebody—not Levin himself; Levin was a silent supporter of the idea—suggested playing a trick on Khariton Maximovich. The trick was to put a small bottle of vodka on the lectern and then see how he would react to the fruit of his desires. On the day of this project, the class was in tense silence when Khariton Maximovich entered the classroom. At the sight of the bottle, he did not show any embarrassment. Instead, he took the bottle in his hands, unscrewed the cap, and then demonstratively took couple of sips of vodka to prove that the trick did not work on him.

Konischev's suspicion of the authorship of the trick fell on Abram Levin. The next month Abram received only low grades in Khariton Maximovich class. That continued until the teacher's wife fell ill and needed foreign-produced medications that it was not possible to buy in drugstores. Levin's father, the head of a pharmacy, personally delivered necessary supply of drugs to the teacher, which restored peace between the educator and the student for a time.

Abram Levin and David Lamm shared a love of writing. They were cooperating in producing school's monthly wall newspaper *Did You Hear?* and provided help to all who wanted to express themselves in poems, short stories, and articles. A talented student in their class, Valeriy Dushenkov, a real artist, provided excellent drawings for the wall newspaper.

To be popular the friends were in constant search of ideas and found one after an event at Beltsy's School Number 2, which, like their own, was one of the largest in the city. School Number 2 was for girls only then. The majority of teachers there were also women; however, the school principal was communist named Jan Petrovich Petrushenko, a married man in his late thirties, energetic and nice looking. He was a stern disciplinarian; in his presence, students were afraid to misbehave. His subjects were literature and poetry. He was not only a teacher of these subjects but was himself an author of original romantic poetry, which betrayed his rich imagination and romantic passion.

Recently, two young teachers, Larisa Osipovna and Maxim Trifomovich Leonovs, a newlywed couple, had joined the staff of Jan Petrovich Petrushenko's school.

Larisa Osipovna taught geography, and Maxim Trifomovich taught physics. In the eyes of the school principal who, under the influence of poetry, saw in women an embodiment of divine beauty, Larisa Osipovna was a woman of inimitable splendor. Her blonde hair was artfully curled, and her lips were a deeply painted red. She was a real princess with high cheekbones; bright, intelligent, sharp blue eyes; and statuesque bone structure. Her laughter was generous, and along with her smiles, it filled men's hearts with joy and excitement.

With all his love for women, Jan Petrovich was a down-to-earth man. He loved his wife and considered her the best. Nevertheless, he fully appreciated the beauty of the female newcomer and demonstrated it in different ways after he met her. Not made of iron, Larisa Osipovna could not resist his intense adoration. For herself, she justified her reciprocity by their mutual love of immortal poetry. Strong love of poetry became a valid reason for the teachers' meetings in Jan Petrovich's personal office between the school's first and second shifts.

Did not the famous writer Albert Camus write, "Beauty is unbearable, drives us to despair, offering us for a minute the glimpse of an eternity that we should like to stretch out over the whole of time"? To make sure that nobody dared to distract their exchange of lofty ideas, the married man and poet in his soul kept the door to his office locked during their platonic encounters.

Following the laws of biology, it could be predicted that our heroes would fall in love.

Unfortunately, all good and bad comes to an end, as Jan Petrovich wrote in one of his poems. During a warm and picturesque October, Larisa Osipovna and the principal held a regular meeting dedicated to poetry. On this day, they read love sonnets by William Shakespeare. As usual, to make sure nobody interrupted their poetic bliss, the door to the office was locked with a key. The power of Shakespearian poetry and the intimacy of the space, or maybe just the warm weather, resulted in a predictable side effect: the poetic couple gradually began to take off their clothes. The poor poetry lovers did not know that behind the locked door were gathering dark clouds. An ancient Mycenaean saying states, "You can be a hundred times innocent, but there will always be evil spirits."

It happened that previously, a colleague of Larisa Petrovna's husband had hinted to him that his pretty wife spent too much time in the principal's office. On this fateful day, passing the second floor of the school, the jealous husband saw a cleaning woman and asked her if by chance she had seen his wife. The school cleaner first put a finger to her lips and then pointed to the principal's office. Previously experienced waves of jealousy in the teacher's chest transformed to a tsunami of the offended feeling. Maxim Trifomovich forgot the rules of subordination. He ran to the principal's door and began to pound on it with his hands and feet.

The couple in the principal's office forgot about Shakespeare and his poetry and went into a panic. Jan Petrovich was devastated: as the Communist Party member, he could be accused of immoral behavior unworthy of that title. According to the official Communist Party line, sex was allowed only for married spouses. Jan Petrovich was losing self-control; he was afraid that he would be expelled from party membership. In despair, he rushed to the window, opened both frames widely, and not thinking twice jumped out.

Fortunately, destiny took pity on him, and a tragic end did not follow. The principal was lucky. His life was saved thanks to the strong fabric of the awning that decorated the front of the school, which was located directly under the window from which the school principal had jumped. He was alive and well, but his honor suffered seriously when the second-shift students, who were on their way to school, saw their principal and strict disciplinarian, dressed only in his old family drawers, trying in vain to hide himself in the awning of the building.

The situation was successfully resolved thanks to firefighters who carefully removed the principal using the truck's ladder. Jan Petrovich escaped with a reprimand for immoral behavior and was forced to pay for a partially torn school canopy out of his salary. The higher-level Communist Party organization decided to transfer him to a smaller school where nobody knew him. There he became a principal again, on the condition that he not to share his love for poetry with married women.

Maxim Trifomovich divorced his wife, but eventually joined her again in holy matrimony six months later. As for Larisa Petrovna, she gave birth to a baby boy, Alik, who, according to her, looked incredibly similar to his father, Maxim Trifomovich.

In the aftermath of this, which was remarkable to the provincial city, Abram Levin and David decided to write a story. Their collaboration was fruitful, and in a week, they had created a short dramatic novel entitled *For the Love of Poetry*. The words they used in the story were more graphic than would be expected from the pens of humble sixteen-year-old boys from nice families. Valery Dushenkov's illustrations of the story were totally incompatible with the puritan Soviet ideology. These crude graphic drawings depicted the misadventures of Jan Petrovich and Larisa Petrovna, both scarcely clad and in compromising poses.

The story written by young authors became an immediate success among their classmates; the entire class read the romantic story about two exemplary teachers, and none of the students betrayed to outsiders the fact of the story's existence. The last student finished reading the story and returned to Abram Levin. It is a well-known fact that a secret is difficult to keep, and despite all efforts, gradually, the teachers at the school learned about the existence of the samizdat underground novel penned by students.

Levin, Dushenkov, and David were under serious suspicion, and the dream of some David's teachers was to obtain the story in order to satisfy their growing curiosity. Elizaveta Borisovna Ksendzovskaya taught biology to David's class. She was an energetic woman of spherical form, short in height and with short hands. During one of her lessons, she showed the class a movie about the meiosis and mitosis of cells. While watching the movie, Abram Levin had the imprudence to hold a suspicious notebook in his elevated and slightly abducted arm. While he was watching the reproduction of cells on the movie screen, Elizaveta Borisovna crept up to him on her short legs and victoriously pulled out of his hand the notebook with the *For the Love of Poetry* story.

Levin, Valery, and David were in a state of shock. What would happen if the principal saw the story with the X-rated illustrations? Would they all be expelled from the school?

Neither Levin nor David inform parents about what happened.

A week after Elizaveta Borisovna took the notebook from Abram Levin, classroom teacher Raisa Chaimovna invited the presumed authors of the story and their parents to attend an extraordinary teachers' meeting. On the agenda was one item: a decision related to the authorship of the story created by the irresponsible and immoral students. David's parents did not share his agonizing worries about the outcome of the situation. They sincerely believed that their wonderful son, David, was unable to participate in such an inappropriate activity as the depiction of an adult love affair.

On the appointed day in the main school auditorium, all the teachers gathered to participate in the pedagogical counsel.

Dushenkov, Levin, and David were expecting the worse and decided beforehand not to admit their guilt; after all, nowhere in the notebook was the author mentioned. In the anticipation of the punishment that awaited them, the ill-fated authors were tensed and worried.

School principal Michail Michailovich Mamaichuk opened the extraordinary meeting. Holding the notebook with the story under the discussion, he asked the alleged authors—separately and together—if we they were the creators of the reprehensible story, which cast a shadow of disrespect on all Soviet teachers. Each of the possible culprits—embodiments of innocent lambs—denied any role in penning the *For Love of Poetry* essay. Knowing that the decision of the teachers' assembly could destroy the defendants' lives forever, they were ready to deny any accusations. After the last denial of guilt, principal Mamaichuk suggested expelling all possible creators of the immoral essay from the school. Valeriy Dushenkov's mother, a simple woman in casual dress with a kerchief on her head, cried out in anguish, "Comrade Principal, we are asking for mercy." David's and Levin's mothers joined these desperate pleas, but not a single teacher expressed any sympathy for the accused.

"Your handwriting appears to be almost the same, and we can't prove which one of you wrote this shameful nonsense, but we're sure that one or all of you are the authors of this horrible composition," principal Mamaichuk continued. "I know that something described in this story might have happened at School Number 2, which competes with us, but that doesn't give you the right to use this event to express your immorality. Your parents should be ashamed of raising such bad children. You're a mold on society, that's what you are, and I suggest expelling all of you without the right to attend another school in the future. Before we vote on that, we want to hear opinion of our *partorg*, the secretary of our school Communist Party organization, Comrade Lichacheva."

Anna Charitonovna Lichacheva was a teacher of the Soviet constitution. In her early fifties, she always wore the same clothes: a gray jacket and a blue skirt. On her inexpressive face were written resentment, anxiety, and concern.

"Let me tell you, comrades, I am grossly outraged, and in principle I support Michail Michailovich Mamaichuk's suggestion to severely punish these students," she started. The accused group shuddered at her fearsome voice. "Two months ago, you asked me to become the secretary of the communist organization at this school, and now I ought to tell you what I think about this matter. With all due respect, Michail Michailovich, you see only a narrow aspect of what these little rascals did. I say no, no and once more, no. Maybe you don't mind messing up your name and the name of my school with this stupid story, but I am against it. Comrades, do you realize what a scandal might happen if somebody in the higher party bodies finds out about this stupid episode? Forget about these brainless students; think about what could happen to us, including you, Michail Michailovich, and me. Do you really want to face accusation that our pedagogical staff overlooked the outrageous behavior of degenerative bourgeois nature that happened in our school? Do you want it said that our school educates a generation of perverts and debauchers? I personally read the trash in the notebook word for word, and with all responsibility, I state that these three dumbbells could not have written this opus. I consulted with teachers of literature, and we all agree that children cannot be smart enough to write such a text. They are too stupid. All they can do is to cheat from cribs. Some adult wrote this wild nonsense, but we are not a detective agency to look for this individual."

"Then what do you suggest we do with these students?" the principal Mamaichuk cried out in despair.

"We're going to do nothing, that's what we're going to do," Comrade Lichacheva answered. "We should not forget that the prestige of our school is above all. These little bastards have already had their lesson. They know well now that they played with fire. They know as well that if something of this kind ever happens in our school again, they will be the first under suspicion, and we will expel them without any discussions. I do not want the prestige of our school to suffer because of this episode, and I suggest throwing this notebook in the garbage where it belongs. That's the end of the story."

The accused students were happy beyond description. Thanks to the unerring logic of the secretary of the party, they escaped a tragic conclusion to the ill-fated story. Such miracles happened in the socialist society daily.

—

The school where David studied was new, but four years after its opening, when David was in the ninth grade, construction defects began to be revealed. The first flaws manifested in the quality of the plasterwork: from time to time, its pieces spontaneously or with an accidental touch fell down.

During one of the midday breaks, David's friend Pyotr Demik started a playful fight with him. At first, David didn't want to respond, but eventually he met the challenge, and with laughter, friendly punches were exchanged. During this "entertainment," David accidentally bumped his foot into a wall corner opposite the door of his classroom. This small bump resulted in a separation of the plaster, first on the bottom of the corner and then higher. Eventually, half the corner's plaster fell down to the floor with a crash. The noise of the minor destruction caught the attention of the chemistry teacher who was walking by.

"Whose work is it?" he asked, pointing the "naked" part of the wall.

Without hesitation, Pyotr Demik pointed at David.

The bell rang; all the students entered their classes and took their seats. In the middle of the lesson, classroom teacher Raisa Chaimovna entered the class. The students stood up to welcome her.

"Sit down, class," she said. "You, student Lamm, continue to stand. Are you the one who destroyed school property during the break?"

"But it was by accident. I only slightly touched it," David responded.

"Put your belonging in your school briefcase and go straight to the principal. Let him sort it out."

"How dare you to destroy our dear socialist school property," Principal Mamaichuk asked when David entered his office, an expression of deepest regret on his face. "Do you understand what you've done? The state builds this beautiful school for you, and students like you destroy it. Shame on you!"

"But I didn't do it intentionally," David answered. "All I did—I was next to it and by accident touched it with the tip of my shoe and *bach*, the wall fell down. That's all."

"I don't accept your excuse. I can't allow vandalism at school. Go home and tomorrow at eleven a.m., I'll expect you and both of you parents in my office. Understand?"

"Yes, I understand."

"Good. Now you can go. Wait a second. Lamm. Is your father the head of some kind of a textile business?"

"Yes."

"OK, now go."

It was the first time David's parents were ever called to see the school's principal. Naturally, they were surprised, and when David described the problem for which he was responsible, Samuel began to laugh.

"But your school has a special budget to fix such petty things," he explained to David, smiling. "It's clear to everyone you didn't do anything maliciously. It is not your fault if plaster fell down from a minimal impact."

The next day David and his parents sat in the principal's office. For starters principal Mamaichuk repeated his accusations against David as if he had destroyed the life of a human being. David's father, who was aware that his son could be expelled from the school, had no desire to argue. When Mamaichuk finished his harangue, Samuel asked only what would be necessary to contribute to the school in order to restore the wall to the appropriate condition.

The principal revived after this question. At that instant, all accusations against David were forgotten, and conversation touched only on practical issues.

"Here's what the school needs," Mamaichuk said, taking out of his pocket a paper he had prepared before the visit. Your son told me that you're in charge of a business, so I don't think it will be difficult for you to provide my school with the materials necessary to fix the wall."

Samuel wrote in his notebook everything that principal Mamaichuk had softly extorted from him. At the end of the appointment, the principal was so satisfied that he shook hands with David's parents and specifically told David not to worry about anything. After three days, the wall was successfully repaired, and the problem was resolved.

This episode occurred in the distant year 1957. Forty-seven years later, in 2004, David visited the city of Beltsy with his wife. Among other places, the spouses visited School Number 6, from which David graduated in 1958. The visit aroused many memories in David, and when he passed by the door of the classroom where he studied, he recalled the defective plaster story. Curious, he approached the ill-fated corner next to the door to the classroom where the incident happened so many years ago. He carefully inspected the corner, and there it was: a seam, a wrinkle, commemorating the border between the original plaster and the plaster used to repair the wall almost fifty years ago.

—

While studying in high school, David was lucky to have many good teachers. A good teacher is a treasure who combines many talents. In particular, a good teacher knows how to discipline students without threats, yells, and lecturing. In David's school life, the best example of such a teacher was thirty-two-year-old Dmitry Iosifovich Motorny, who taught the ninth class the seemingly simple and undemanding subject of drawing. Before the new teacher appeared at the school, students considered drawing to be a subject of secondary importance. Amazingly, this teacher was able, without visible effort, to transform this unimportant subject into a subject of primary importance.

Dmitry Iosifovich Motorny, a tall, athletic, handsome man with manly features in an accurate three-piece suit with a tie, was a veteran of the Second World War. He was born in a Ukrainian village and was an excellent drafter himself. Each time, after a short introduction at the beginning of the lesson, he turned to the blackboard, carefully cleaned it with a wet sponge, and then made a drawing of such a beauty that, when the class was over, students did not erase it and tried to preserve the image on the blackboard as long as possible.

Even more amazing was that he was able—never raising his voice—to maintain an iron discipline in the class. When it was necessary, he had an armamentarium: not insulting, but effective healthy sarcasm and irony. From the moment he entered the classroom, the silence was so profound that it was literally possible to hear a pin drop.

Small talk and vulgar humor were not in Dmitry Iosifovich's nature. During his lesson, attention to the subject was undivided. When students, almost shaking from excitement, presented their drawings to him, his praise, which consisted of a short but meaningful phrase, was the best award they could dream of.

Once, Mr. Motorny brought with him a metal detail. He gave the class its measurements and assigned them to make a drawing of this product. Working at home on a round dining table, David spent a lot of time trying to make a good sketch. The next week, during the drawing lesson, Dmitry Iosifovich summoned David to the blackboard to present his work. With drawing in hand, David confidently approached the lectern where the teacher sat. Dmitry Iosifovich looked attentively at his work and then unexpectedly frowned.

"What is this?" he asked David sternly, pointing to an oily spot on the drawing. David had no idea where it came from.

"I'm sorry. I don't have any idea how it got there, Dmitry Iosifovich. Honest."

A difficult-to-forget repartee followed after a meaningful pause.

"Tell that to your grandmother when you're taking a nap with her, lying on the Russian stove," said Dmitry Iosifovich, looking at him with a hypnotic look. The students laughed carefully, not quite sure that they themselves would not soon become a subject of this type of a joke.

A Russian stove was a large, multifunctional device, where the usable part of the stove heated the house and the rest served for cooking, provided a warm place for sleep, and, when necessary, was used for the treatment of colds.

Teacher Motorny never showed that he was not confident in what he said and what he taught. He never became defensive with those who tried to challenge him; he silently gave them a piercing glance, and—if that did not help—he asked them to stand up, and in a quiet but assertive voice that manifested his unquestioned moral and personal authority, achieved the desired result.

Dmitry Motorny only taught David's class for a year and couple of months, which was very unfortunate for the students, but fortunate for the teacher. When he came to class for his last lesson, the stern and resolute expression disappeared from his face. To the amazement of the students, who had no idea that he was leaving, their strict teacher appeared joyful, open, and relaxed on this day. Not only that: he was friendly and warm, and the grades he gave to the students appeared to be higher than usual. Forty-five minutes of his farewell lesson passed like one second. When only five minutes were left of the class, Dmitrij Iosifovich stood up and announced that it was his final lesson.

"Why?" the students asked him, astounded. "Are we bad?"

"No, you're good. I like you, and I'm grateful to you for giving me an opportunity to teach you," Dmitrij Iosifovich answered with a wide manly smile they'd never before observed. "A while ago, I graduated a cinematography college, and yesterday I received an invitation to take a position as a movie operator at the Moldova Film Studio immediately."

His news of a prestigious profession produced a great impression on the students of David's provincial town. Soon Dmitry Motorny became a famous man in the field of cinematography; he was involved in the creation of more than a dozen famous films.

The week after Dmitry Motorny's departure, a new drawing teacher came to David's class. He was Oleg Andreevich Martinov, an average-height, fair-skinned man in his late forties, with straight blond hair and an already-receding hairline. The new teacher had an absentminded air about him.

With the appearance of the new teacher, the students had an unpleasant opportunity to find out what a great teacher they had recently lost. From the moment the new teacher appeared, discipline became a forgotten word in the class. Oleg Andreevich did not have any idea how to control his students. Or maybe he just didn't care about discipline in the classroom. In any case, those students who chose to misbehave moved freely in the class, noise was intolerable, the quality of teaching reduced to zero, and drawing class became a secondary subject.

Teachers like Oleg Andreevich were on the other pole of those who were able to effectively control and lead a class. There were not many teachers—men or women—like him at the school. Teachers who could not discipline students ignored the chaos in the classroom. Male teachers tried to show that the misbehavior of the students did not bother them, while female teachers periodically resorted to crying, which had the opposite effect on students.

The majority of teachers did not have a big problem with student discipline. Nevertheless, during their classes, a constant white noise produced by students talking among themselves did not stop for a minute. This constant noise produced by boys and girls could be stopped only on those rare moments when students were directly threatened or voluntarily shut their garrulous mouths.

CHAPTER 6

Pioneer Camp

After David graduated the first grade, Ilana and Samuel decided to send him to the pioneer camp. They did it out of the best intentions and were sure that it was a nice gift. However, despite their true love for their son, they were pretty naïve thinking that David would enjoy a place located far from his home and without any means of communication with his parents.

Samuel took his son to the pioneer camp early in the morning. On a bus, they traveled to the capital of Moldova Kishinev, 105 kilometers from Beltsy. They arrived in Kishinev in the morning. Before taking his son to the pioneer camp, Samuel left him with a woman acquaintance who lived in downtown. He said that he had to take care of "important business," not letting David know when he would be back, The acquaintance was a small old woman in her late sixties, who lived in a garden-level apartment. As soon as Samuel left, the woman asked David to sit on a stool in the middle of the living room. And so, for the next couple of hours, he sat where he was ordered while his hostess stared at him with curiosity from time to time as if he was an interesting specimen in a zoo. When Samuel finally arrived, he told David that he'd just discovered his medical form was not ready yet, and that for him to be accepted to the pioneer camp, they need to find a medical office where it could be filled out. Samuel found such a medical office not too far from where they were. They went there, and after half an hour of waiting, David was called in. The doctor was a tall young man with a pleasant face. For David this visit was hard to forget because, when the time came to examine his throat, this "pleasant" doctor shoved the spatula down his throat so far and with such a great force that David was not able to get rid of pain for the next week. What was the problem with the doctor? He could have acted this way because he was inexperienced, because he was under stress, or because he just was a medical sadist. All were possible.

In the afternoon, the father and the son arrived at the pioneer camp, located in a remote suburb of Kishinev, via the local bus. When David's documents were accepted in the registration room, Samuel kissed him on the cheek and forehead, said goodbye hastily, and left him in the care of the pioneer camp employees.

It did not take David long to discover that he was now in an inhospitable place where children were treated as a commodity. As for any little child, it was a difficult for him to be there. His parents had no idea that the four weeks that David would spend at the pioneer camp would be traumatic and painful for him. There, David was a boy without name, whose face hardly anyone could recognize. At the camp, David received enough food and beverage, slept well, and was not physically abused, but he ceased to exist as a person. Telephone connection with his parents was not possible, but even if it had been possible, there was no chance that David could have explained to his parents what was happening to him. Not without reason—in one of his children's books, he read that to live in decent poverty is better than to be an orphan in a royal palace.

—

On the day after David's arrival, many more children came to the camp. On this day, David was introduced to the sexual life of human beings.

His first encounter with sex had happened two years before when he was six and a half years old and lived in Pontonnaya Station. On that day, Ilana took him with her to visit her seamstress. While David looked at a children's book that he found on a table, the women were involved into discussion about fashion. In the middle of the conversation, the seamstress's daughter came in. She was two years older than David, thin, tall, agile, full of energy, and radiating beautiful smiles.

Entering the room, she greeted everyone and then cast a quick appraising glance at David. "Mom, we are going to play outside," she announced and, taking David's hand, went with him out into the backyard. "My name is Varvara. What's your name?"

David named himself.

"Good, David. Now follow me."

"Where are we going?" David asked Varvara as they went along the path surrounded by bushes on one side and a river on another.

"Don't worry. Follow me and don't fall behind," she answered in a conspiratorial tone.

Soon Varvara brought her new young acquaintance under a bridge over the river and sat with comfortably David on the grass.

"What are we going to do now?" David inquired of the girl.

"You'll see right away," Varvara said, smiling mischievously and examining David from head to toe.

"Do what I do," she said, taking off her dress. Puzzled, David took off all his clothes. At his young age, he was surprised that they should be facing each other, naked, on this relatively cool day as if there was nothing else to do.

The girl looked at David, touched a part of his body she was not supposed to touch, and minutes later, having carefully examined her partner from all sides and satisfying her curiosity, she whispered that she thought somebody was coming, and therefore, they must get dressed and run home. The couple quickly dressed and in a short time were in the girl's house.

Now, at the camp, David was again exposed to something he was not supposed to be exposed to in his age. Standing next to a group of older children who were not paying any attention to him, he heard their loud whispered discussion, which he could not initially understand. It took a while for David to understand that the children were talking about a male and a female camp counselor who had left the main building and gone deep into the cemetery adjacent to the camp. The point of the story was that the male counselor had a raincoat with him, which, in their "expert opinion," would prevent his female companion from the inconvenience of laying on the bare ground.

When the discussion was over, David joined a large group of boys who ran into the cemetery, looking for the couple hiding among the gravestones.

"Why are we looking for them?" David asked the camper who was next to him.

"Don't you understand? We want to see how they're fucking," the teenager declared authoritatively.

David did not have any idea what the word *fucking* meant, but he understood it was something intriguing. In search of the couple,

David went his own way, different from the older children. Five minutes later, using his own intuition, he found the couple of interest. Lying on a raincoat thrown on the grass, they were performing—with the enthusiasm of youth—the act mentioned by the teenager with the definition as yet unknown to David. David did not have any idea why the male counselor was on top of the female counselor, or why they were producing peculiar movements and strange sounds. Not knowing what exactly was going on, David felt that it was not something for young children to see.

Most of David's knowledge about life arrangements was gleaned from his life experience. Parents and educators assumed that the child would learn about the intriguing issue of the relationship between the sexes through osmosis, observation, and trial and error. In their turn, children don't usually ask parents questions regarding the intimate life of human beings.

The primal scene that David witnessed imprinted itself in his memory.

Georgiy

Every day at the pioneer camp was a replica of the previous one. At seven o'clock in the morning, the pioneers woke up to the sounds of the bugle. After making their beds, washing up with cold water, and getting dressed, they ran outside on the court to line up in two rows in the shape of a square. Each camper stood with his corresponding squad. When all the participants had taken their positions, the leaders of each squad marched one after another at a solemn and measured pace toward the chief pioneer leader, who stood in the middle of the square. Coming close to the chief pioneer leader, the squad leader gave a pioneer salute—right hand lifted to the level of the shoulder or applied to the headdress (if it existed)—and then pronounced the words of the report: something like, "Comrade Chief Pioneer Leader, my squad has so-and-so many members. All members are present for today's inspection." After the chief pioneer leader was done listening to all the reports, he gave the order "Raise the flag!" and two children chosen for this occasion slowly raised the red flag on a high pole.

A child does not need too much to be pleased. David was on top of the world when he, a small, thin, undetectable, abandoned kid, was chosen to participate in the ceremony of the flag rising one day.

There was not much entertainment in the camp, so after each of the three meals, the pioneers were left to their own devices. Early one evening during this free time, David had only one memorable encounter with a Moldovan boy, Georgiy, who was a year older than he was. Georgiy lived not far from the camp and visited it alone to hang around with the children on the camp playground, which was located in the church garden.

Georgiy, dressed in a loose black shirt with big white buttons, was thin, tall, and of rather swarthy complexion. He and David were so carried away with their conversation that they did not notice when it became dark. All the other children playing in the garden had gone back to the camp. Only David and Georgiy stayed behind, walking along the alley lined with old trees, slowly approaching the garden gate.

In the gathering dusk, Georgiy mentioned the word "God" several times.

"What does 'God' mean?" David asked his new friend.

"God is the One who created the world," answered Georgiy firmly and confidently. "My parents told me about God, and they know everything. God sees all, knows all, and helps all the people, especially us children. He can do anything. God is in heaven, in the air, in the trees, everywhere, in every place. He is always with us," the young mentor stated with certainty.

"But where is He? Can we see Him? Does He see us now?" David asked Georgiy impatiently.

"If you really want it, you might see Him yourself. God is everywhere. In heaven, in the sea, in the air. He watches us, and when we need Him, He comes to our aid."

"But where is He now? Does He see us this moment?"

"Yes. Of course He does. Just look carefully and you'll be able to recognize Him."

Little by little, the gathering dusk began to intensify the bright light of the rising moon sailing up from the horizon. The moonbeams made their way through the tree crowns, spreading a wide, openwork lace of shadows on the paths and grass in the garden.

The definition of God that David had just heard produced a lasting impression on him. At that moment, David, a painfully lonely child with his eyes wide open in search of kindness, stared into the darkness, trying to discern the face of the One Who cared for him, for a tiny breathing wet dot in the vast expanse of the universe. To his amazement, a vision suddenly appeared before his eyes: on the top of the thick trunk of one tree and then on the other, in the vague outlines, he saw the face of He Who would never abandon him.

Having reached the gates of the church's garden, David and Georgy parted. David never had another chance to meet that mystical stranger who told him for the first time in his life that the One Whom David, as other people, subconsciously sought did, indeed, exist.

—

As there was no running water in the buildings at the pioneer camp, the children washed up with cold water from primitive washstands. Only once during the second week of the month-long stay did the children have an opportunity to wash themselves with soap and hot water in a public bath. David's squad went there in the afternoon. The bathhouse, located two miles from the camp, was a brick building, old and dilapidated both inside and outside. A stuffy and damp dressing room boasted dirty cement floors and no individual lockers. Boys took off their clothes, put them on the common benches, and were then directed to a large, dark, steamy hall.

Cold and hot water trickled intermittently from faucets operated with oversize wooden handles. Each child received a piece of unpleasant-smelling laundry soap and a basin. They brought the basins to the faucets, filled them with water, and took them back to benches where they could wash themselves. When David carried his basin of water to the bench, he saw a tall, large man in army boots in front of him, probably an employee of the public bath. Ignoring David's presence, the man passed him by and with all the weight of his big body, stepped on his foot. David screamed from severe pain, but the man did not even think to apologize to a young child. Instead, he yelled at him, using coarse profanities the meaning of which was not known to David. In conclusion, he hit David's back hard with his open hand and, muttering under his breath, left him. David was lucky; at least this man did not break his foot.

—

The next day, the camp expected a treat. During breakfast that day, one of the counselors notified the campers that in the afternoon they were going to watch a real movie—the first and last one during their stay.

The movie that David watched that day was great beyond all his expectations. The film *Vesyolie Rebyata* (*The Jolly Fellows*) took him back to the world of joy and humor from which he was temporarily barred: the abandoned thing that he temporarily became apparently had not forgotten how to have fun and laugh loudly.

The next day, a monotonous and boring life returned to the camp, but the children continued to discuss the movie among themselves.

David did not remember if he ever changed any piece of his clothing at the camp, but the most upsetting were his shoes. He outgrown them, and now they were too small for his feet. Since his feet did not fit his shoes, David walked on the inner side of them, which completely deformed his footwear, making walking a painful task to which, as a child, he did not pay attention.

The worst of all was the lack of opportunity to communicate. Maybe if David were an orphan, he might have adapted to such conditions, but he grew up with his family around him, and the present emotional vacuum deafened him.

Then, to his great relief, came a day when his mother and Victor, his brother, visited him to say hello and to see how he was doing. David was immensely happy to see them, and for a short time, he forgot misery of his daily existence. In the camp's dining room, the family enjoyed delicious food that the guests had brought with them. Finishing the meal, David showed Ilana and Victor the camp. After a short walk, they reached the cemetery, which was a part of the church property. On this beautiful warm day in July, they found a nice grassy spot. Ilana took a thin blanket out of her bag and spread it on the grass, and they all settled comfortably under the shade of a big tree.

Ilana, periodically kissing David and stroking his face, told him about different things that had happened recently in the city of Beltsy. When Ilana and later Victor were through with the news, David pleaded with them both to take him home.

Since birth, David had hardly ever complained, but even if he were a complainer, at eight years old, he did not have the words to express his frustration. At his young age, he had not yet reached the cognitive level to explain to adults why he suffered morally at pioneer camp despite the fact he was not hungry, had slept well, and nobody had taken advantage of him. He was only a child, and it was beyond his ability to explain to his mother and brother how alone and neglected he felt at the camp. Maybe if his mother and older brother had not been in a hurry and were ready to ask him questions, they might have understood what was going on in David's life.

Ilana sincerely thought that his complaints were nothing but a childhood whim, and gently smiling, she told David to calm down and that his father would bring him home when his term at the camp was over. David—who rarely cried—this time began to cry, time after time asking them through tears to take him home. Ilana, not understanding the seriousness of his plea, told David that he should be patient and positive and that everything would be just fine. David cried even harder, now frustrated that he was unable to explain how miserable he felt. When his cries did not produce any effect on his mother and brother, he stopped crying. An hour passed. Ilana gave him a kiss, Victor embraced him briefly, and David was left alone again like a bird in a golden cage.

—

Three days later, with only two days left for David to survive in the emotional desert of the pioneer camp, he had another episode that left one more notch in his heart. In all the pioneer camps in the country, including the one where David was, children were obliged to have an afternoon nap. This period was called *мёртвый час* (literally, "dead hour," but actually "an hour of complete rest"). Boys and girls slept on their cots on a top of a coarse cotton fabric, stretched between two backup frames producing an X-like shape. According to the rules, during of *мёртвый час*, each child was supposed to be in a deep sleep.

On that day, David lay quietly between the sheets during the nap, ready to fall asleep. On the cot next to David lay Kira, a girl his age with whom he had not exchanged more than a couple of words. She usually slept deeply during the nap time, but today she was awake and was periodically turning from side to side. Noticing that David had opened his eyes and was looking at her, she asked him in whisper to watch what she was going to do. David was a disciplined child and did not want to break the rules, but he also was taught to be polite and not to refuse the requests of girls.

When he opened his eyes wider, Kira began to demonstrate her achievement. Lying on her back, she moved her belly sharply from side to side with her hands, which produced loud sounds of splashes in her stomach. Unwilling and unable to speak, David only smiled and laughed softly a couple of times, observing his neighbor's silly activity.

When "the dead hour" was over and the cots were folded and set aside, David and the other children were on their way from the bedroom to the playground. At the door of the bedroom stood three kindergarten teachers, including Nadezhda Maximovna, who sat on a chair and read a book while the children were asleep. She was in her early twenties, a very beautiful blonde woman. When she saw David, she took his hand in hers, pointedly looked at the other teachers, and asked him, "So, what is your name?"

"Aha, so your name is David," Nadezhda Maximovna said with undisguised menace when she heard the answer. "How dare you not sleep while all the rest were sleeping? Do you think I didn't see that you and your neighbor were talking all the time? You even laughed twice. Do you think that the rules aren't written for you? You broke the rules, and therefore I will punish you so you'll know how you're supposed to behave.

Demonstrating her pedagogical talents, Nadezhda Maximovna looked victoriously first at the small object of her anger and then at the rest of the teachers.

David stood, unable to say a word in his defense. What could a child say if even adults' defense is done by lawyers? Who would listen and believe his explanation if the sentence on this case was already rendered? All that children can do with this kind of attitude is to apologize. The next moment, Nadezhda Maximovna looked at the other teachers triumphantly, inviting them to witness the final blow.

"OK, David, for your outrageous behavior, go to your room, gather your things in one package, and get out of here. Go home," she said, smiling cunningly.

"I don't live here. I live in another city" was all that David was able to mutter, shaking under glances of the teachers who, enjoying the reaction of the small child, were smiling.

"That does not concern me, boy. Pick up whatever you have and get lost."

David stood before his "judges" as if he had been sentenced to death. In his rich imagination, he saw himself, a little child with a piece of luggage in his hand and deformed shoes on his feet, leaving the camp and walking, walking, walking in a direction unknown to him in the darkness of the night. Chilling fear was now affecting each cell of his body.

"Go! Get ready!" his teacher repeated, pushing David's back in the direction of the exit.

"I don't have anything to take with me," David whispered and went straight to the exit. He passed the territory of the camp with tears running down his cheeks. In a hundred yards, he felt a hand on his shoulder. It was his recent prosecutor, the beautiful Nadezhda Maximovna.

"Where are you going, crazy boy?" she asked, looking at him with a reproving gaze.

David was silent.

"Go back to the camp immediately! Are you doing this so they can fire me?"

David turned around and, with a pounding heart, followed his teacher.

If someone had suggested to Nadezhda Maximovna that she should apologize for her emotional cruelty, she would have been genuinely surprised. She definitely would have said that all she wanted to do was to teach the child a lesson. She would never agree with the fact that what she had done was an example of mental cruelty.

People are different: some of them are angels, some of them are insensitive human beings, and the majority are in between. Compassion is a foreign word to those who are insensitive.

—

Eventually, everything in the world ends. On the last day of David's stay at the pioneer camp, his father took his son home in the morning. After four hours of travel by bus, David was back to his native home. While on the way home, Samuel handed him a gift: the book *Robinson Crusoe*, adapted for readers of a younger age. David read it nonstop. The book was illustrated with beautiful pictures, and reading it, he soon forgot about the miserable times at the pioneer camp.

When David entered his home, his mother covered his face with kisses and then handed him her present for him: a primitive metal flute with a plunger inside. By blowing into the tip of the device and moving the plunger, it was possible to produce a primitive but pleasant melody. This simple musical instrument, along with the interesting book, distracted David even more from recollecting the place where he spent the previous month.

David was practicing his toy flute on a bench outside his house when one of the chimney sweeps working at the Lamms' residence that day walked by. Seeing David, this man whose skin was covered with soot smiled at him.

"Hello, kid. My companion and I were listening to your performance, and we enjoyed it a lot. Especially when you were imitating birds' songs on your flute. Well done. With time you might become a real musician."

A child needs little to be happy and satisfied. David now was a happy child. The words of praise were oxygen for him.

CHAPTER 7

Twelfth Birthday

On the evening of the day preceding David's twelfth birthday, his parents informed him that this year, instead of giving him birthday party, they had decided to present him with a nice shirt, pants, and a pair of shoes. David expressed his gratitude and was ready to leave the room when his father, Samuel, overwhelmed with feelings of paternal love and despite Ilana's disapproving glance handed David thirty rubles—a lot of money for a young boy—and told him that he could use this money at his discretion.

Before going to bed, David thoroughly thought over how he was going to spend thirty rubles on his birthday and came up with a plan for the next day. He woke up early in the morning and after a quick breakfast, carefully placing his father's gift in his pants pocket, first of all went to the boat station located on the city lake. There he rented a boat for a trip. After an hour of rowing, he returned the boat to the station and went to the city's downtown. Instead of going the long way, David took a taxicab—the second luxury of the day. Traveling in the taxi, he felt as if he were already an adult.

Reaching downtown, first he went to the central bookstore. Buying a good book in these times was a difficult task. Most of the books during the Soviet period contained political propaganda while interesting literature was hidden under the bookstore counters and sold only to a select public. Today, however, David was expecting a pleasant surprise: on the floor of the store, he saw boxes of books not yet opened. Reading the labels on two of them, he learned that the boxes contained the book of his dreams: Jules Verne's *Mysterious Island*. This book was so popular among his peers that it was never available in the library.

Fortunately, one of the salespersons in the bookstore today was Dora Berman, a cousin of the Lamms' neighbor Yankel Melman. At least once every two months, David met Aunt Dora in his backyard when she came to visit Uncle Yankel. In the expectation that he would soon own the coveted book, David became excited.

"Good morning, Aunt Dora. Remember me? I live next to your Melman relatives." David addressed the saleswoman.

"What do you want, boy?" answered Aunt Dora dryly, in a tone so different from the sweet one she used when she met David in his backyard.

"I would like to buy the book *Mysterious Island* by Jules Verne. Here's the money."

"Why do you think we have this book, boy?

"Because this book is inside these two boxes on the floor in front of you."

"Oh, you're talking about that. These boxes just came; we need to unpack and register them first. Do you understand?"

"So when can I buy the book?" David asked.

"Well, boy, if you want, come back here in an hour and a half."

To kill time, David went to the popular cafeteria Be Our Guest. As he still had plenty of money, he ordered theatrical cake, a napoleon, and—in conclusion—Ice Cream *Plombir*. To wash down the delicacies, he ordered two glasses of lemonade.

It was too early to return to the bookstore, so—experiencing a slight discomfort in his stomach from too many sweets—David went to the market to see what was going on there.

Passing by a shooting gallery, he learned from a large poster that for each four air rifle shots, the shooter got one shot extra. David had never shot a rented rifle before, but today was his birthday, he still had money, so why not try his luck?

The shooting gallery David entered was a large rectangular room. The targets were located on the back wall of the room. On the right side of the counter for the shooters, David noticed a woman in her fifties in charge. After the customers paid her money, she provided them with an air rifle and bullets. Besides regular bull's-eyes, there were different gadgets in the shooting gallery; each of them had a metallic circle on a side. When a small bullet shot by an air rifle hit the target, a metallic sound was heard, and the corresponding toy in a shape of a water mill, a dog, a doll, a tiger, or a chicken fell down. A longitudinal bullet consisted of two parts: a metal cylinder sharpened at front and a little hairy "tail," actually a tassel, to provide a steady flight for the bullet. After five successful hits, the shooter was entitled to an additional five shots.

There were two customers in the shooting gallery besides David. The woman in charge did not pay any attention to David when he approached her. At his request, she gave him a rifle and five bullets. Of the five targets, David hit only one. When he was done with the first five shots, he twice ordered an additional five shots. At this moment, the indifferent attitude of the woman in charge underwent a remarkable transformation. When she understood that David was ready to pay for services, he became an important customer. Instead of being morose and discontented, now she became agile and full of life. Every time David managed to hit another target, she applauded and smiled widely.

The time passed, and David became bored with shooting. He was on his way out of the gallery, but the woman in charge did everything to encourage David to purchase more and more shots. It was not difficult to understand that though she was dealing with a child, she was manipulating him, pumping out his money.

"I'm so glad you came here. You're such a good shooter! How many more bullets do you want?" she kept repeating each time David finished another five-bullet set.

"Thank you. I'm done," David said, displeased with the pushy salesperson who continued to entice him to buy more shots as if he did not have his own mind.

Leaving the shooting gallery, David realized that it was time to go back to the bookstore.

"Aunt Dora, I am back to buy Jules Verne's book." David addressed his acquaintance in the store.

Again Aunt Dora looked at him as if she had never seen him before.

"I'm too busy now, boy. Come later," she told him squeamishly, not hiding her contempt for her young customer.

"But Aunt Dora, you told me to come in an hour and a half to buy this book from you. You got two boxes of this book."

"I don't remember promising any books to you."

"Yes, you promised me to sell Jules Verne's book."

"Jules Verne's books are very popular, so whatever we might receive is already sold out. That's all I can tell you. Goodbye."

It was not the first time David had heard adults lie, and he knew that it was useless to argue. He decided not to get upset and to continue his birthday celebration.

It was still early to return home, so to finish the day on a good note, he decided to entertain himself at the Circus Shapito, which had recently begun its performances in the city market.

The word *shapito*, translated from French, means *hood* and designates a tent, a collapsible structure of masts stretched with red and yellow canvas. This type of mobile circus was touring in large and midsize cities. David was lucky: the next show started ten minutes after his arrival, and there were empty seats. The ticket was not expensive, and even after the money David had spent today, he still had some left.

The circus performance was in the open air. David found a seat on a bench next to a boy his age. As David still was in a birthday mood, he perceived the circus performance as interesting and fascinating, though on the second thought, it was rather mediocre.

During the performance a dog was correctly solving simple mathematical problems; a juggler was catching discs, balls, and knives; and four acrobats were surprising the public with the flexibility and coordination of their bodies. One performance made a special impression on David. A woman gymnast stood on two narrow beams, which lay on the shoulders of two athletes. She jumped up high in the air, tumbled, and then landed exactly on the beams. She did it perfectly, but David thought that she was performing a very dangerous trick. Each time she landed on the narrow beams, he was afraid she might miss them and fall on the floor, injuring herself. He felt sorry for the poor woman who was risking her life for the spectators' entertainment.

While David watched tricks performed by a magician, his neighbor suddenly stood up and ran away from the circus. Meanwhile, the cascade of magic tricks continued, and explaining how they were done was not possible. Some people around David were not happy that they couldn't understand how the magic tricks were performed. After each new fascinating trick, they repeated the same phrase: "Everyone knows how he does this trick. It is all smoke, mirrors, and fog."

David was curious to hear what people said when they did not understand what they saw. He asked a young woman next to him to explain to him how the magic trick that had just been shown was performed.

"As if you don't understand it yourself! He creates a fog in our brains and acts on our minds. That's how he does it," the woman answered confidently.

David was still not satisfied with such a strange explanation and asked a man who was sitting in a row in front of him the same question.

"You see, boy, he is screwing with our brains. It's something like hypnosis" was the man's explanation.

Meanwhile, a light rain had started, and the audience began to leave their seats. Before David left the circus, he wanted to know how much money he still had. He checked his wallet and to his displeasure realized that his wallet and the money had disappeared. No doubt, David's young neighbor, the one who had run away in the middle of performance, had stolen it. David followed his principle: he had no right to be upset at his birthday. Money comes and goes, but a twelve-year birthday happens only once in a lifetime.

It was early evening when David returned home, full of impressions of the remarkable day with so many adventures.

"David, why are you so late?" his mother asked him when he appeared at the door. "Come in. Look what I prepared for you."

His father, Samuel, who sat at the festive table, was smiling joyfully. "Sit down, David. We're going to have birthday dinner in your honor."

From the kitchen Ilana appeared with all kinds of delicious food on a tray.

Life is good—especially for people who have positive thinking!

CHAPTER 8

LIFE OUTDOORS

After military service in Karelo-Finn Province, Samuel was transferred with his family to serve at Pontonnaya Station in Leningrad Province. Pontonnaya Station was a peaceful place to live, and Ilana, like other mothers, did not see anything wrong in letting her younger son spend time outside without supervision. She combined this liberal attitude with a peculiar attitude toward David's clothes. Until he achieved the age of independence, Ilana was obsessed with the thought that he might catch cold. As the previous object of her obsession, Victor, was old enough, to resist mother's exaggerated concern, all her efforts to prevent cold, flu, virus, and other infections were now concentrated on her younger son. Frequently, when David was outside during the winter, he was overdressed to such a degree that he was sweating and immobilized by layers of clothing.

At the same time, Ilana most probably was still under impression that as long as the war was over, a full peace now reigned in the world. Because of this conviction or because she herself grew up in a small town where everybody knew each other without any worries about their children, she allowed her younger son to play and walk around outside their home without supervision.

Thanks to that, David grew up independent and streetwise, learning from early childhood how to stay away from trouble and how to fight back for himself when somebody wanted to take advantage of him. But he wasn't always lucky enough to avoid a difficult situation. One early winter day, minding his own business, David was walking down the street where he lived, on both sides of which stood houses, some of them built of logs. That day, Ilana hadn't overdressed him too much: he was wearing a warm coat and mittens on his hands. To make sure he did not lose the mittens, they were connected with a string that passed through both sleeves of his coat.

Passing by one of the log houses, which was of unusual architecture, David was carefully examining it when he heard a dog's growl beside him. He looked over his shoulder and saw a large and tall dog. It was a German shepherd, and its appearance did not portend anything good for David. Alas, that was only the beginning. In no time, four more big German shepherds, behaving the same way as the first dog, surrounded David from all sides. Gradually, their growls became louder. Some dogs periodically barked; some just showed their teeth.

David was too young to understand what might happen if the dogs attacked him, and staying in the center of the narrow circle produced by the vicious dogs, he looked at them with naïve childish curiosity. To create a space between himself and the dogs, he instinctively extended his arms shoulder level and slowly moved them left and right, trying to prevent the dogs from getting any closer. This episode could have had a tragic ending if not for the appearance of one more guardian angel in David's life. This time it was the dog pack's owner, who appeared as if from nowhere on his skis with ski poles in his hands. Shaking ski poles in the air, he stopped next to the dogs and sternly ordered them to scram. The pack obediently ran away and left David standing. The dog's owner, not paying any attention to the subject of the potentially life-threatening attack, went straight into his house, leaving to David a memory that woke him up with nightmares later, when he understood what could have happened to him.

—

Life in a provincial town does not present much diversion, and in order to see and learn something new, David asked Samuel to take him along when his father traveled to different places for matters related to his work. Samuel and David were friends, and Samuel himself liked when his son was with him. Such trips exposed David to far corners of the city, the existence of which he did not suspect.

Years did not change Samuel's character. He was still a sociable person with an optimistic nature, and he enjoyed entertaining those who were close to his heart with delightful surprises. It was normal for him, for example, to wake David or his older brother, Victor, in the morning by bringing to their bedroom a dog, a puppy, a rooster, a piglet or, in rare cases, even a turkey. While David was opening his sleepy eyes, Samuel laughed, enjoying his son's reaction.

The weaving business of which Samuel was the head had a horse. Sometimes, Samuel would let the coachmen go home and drive the horse cart to his house by himself. There he tied the horse to a tree and ran inside.

"David, forget about everything and come with me," he yelled. "I have a horse cart outside! Let's go for a ride!"

Who could refuse such a trip at David's age? Under his mother's cautionary remarks, David would immediately dress up and run with his father to the horse cart. The two of them sat down on a bench in the front of the cart, Samuel took the reins, and they went for a ride. Usually, the horse was not as enthusiastic as the riders were, so their speed was slow, but it was a real horse, and it was a great experience. In the middle of their short trips, Samuel would pass his son the reins and a whip, and David became a driver. When David was in charge of the horse, he never used the whip, not only because he did not want to hurt the horse but also because he did not want the horse to have a bad impression of him. The trips lasted an hour or less, after which, with the help of the faithful and sleepy horse, Samuel and David returned home.

Sometimes, in the warm times of the year, Samuel took David with him on business trips as far as city of Kishinev, the capital of Moldova. David's place was usually in the body of the truck. Being there was his own choice: he enjoyed being face to face with the elements of nature. He enjoyed bird songs; he loved when a stream of fresh air enveloped his face and when his shirt became inflated with the pressure of the air and his hair fluttered in the wind. But he discovered a special entertainment, an effect that hardly anybody knew: when the truck was driving through the section of the road where trees grew on both sides, the musical tone of the wind changed.

It was an early morning in the middle of the August of 1954 when Samuel ran into his house, opened the door to David's bedroom, woke him up, and offered him a ride in a truck waiting for them outside. In this truck, Samuel needed to travel to a small stone quarry in the Gypsy suburb to buy stones to build a new plant structure. Their driver was a Gypsy man who lived near the quarry and knew the area well. The trip promised to be interesting.

David did not need his father to ask him twice. In a minute, he was ready to leave. Ilana, his mother, who was at home, did not have anything against the trip: she thought it was better to let her child to see the world than have him spending endless time reading books.

The truck was designed to transport construction materials, so after a short time, David moved from the body of the truck to the cab, next to his father. The driver, Motshan, was a man in his late twenties, swarthy and with broad cheekbones. He was tall and underweight. He had knowing, angular dark brown eyes, a large nose, and a cleft chin. While driving, he concentrated on his thoughts and talked only when Samuel addressed him.

After a while, the truck arrived at a suburb the existence of which the father and son had no idea about. The Gypsy population here lived mostly in small adobe houses with thatched roofs. When the truck stopped in the middle of the suburb, four adults and six children of different ages surrounded it. They all were relatives and friends of Motshan.

The driver opened his door and involved himself in a vivid exchange of news with his relatives and friends. Meanwhile, Samuel invited David to come out of the truck. When David left the truck, he looked around to see where he was. What he saw was an example of urban development where the cart was placed before the horse: first, the residents built houses here, and after that, the other elements of urban development, such as roads and electric poles, appeared. The general impression was that the residential area was in chaos.

Motshan left the truck on a hillock. In front of the car was a slowly descending flat space, which, in a hundred yards, ended at a cliff more than twelve yards in height, a leftover of the abandoned quarry. To the left and right of the path were little hillocks covered with weeds. As there had been no rain for a long time, pulverized dust covered the path and vegetation. Flies were swarming as if the space belonged to them.

David's father invited David to follow him. In fifty yards, a surprise expected David. In the midst of the dirt and dust, he noticed a spring. At the hillock's base, water was running from a little pipe inserted in the ground to a small pit. Someone had paved the pit with rough pieces of stone. An old communal tin can stood nearby on a flat place.

Samuel carefully rinsed the can and put it under a stream of water that was flowing out from the pipe to the ground. "Try it, David," he said with the pride of a discoverer. "You never tasted water like this."

David's father was right: the water was truly outstanding. On this hot day, in this unclean environment, it was surprising to enjoy crystal clear, cool water that seemed to have some sweetness in it.

While David was savoring the last gulp of the exquisite water, a man from a stone quarry came to see Samuel. Neither the children nor the adults paid any attention to David when he returned to the truck's cabin. This time, for fun, instead of the passenger seat, he took the driver's seat. Though the windows were open, the car's cab was hot and humid. All controls in the truck—the brake pedal, the clutch, and the accelerator—were manual. David had forgotten to bring a book with him, and with nothing to do, he began to entertain himself by turning the steering wheel to the left and to the right, pulling handles, and imitating the sounds of a moving car. He tried to move the handle of the stick shift, but it was unmovable. When he came to the brake and clutch pedals, David pressed on one of them with both legs, and to his amazement the truck—for reasons that were incomprehensible to him—began to move down on the declining surface, straight toward the edge of the cliff. Frightened and not knowing what to do, David became paralyzed. Only when he was a meter or two from the cliff did he come out of his stupor and removed his feet from the brake and clutch pedals. When the truck stopped, it was a foot away from the edge of the cliff.

What else but a miracle saved David's life? If the car had fallen over the cliff, our hero, not restrained by a belt (seat belts did not exist at that time), surely would not have survived.

David looked out the window and saw that Gypsies of all ages, most of them with their mouths open, looked with curiosity at him. Suddenly, the door of the cab opened sharply, and Motshan jumped into the car, unceremoniously pushing David from the driver's seat. He inserted the key into the ignition, started the motor, and returned the truck to its previous place. Then, not saying a word of reprimand, which David expected, he left the cab and went about his own business.

Samuel was at the quarry and did not know what had happened.

When the adults returned to the truck, David understood that Motshan never told Samuel about the incident.

On the way back to city, Motshan offered to show the passengers a small lake where it was possible to swim. Samuel agreed, and soon the truck reached the lake. Trees and bushes surrounded the lake, making it invisible from the road. David immediately jumped out of the truck and ran into the lake. The water in the lake was cool and pleasant. After a short swim, David ran toward the bushes to wring out his drawers. To his surprise, in the bushes he saw a young man he had not noticed before. Hidden by trees and bushes, he sat on a big stone and looked at David. Judging by his appearance—the hair on his head was disheveled, and he was dressed in rags—David decided that before him was a homeless man or a poor tramp. When David returned to the truck, he told the adults about a man he had seen. Samuel, who never missed the opportunity to strike up a conversation with different people, came out of the truck and went in the direction of the stranger. David followed him.

Coming closer to the stranger, David was once again convinced of how poor the man was. His clothes were dirty, and there were holes in his old jacket and his pants. His shoes were old, deformed, without shoestrings and with holes in the soles. The stranger was dirty and unshaven with stuck-together brown hair. When Samuel and David approached him, he behaved as if he did not notice his visitors.

"Young man, what are you doing here?" Samuel asked.

"Nothing. Just looking at the lake."

"What is your name?"

"Fedot. Why?"

"Where are you from, Fedot?"

"From Vinnitsa. Why are you asking?"

"Before I give you money, I want to know who I'm giving it to."

"Why?"

"Just to feel better. Here are twenty rubles. Hold them."

"Well, thanks for that. Right now I have only two rubles."

"So, how do you survive, Fedot? Where do you get food, for example?"

"Kind people never let me go hungry."

"How did you end up here?"

"Simple," Fedot answered reluctantly. "I was walking from Sinjereya to Beltsy, and people told me about this lake where I can wash up. After I have enough rest, I will be on my way."

"I wish you a safe trip. Be healthy and try to stay away from trouble," Samuel told Fedot and, not waiting for an answer, went back to the truck with David behind him.

Before this episode, David had read books about homeless people written by Victor Hugo, Charles Dickens, Fyodor Dostoevsky, and Maxim Gorky. These writers wrote many stories about the "humiliated and insulted" exiles of human society. However, this was the first time in his life that David had seen a real homeless man. He felt sorry for the human being, who, despite his appearance, was able to maintain reasonable conversation, who was not in possession of even elementary conveniences, and who lived in the utter poverty.

"Dad, please, can you offer this man some kind of work in your business?" David appealed to his father. "He won't survive if he stays homeless. Please take him, Dad. I'm sure he'll really appreciate what you're doing for him."

"Fedot, do you want to work at my plant? You'll get your first salary in two weeks, and then you'll be paid monthly. Meanwhile, I'll give you enough of my own money to get you to your first payday. Agreed?"

"Well, why not? I agree," Fedot responded after a minute of hesitation and without enthusiasm.

"All right, David, I'm giving him a job, though you seem quite naïve to me. In the beginning, he'll work as a janitor, and later I'll see what else he can do in the plant."

Fedot lifted his old knapsack from the ground and went toward the truck with Samuel and David.

Though Fedot had swum in the clear water of the lake, his clothes smelled very unpleasant, and Motshan offered him a seat at the truck bed. Though the truck bed was not intended for the transportation of people, David joined him. In vain, David tried to speak with Fedot during the trip. Not willing to maintain a conversation, Fedot responded to him in one or two words.

When the truck stopped at the Lamms' house, David got out while Samuel continued the trip. Before taking Fedot to a place he could live, Samuel took him to a disinfection station to make sure he did not have lice. From there, they went to the public bath, then to the barber, and finally to a men's store to buy Fedot some inexpensive clothing.

In the following days, David's dream was coming true. On rare occasions when he had an opportunity to see Fedot, his ward looked quite different from the way David saw him at the lake. Though Fedot did not have a neat look, his clothing was clean, his hair was combed, and he was shaven. Fedot hardly responded to David's polite greetings. He was all in his thoughts, but he worked well and performed his duties adequately. Fedot's transformation filled David with satisfaction, and he was grateful to his father. It was pleasant to him to strengthen his opinion that people like Fedot improved under favorable circumstances.

Eventually, Samuel became annoyed with David's daily inquiry about his protégé, Fedot, and returning from his job, not waiting for David to ask, he told him, "Your Fedot is doing well." That lasted until Fedot received his first check. On that day, when Samuel returned from work, he told David that Fedot was not working in his plant anymore. After receiving his first check, Fedot thanked Samuel and told him that he needed to leave. Samuel offered to raise his salary, but Fedot responded that the work did not fit his character. When Samuel asked him where he was going, Fedot answered that he did not know yet; he would make this decision when he hit the road.

David was upset that his dream had not come true. Fedot had everything necessary for a productive life, but he chose to return to his wandering lifestyle. David discovered that human beings are more complex than books describe them. To each his own. What a pity; this time the miracle did not happen.

—

David's older brother studied at the Leningrad Textile Institute. During summer vacation, which lasted a month or more, Victor came to Beltsy to spend his time with the family. As the firstborn, Victor received more attention and signs of parental respect than his younger brother. A week before his arrival, the house was thoroughly cleaned from threshold to threshold, linens and curtains were changed, and the kitchen stove worked twenty-four hours without interruption. The entire Lamm family, armed with flowers, arrived at the railway station to meet Victor an hour before the train's arrival.

After Victor came home, a generous rest was provided for him; for the first two days, he slept all day, waking up only for the rich meals carefully cooked by Ilana. While Victor slept, his parents would not allow David to produce the quietest sound "because your brother is very tired after hard study and the long road home. He needs a lot of rest. Don't bother him, David. Go outside and play there."

David just graduated the fifth grade, and his vacation coincided with Victor's. On the third day after his arrival home, Victor had had enough rest, and to David's surprise, he woke him up at seven-forty in the morning.

"Wake up, David," he told him, not expecting objections from his younger brother. "Enough sleep. Get up, wash up, and get dressed. We are going to the city lake."

"I'm ready, Victor, but you should know that I don't know how to swim."

"That's not a problem," Victor said. "Come with me, and I will teach you."

David was more than happy. Like any other child, he was eager to learn how to swim. At that time in Beltsy, there was a man-made lake with a little dam. It was large enough to have a boat station, where David's father occasionally took his wife and son for a boat trip. It was before the time when life jackets were required. The only available rescue equipment was a heavy life buoy made of cork that hung on the wall of the water station, attached with nails in such a manner that "nobody could steal it." Boat trips were always entertaining and pleasurable.

Another thing to do at the lake was swimming. It was true that the bottom of the lake was nothing but the famous Moldavian black earth mud and that any bather or swimmer in the lake was exposed to such "mud baths." The secret to avoiding a mud bath was to arrive at the lake early in the morning, when nobody had muddied the water yet.

Victor and David woke up early every morning and were as a rule the first comers to the lake. At that time, the water in the lake—not yet disturbed by swimmers—was clear and cool, and entering the water was sheer pleasure. Learning how to swim was not as difficult as David had thought. Victor was a good teacher, and soon David began to swim on his own: an accomplishment of which he was very proud.

Having had enough of swimming, the brothers lay on a blanket, tanning, reading books, playing cards, and talking.

The brothers returned home when the sun was higher on the horizon and when its rays became hot. At home they took a shower in the courtyard from a makeshift metal barrel to bottom of which was soldered a funnel with a valve. Water in this barrel was pleasantly warm thanks to the free heating provided by the sun.

After Victor returned to the institute, David, who now knew how to swim, visited the lake almost daily. David loved to swim in the lake, and when his friends could not accompany him, he went there alone. On the lake, a dam regulated the level of the water, and David and the other boys used a barrier of the dam for diving. David never was a good diver. He rarely dived with hands and head forward. Usually he dived legs first or, as is said in Russia, "*солдатиком*" ("like a little soldier"). Despite all his efforts to overcome his fear of heights, each time before a dive, David was hesitant to jump into the water. He overcame this hesitancy by making mental efforts to force himself to leap down like other divers.

One day after David had had enough of diving, he dried his body with a towel and, taking his belongings with him, went toward another part of the lake that was used for swimming.

Along the road to the lake, he noticed two teenagers. They were at least three years older than he was. At the same time, to the left of the road about three hundred yards away, David noticed the rest of the gang to whom his counterparts belonged—another three boys of approximately the same age. They were sitting on the ground staring at David.

When David approached the two teenagers, one of them confronted him.

"What are you doing here, kid?" he asked, looking menacingly at David and clenching his fists.

"Oh, so you're going swimming," the teenager replied when David explained to him what he planned to do. "You better go back where you came from!"

"I'll do it if you tell me why you object to my intention," David answered.

"Oh, you don't ask questions here! What are you going to say if I slap your face? What are you going to say if I hit your dirty face?" the boy answered and struck two strong blows against David's jaw. His silent friend joined in the beating.

Since it was one against five, David came to the only right decision in the situation: against this many, he did not have a chance. Fighting back would only give his opponents the right to attack him with all their force, which would be counterproductive. Instead, he intentionally chose "civil disobedience." He opened himself up as much as he could; standing with his arms along his body, eyes wide open, chin up, he consciously or subconsciously reminded his executors that he was not a punching bag but a living human being, the same as they were.

The beating continued, and David felt the blood flowing from his nose. His strategy had its own risks, especially if he was dealing with criminals, but there was a chance it could affect the gang of teenagers, who—hopefully—were not yet fully immunized to performing violence against innocent human beings. Some time passed, and David became convinced that he had chosen the right tactic: the blows to his face were becoming less strong, less resolute, and more hesitant. Emotional stress prevented David from feeling much pain during the beating.

Eventually, one of the three boys who were sitting on the ground and observing the beating, most probably the leader of the group, yelled to the hooligans to stop. Purposeless, "just for fun" beating of innocent weaker people was a well-known phenomenon among teenagers and could be used as an act of initiation into the gang. Angry with the gang, David decided to show them his contempt for their intimidation, and instead of his initial plan to go swimming, he returned to the dam where the gang could easily see him. He took off his T-shirt and resumed diving into the water as if nothing had happened to him.

David was sitting on the edge of the barrier taking a rest between dives when he felt someone take his hand. He turned around and saw before him the leader of the gang that had just attacked him. The leader was dressed in pants and a short-sleeve shirt, while other members of his gang had taken off their clothes and were in their cheap swimming trunks.

"So, did you get a good lesson, kid?" the leader asked David, without menace, in the patronizing tone of a godfather figure.

Not knowing what to answer, David looked at him silently, waiting for what would happen next. The leader of the gang was a handsome-looking teenager of middle height, thin, with recently cut thick black hair. Most impressive was his innate, unfeigned arrogance and an attitude of superiority to others—qualities that made him a leader.

"Well, you probably think you are brave, kid. I saw you could take pain well; you did not cry a bit, though I can see you have a black eye and bruises on your face. But you must understand, you are dead wrong. You must defend yourself when somebody is attacking you regardless of circumstances. What kind of a man are you if you do not resist?"

The gang leader changed his arrogant tone of voice to an almost-friendly one. "Stand up. I'll show you some fighting techniques you could consider using in the future."

In the next quarter hour, the mini-godfather demonstrated to David several methods of martial fighting. It appeared that the gang leader was satisfied with his "disciple" when the free-of-charge lesson was over.

"What's your name?"

"David."

"OK, David. My name is Maxim. You listen carefully to what I'm going to tell you," he said with a solemn expression on his face as if he were somebody who opened the doors to paradise. "I see you are not a bad fighter yourself, and your attitude toward pain is commendable. Congratulations. Consider yourself accepted into my gang. I don't offer membership easily, kid, but I like you. Come to the northwest corner of the city market tomorrow at six p.m. I will introduce you to my guys, and we'll possibly initiate you."

David never saw the rising star of hooliganism again. As for his advice to return punch for punch, David knew better than Maxim: everything depends on circumstance. Life is not that simple; sometimes it is much more beneficial to be cool and vigilant and to respond to provocation with civil disobedience than to respond an eye for an eye, a tooth for a tooth.

—

The Markus brothers had been friends of David's since the beginning of the high school. Lev Markus was his classmate, while William was two years younger. The brothers looked very different. Lev had fiery red hair while William's hair was jet black; Lev's face was covered with freckles while William's skin was clear white.

David and his friends loved boating on the lake, but the problem with boating was that the boat-rental fee was relatively high, and in order to get the boat, the friends needed to come to the boating station with an adult. Eventually, Lev and his brother came to a great solution. "Are we worse than other young artisans?" they asked. "We're going to build our own boat!" The next day, the work was in full swing. The main materials for building a boat, a punt, and oars turned out to be plywood, sticks, and tar. Tools required for the project were a pair of pliers, a saw, a hammer, and nails.

It took one and a half weeks to turn the plan into reality. David's father provided the builders with plywood from his plant; as for tar, that was not a problem, either. Nearby, a team of workers was covering potholes on the road and, when they went for a break, the boys "borrowed" half a bucket of tar from them. Under Lev's guidance, the work of creating of the boat was undertaken with a sincere enthusiasm. First, the boys sawed out the sides and the bottom of the future punt and connected them with pieces of wood and small nails. The next step was to smear all the seams of the punt generously with tar, to make sure it was safely sealed from the water.

After creative and entertaining work, the boat, a punt six feet in length and two and a half in width, was ready to be tested. If the testing were successful, the boys were planning to paint the punt dark gray—the same color used for the rental boats. The boat builders, along with David's father, marched all the way to the lake. Samuel had joined the group voluntarily, after a short secret conversation between him and Ilana, his wife, at home, during which they threw anxious glances at the children. Under the curious glances of pedestrians, the boys, full of self-esteem, solemnly carried the punt by its sides until they finally reached the water.

After arriving at the lake, the friends impatiently lowered the punt into the water. William was the first who expressed his desire to test the punt. While his friends held the boat, William stepped into the vessel, sat on the board that served as a seat and, took the oar in his hands. Even before he announced it, his friends on the shore could see that the boat was extremely unstable. William tried to row but instead of moving in one direction, the unmanageable boat was going in different directions at the same time, and after William was able to cover distance of four feet, it turned bottom up with William in it. Fortunately, William was a good swimmer. He reached the boat, turned it over to the upright position, brought it to the shore, and then once again, with the help of his friends, took his seat on the boat's bench. In response to his new attempts to paddle, the boat stubbornly resisted his efforts; soon the rower again lost his balance and plunged into the water.

After that, William decided to take a pause in the taming of the boat, pushed it to the shore, and invited his older brother to give the punt another chance. Lev was more successful. As if he was performing a circus number, he balanced with his body and the oar and was able to keep the boat on the water for several minutes before it turned over.

Samuel Abramovich, who until this moment had watched what was going on with the boat attentively from the shore with philosophical air, reminded the group that it was time to go home.

"Dad, what are we going to do with the boat?" David asked. "Should we take it home or keep it somewhere else?"

"Don't you worry, son," Samuel answered pointedly. "I'll take care of it personally. Bring it to the boat station, and we'll arrange storage there. When one of you needs the boat, you can come and take it out.

"How much are we going to pay for the storage, Dad?"

"Five rubles a month," his father answered without hesitation.

The boys brought the boat into the boat station and placed it in a vacant spot while David's father negotiated the conditions of the storage with a boat station supervisor.

Pleased with the results, the boys returned home, discussing on the go the results of today's experience.

Four days later, David, William, and Lev went to the boat station and—anticipating new adventures with the unstable punt—asked the supervisor for the fruit of their ingenuity and labor. The supervisor told them that he knew nothing about their "self-made boat, a punt." When with one voice David and his two friends told to the supervisor that he was obliged to return their punt to them, the supervisor sent them all very far to a very vulgar place.

Upset and disappointed, the boat builders left the boat station empty-handed.

Back at home, David could not wait for his father to return from work.

"Daddy, the boat disappeared. Maybe you know what happened to it?" David asked Samuel after he shut the door behind him.

"What do you mean, 'what happened,' my son? Very simple. I sank your boat before one of you drowns because of it. I want you to be alive, son. Period."

David was silent. He was brought up in the era when the word of mothers and fathers was unquestioningly respected, when children were supposed to remember the good things that parents did for them, when the phrase "I hate you," addressed to a parent by a child, was considered to be an absolute taboo. Only half a century ago, it was parents who taught their children how to live and not the other way around, and the adults then were not afraid of traumatizing a child's soul forever with one unpleasant word. Children of these generations eventually became responsible adults without armies of mental health workers and without a monthly supply of Ritalin or other psychotropic medications. Children knew that life was not "a bowl of cherries," and that it was their responsibility to adapt to reality and not the other way around.

David and his friends were upset with disappearance of their self-made creation, but their disappointment quickly vanished when they witnessed a case of drowning in the muddy waters of the Beltsy lake.

—

Approximately fifteen miles from city of Beltsy where David lived was the small Moldovan village of Kubolta. Thanks to a river with the same name, which was not polluted and had comfortable sand beaches, this village was popular among the city residents as a place of leisure.

Together with his parents and friends, David visited this resort-like place on several occasions.

He was fifteen years old when, in September of 1957, he noticed that Kirill Gusev, his three-years-older neighbor from across the street, was fixing his new motorcycle on the sidewalk next to his house. Though because of difference in their ages, David and Kirill did not communicate frequently, Kirill was benevolent toward

David, exchanging one or more phrases with him when they met on the street.

Driving a motorcycle is the dream of any teenager. At the sight of Kirill repairing his bike, David approached him and asked if he possibly needed help. Kirill answered that he was almost done with the bike repair, and now he was planning to drive to Kubolta village for fun. In a voice trembling with unconcealed excitement, David asked Kirill if he would take him for a ride. Receiving a positive answer, happy, David ran to his house, received permission for the trip from his mother, and right away returned to Kirill.

Kirill finished fixing his bike, started the motor, and soon, traveling at a high speed, the neighbors were on their way to Kubolta village. David was beside himself with happiness from the unusual experience: he enjoyed riding the iron horse that was quickly bringing the boys to Kubolta. The wind whistled in David's ears while he held on to Kirill's waist. David breathed the fresh air deeply, admiring the constantly changing views on both sides of the road. Motorcycle helmets were not available at that time, and the wind was playing with his hair, throwing it in all directions on his uncovered head.

In the middle of the trip, potholes began to abound on the road, which forced Kirill to reduce their speed. This was not enough to avoid the obstacles, and on a narrow curve, when Kirill tried to avoid deep potholes, the motorcycle fell to the ground along with its passengers. But who paid attention to such small things as a fall from a motorcycle? Youth differs from the older age in its contempt for danger, and after Kirill and David shook the small stones and dust from themselves, Kirill picked up the motorcycle, sat on it, and took off with David as if nothing had happened. They drove another kilometer and again encountered potholes, which resulted in another fall, again without any unpleasant consequences. Closer to Kubolta, the road's condition improved, and now they drove at a greater speed. Additionally, Kirill decided to entertain himself by driving from one side of the road to the other in a sinusoid curve. Soon the boys heard honking behind them. For a while, Kirill pretended not to hear the signal, but eventually he stopped.

The man who was signaling Kirill to stop was the driver of a large truck. He was a middle-aged man with a weathered reddish face and thick eyebrows. He was dressed in cheap dark-colored cotton clothes, which drivers in the countryside usually wore. Tall and thin, he left the truck cab, approached the motorcycle, pulled a certificate from his pocket, opened it, and showed it to Kirill.

"I am a voluntary public auto inspector, and I have the right to stop vehicles at my discretion," he said. "I stopped you, young man, because—judging by your driving—I think you are drunk. I don't have a breathalyzer on me, but it is obvious to me you are not sober. Tell me the truth!"

As could be expected, Kirill, who was the picture of complete innocence, hotly denied that he had consumed alcohol in any form. Meanwhile, David understood why before, sitting behind the driver, he periodically could smell alcohol vapors.

"You are lucky, young man. I am in a hurry and cannot call the road inspector, but you better take a rest somewhere until you are sober enough to drive your bike steadily. If I see you again driving the way you are, I will personally take you to the road inspectors, and they will take away your driver's license. Understand?

Kirill promised to follow the instructions, and the volunteer road inspector drove away.

Kirill gave David a sign to take the back seat, and as if nothing had happened, in a minute, he was ready to continue the trip. Even if David had known for sure that Kirill was drunk, what could he do in the middle of the road? Nothing. There was another reason David did not protest: he could not show Kirill that he was a coward. Such is youth: honor above all.

Fortunately, the effect of alcohol on Kirill gradually passed, and until the moment when the boys approached shore of the Kubolta River, he drove his bike more or less steadily.

The companions had a good swim in the river and returned home without incident. At the end of the trip, David was happy that it was over and that nobody had been killed.

When the motorcycle stopped at the Gusevs' house, a family of the Gusevs' neighbors sat on the front porch of their house: grandparents and parents with their children, a five-year-old boy and a six-year-old girl.

Kirill parked the motorcycle and was on the way to the porch when an ingenious idea came to David's mind. Though he was a good bicyclist, his experience with motorcycles was zero, but he decided that there was little difference between a motorcycle and a bicycle. Big deal: a couple more pedals and buttons than on a bicycle.

"Kirill, can I ride your motorcycle a little?" David asked in the tone of voice of an innocent lamb. He thought he had nothing to lose: if his older friend refused his request, he would survive, but if he agreed, oh! Then he would get the greatest excitement of his life.

To David's enormous satisfaction, Kirill handed him the key to the motorcycle without a word and in a minute disappeared into his home.

It turned out that entrusting the key to the motorcycle to David was a big mistake. He only learned about it later, but now, with the key in his hand, he was in the seventh heaven.

Trembling with excitement, David inserted the key in the ignition and turned it, pushed the foot pedal, and voila! The motorcycle's motor obediently began to work, ready to do its job. The family of the Gusevs' neighbors, who sat not far from him on their porch, looked at David with curiosity, especially the five-year-old boy: such a young driver, but he already knew how to handle the iron horse.

David sat firmly on the saddle of the motorcycle, twisted the right handgrip to operate the throttle, and—hooray—his long-term dream came true: windblown, with disheveled hair, subordinating the iron horse to his will, he rushed back and forth along the street where he lived, surprised by his own ability to control the noisy machine successfully. When to David's satisfaction he noticed two of his friends walking on the sidewalk, he intentionally increased the speed of the vehicle to the maximum. Another victory: judging by their gaping mouths and surprised eyes, he had made a great impression on them. One more time, David was happy to prove to himself that he could reliably control the motorcycle.

Twenty minutes later, David decided that it was time to return the vehicle to its rightful owner. The Gusevs' house was located in the middle of the block. Using the throttle, he slowed the motorcycle down to the minimum speed. Now he was moving forward by inertia. The vehicle was moving slowly when it entered the sidewalk in front of the Gusevs' house. The Gusevs' neighbors were still on their front porch.

The motorcycle continued to slow down, ready to stop. Only seconds before it came to a complete stop, just a yard away from the motorcycle appeared the curious five-year-old boy from the Gusevs' neighbors' family. He stood still, right in front of the motorcycle, with an expectation that it would stop. However, the motorcycle—though very slowly—continued to move by inertia toward the child because David, its lousy driver, knew neither where the brake-controlling handle was located nor how to use it.

Now in a state of trance, with horror, David continued his slow approach toward the kid. David expected the worst: another second or two and the motorcycle would crush—God forbid—this poor child. He knew if that happened, his own life would also be over because neither kid's family nor his own conscience would ever forgive him. He froze to such a degree that the idea of simply turning motorcycle sharply did not come to his mind. But there was a God in heaven. The motorcycle's front wheel touched the child's leg slightly, and as if by magic, the motorcycle stopped! Yes, it stopped!

When David had returned the motorcycle key to Kirill and was on his way home, the grandfather of the child he had almost knocked down called David to come to him. Awaiting an ugly reprimand, profusely blushing and embarrassed, David approached him.

"What's your name?" the grandfather, who was in his seventies, cordially asked the embarrassed rider.

"David."

"Listen, David, to what I, an old man, will tell you. I sincerely admire how you, yourself only a child yet, were able to stop the bike right in front of my grandson's nose. My whole body trembled as you approached him, and I really appreciate your skill, David. You're a great rider. Congratulations!"

David did not want to disappoint the old man and remained silent.

—

Having a pharmacist for a father, David's classmate Abram Levin had a certain knowledge of folk medicine. Once, in beginning of May when the school year was coming to an end, Abram persuaded several eighth-grade boys that they needed to collect daises or chamomiles. By selling these medicinal plants, Abram told them, they could make good money. From his father the pharmacist, Abram had heard that daisies and chamomiles were useful for skin problems, stomachaches, and simply for relaxation if taken as an elixir by mouth.

Abram suggested that they cut mathematics class; he had an unpleasant relationship with its teacher, Konischev. Abram had seen him earlier in school and could swear that the teacher was slightly inebriated. In such a condition, he was sure the teacher would hardly notice that six students were absent from his class.

During this part of the year in the city park, which was located close to the school, the daisies blossomed magnificently.

"I'm not talking nonsense," Levin kept telling the boys. "Daisies are medicinal plants and we'll make good money by selling them. The pharmacists will reward us with extra money, and we'll have a great opportunity to help people."

The park to which Abram, David, and the five other students came for daisies was in the initial stages of construction, and the territory was mainly uncultivated. The park consisted of dirt roads and paths enforced by broken calcareous stone and patches of land covered mainly by weeds. Here and there, small ravines formed after previous rains cut the ground. A white-and-yellow carpet of daisies along with the greenery created a festive look in the park.

Within twenty minutes, the motivated daisy harvesting team began to work. The promised profit inspired its members with future perspective. The day was wonderful, the weather was beautiful, everything around them was growing, the sun was shining—all this provided the team with a powerful surge of energy.

With real enthusiasm, the members of the group dispersed in different directions. If their parents could have seen the diligence of their hard-working and disciplined children, they would have been proud and happy.

The boys were collecting the flowers in a burlap bag, which they had prudently brought with them, but to their surprise, the bag filled very slowly. That quickly demoralized them, and after a short time, they discovered that the manual work was not as easy as they initially thought. Nevertheless, Abram Levin, a man born to be a leader, was maintaining good order among the young workers. Whenever he saw a lack of enthusiasm, he addressed the irresponsible member of the group and reminded him about the future generous financial reward.

When the general enthusiasm had significantly diminished, ignoring the man who was born to be a leader, the daisy harvesters decided to play a game of war. Of course, only small children play such games, but the group could not think of another option. The boys split into two groups; the objective of the play was to find the opponent and touch him with a "rifle," which was symbolized by a stick made from the stem of a plant. Forgetting about their daisy business, the students filled the field of daisies with bellicose screams.

The end of the game was unfortunate for David, though it was entertaining for the rest of the group. When it came David's turn to perform a "combat mission," he jumped out of the weeds and began to run to an explosion of laughter from his classmates. They laughed because the front of his new white pants, which had been a birthday present from his mother, was now all green after his crawling in the grass.

After the war game was over, the group resumed the collection of flowers. Despite their friendly collaborative effort, overall the group managed to collect not more than half a sack of daisies. In the late afternoon, the team went to Pharmacy Number 7, the largest in the city, in expectation of a good financial reward.

The pharmacy was shining with cleanliness and smelled of all kinds of chemicals. Abram Levin began official negotiations with a pharmacist. Proud of the achievement of his team, he spoke from a position of strength until his eloquence was exhausted. Following his presentation, the pharmacist told him that the pharmacy was not interest in his merchandise. The main reason was that, in order for the plants to be offered for sale, they were supposed to be dried. After the unfortunate negotiations, a disappointed Abram Levin walked away from the counter and asked the others who had an attic in his house where the collected daises could be dried out. It turned out that the appropriate conditions for performing such a task were only available in David's house.

David's mother was surprised when her son arrived home with a sack over his shoulder and even more surprised that his recently dazzling white trousers had acquired a bright green color. Under her supervision, David climbed up to the attic on a ladder, spread a sheet on the floor, and placed on it the recently collected precious load of healing flowers.

Exactly two months later, all the participants in "Operation Daisy" appeared at David's house to take the dried plants to the pharmacy. David climbed up the ladder to the attic and brought down all the daisies that the group had harvested earlier. When David's friends saw a miserable pile of shrunken dried daisies instead of a large pile of flowers, they could not believe their eyes. Ilana provided the boys with a pillowcase in which they placed the dried flowers, and the group paid a second visit to the pharmacy. Now the dream was coming close to its embodiment in life.

When the group entered the main pharmacy, Abram Levin, born to be a leader, pillowcase in his hands, approached the pharmacist who specialized in medical plants with dignity. She was a short, elderly woman whose face was strewn with a web of wrinkles. Her look was astute and intelligent.

"What can I do for you, young men?" she asked the leader, whose eyes were shining in anticipation of a fat financial reward.

"We, students of School Number 6," Abram began in a solemn voice, "brought to your pharmacy this precious medicinal plant which is dried and ready to use." Intentionally slowly, he untied the pillowcase and with the pride of a humanitarian showed the pharmacist its precious content.

The pharmacist looked attentively at the merchandise. "Oh, that's wonderful. We're going to take it from you, thank you," she commented.

"We're very satisfied," Levin answered, "and we're ready to accept the financial remuneration for our noble efforts."

"Naturally. Let me weigh your merchandise," the pharmacist answered. She took the bag with the medicinal plants and went to the back door.

"Don't worry, guys, we're not going to sell our daisies cheap," Abram told his hard-working team.

Shortly the pharmacist returned and announced that the group was entitled to five rubles and twenty kopecks for their healing merchandise.

Abram Levin was extremely disappointed, he was shocked, he was speechless, but then—as a good leader—he pulled himself together.

"Does this mean that for all our work collecting this health product for working class and vulnerable populations, we're going to receive only five rubles and twenty kopecks? It's extremely unfair. To collect them we even skipped classes at our school, and one of us even spoiled his trousers," he said, appealing to the power of justice.

"Why? It's not unfair at all," retorted the woman. "With your noble work, you helped . many Soviet people to have nice skin, for example."

Then followed the unforgettable moment when David and his friends learned that their role model, their born leader Abram Levin, was hopelessly alien to socialist thinking and not worthy of being a Komsomol member.

"So, you want me to help our society," he said, dramatically raising his voice, finishing eloquently and with indignation, "but who will help me?"

The team took their production back and decided that David would takes the dried daisies home until a better solution than "for five rubles" could be found.

The unexpected beneficiary of this story was David's mother, Ilana Lvovna Lamm. For the next two seasons, she used a home-prepared decoction of dried daisies to maintain her hair in exemplary condition. Therefore, the work of the students under the leadership of Abram Levin was not completely wasted.

CHAPTER 9

Adventures in Health

David, who was born on the first day of the fascist German attack on the Soviet Union, could be considered a child of war. During the first years of his life, the country was not up to celebrating birthdays. Only when he turned nine years old did his parents finally organize a formal celebration of his birthday.

June 22 was a very beautiful day. Like other children who love their birthdays, David was proud that on that day, he received all the attention and that he was important enough that guests—some of them with presents—came to his party. Everything on this day was bright, green, and fresh. The sun was sending to earth its warm rays, so pleasant in combination with a cool breeze.

Before his young guests took their seats at the table, they played different games and were jumping and singing. Early in the morning, David's parents had given him a precious present, a pair of leather shoes, and now David was running in them faster than anyone, sometimes thinking that with a little more effort, he could fly like a bird.

Later, when the children got tired, everybody gathered in David's backyard, splashing and pouring on each other water from three buckets that was warm enough, thanks to the hot rays of the sun.

Later, one of the Lamms' neighbors brought his accordion and began to play melodies to which children sang, and some of them danced. Finally, it came time to sit down at the festive tables. There was a lot of food on the tables, but the most important thing was not the abundance of food but the festive atmosphere. David enjoyed each moment of his birthday.

At the culmination of the festivities, David's mother brought to the table chocolate cake and napoleon torte. David was in seventh heaven finishing his second piece of cake when he heard a knock at the door. David's father went to open the door and let in two young, nice-looking, pleasant women. They explained that there was an epidemic of scarlet fever in the community, and they were performing a medical exam on children in the neighborhood to prevent the spread of the disease.

The visitors were happy to accept Ilana's invitation to be guests at her son's birthday. They took seats at the table and enjoyed the food spread out on the table. When they were done with the treats, they asked David to follow them to another room. There one of them took a stethoscope out of a worn bag and began to perform David's physical examination. The only very small problem they found during the physical examination was that the skin on his palms and fingers was peeling; otherwise, everything was normal.

"Oh, you're very observant." Ilana smiled. "David's hands peel frequently because they sweat. It's normal for him. His hands look better if I smear them with Vaseline."

"We understand what you're saying," answered a nurse, "but it's our responsibility to mention this fact in our report. It's not for us to decide who's healthy and who isn't. We just obey orders."

"But one of you said yourself that he's healthy. It's obvious: my son is active, running, jumping; his temperature is normal. The people you're going to show your report to are bureaucrats. They understand nothing of medicine, and they can completely misunderstand your finding, which will result in serious trouble for my son."

"Don't worry, woman. Nothing will happen," one of the nurses reassured Ilana. "It's nothing more than a formality. Believe me, no one is looking at these reports. Thank you once again for the dessert. It was delicious. Enjoy your birthday, little boy."

When the nurses left, David returned to his guests to celebrate his birthday. It was a great day, and he enjoyed each second of it. How could he know that soon he would live through a medical imprisonment?

—

In a week—it was a Saturday—on the quiet street where the Lamms lived, a prewar model ambulance stopped in front of the house. A man in a dirty white gown got out of it and went to the Lamms' house. After the man knocked on the door, Ilana opened it.

"What do you want?" she asked.

"I am a sanitary inspector. My name is Portesku. I came from the sanitary-epidemiological station to take David Lamm to the hospital. He is your son, right?"

"Are you out of your mind?" Ilana answered indignantly. "What kind of a mistake is this? Why does my son need to go to a hospital if he is in a perfect health?"

"I know nothing," the sanitary inspector answered. "I only obey orders. Dress your son; I'm taking him to the hospital."

"Before you do anything, let me know why you want to take my son to the hospital," Ilana protested.

"Your son is a carrier of scarlet fever. His hands are peeling."

"My son is perfectly healthy. Look at his hands now; there's no peeling or anything wrong with them. The nurses saw the peeling when I forgot to put Vaseline on his hands; that's all."

"Woman, I don't want to hear your explanation. I follow orders. Understand?"

"Show me the permission to take away my son to the hospital," Ilana said.

"Here it is. This is an order to take your son to the isolation unit. Dr. Reznik signed it. He's the main infectious specialist in our city. What else do you need? Do you want me to call the militia? I can do it easily."

Ilana ran out of arguments. She had no choice but to give a bribe to the sanitary inspector in exchange for a delay in David's hospitalization. The miserable salaries received by workers during the time of socialism made bribes a universal lubricant in human relations.

The bribe did its partial work. Portesku softened and told Ilana that the most he could do was to delay David's isolation by two days, until Monday instead of Saturday.

When it rains, it pours. For the past month, Ilana had felt bad. She had a slight fever and an upset stomach. On Saturday, she noticed that the whites of her eyes had become slightly yellowish. The district doctor who examined her the same day diagnosed infectious hepatitis A and, taking into account the mild form of her disease, prescribed her bed rest until recovery.

Meanwhile, on Sunday, through mutual friends, Samuel learned where Dr. Leo Reznik lived and without delay took David to the doctor's residence. Dr. Reznik was a handsome, well-built man. He had an angular face with a rounded jaw and an English moustache. He was dressed in decent clothes and smelled of an expensive cologne.

During this private visit, Dr. Reznik was formal and behaved as if David's destiny was in his hands. After a thorough examination, he admitted that, indeed, he did not see active disease. It was true that such an isolated symptom as the peeling of hands, he said, could not prove a diagnosis of active scarlet fever. At the same time, he continued, he could not rule out David's having scarlet fever. The peeling of hands noted by the nurses could be a sign of recovery after scarlet fever, which meant that there is was possibility (yes, very minimal, he admitted) that David might be a carrier of the disease. In any case, he concluded, as long as David's name was on the list of the "all-powerful sanitary-epidemiological station," which he had signed a week before, he was unable to change his own decision of isolation in the hospital. It was against the rules.

"Dr. Reznik," Samuel interrupted him, "for any person with common sense, it's as clear as day that my son is healthy. Look at his hands: today there's no peeling there anymore. Only yesterday, he played soccer with his friends."

The doctor was inexorable. "Yes, there's truth in your words, and you might be right, but now, when he is on the list, if any new case of scarlet fever happens in your district, both the sanitary-epidemiological station and I will be responsible. And who want that to happen? Listen, your son needs to be isolated only for ten days or less. Let it go. Ten days is nothing. Sometimes we keep people more than a month."

"It's nothing to you," Samuel objected. "Imagine if one of your children was in the hospital for no reason. How would you react then?"

"Let's not point fingers," Dr. Reznick answered. "I cannot change anything if your son's name is on the sanitary-epidemiological station's list. That's the law."

The next day, Portesku, the sanitary inspector, arrived at the Lamms' house in the same ambulance to take David to the hospital. Samuel was at work at the time, while Ilana was in quarantine at home for infectious hepatitis and was not allowed to leave the house. Without parents, with a small package that Ilana had given him in his hands, David rode in the ambulance to the hospital.

The nurse in the admissions office where the ambulance brought David was tired and in a bad mood. She ordered the new patient to undress and put on hospital pajamas. Then, without saying a word, she took David to the hospital room intended for patient observation at the First City Hospital, in the basement of which David had been born nine years before.

In the hospital room, where prevailing color was gray and the environment was dusty, eighteen children were hospitalized, all of them suspected of being in the carrier stage of scarlet fever. Their ages varied from five to thirteen. Younger children were with their mothers. The room was large, and it was located on a high level. Two normal-size windows were on the north and south sides. David's adult-size bed stood along the eastern wall. On the north side were doors to auxiliary quarters; patients were not allowed to enter there.

The main content of the ten days of David's imprisonment were chronic boredom and homesickness. Dr. Reznik, in white gown with a stethoscope around his neck, performed morning rounds daily. His nurse accompanied him, carrying patients' folders in her hand. They addressed patients in a dry and formal matter, as if these children were a faceless commodity.

Except for the patients with parents, the children were on their own. Table games and books on the floor where forbidden because they could transmit the infection from one patient to another. Every day was like the previous one: only three meals a day, which consisted mostly of carbohydrates, served as diversion from the daily monotony. There was nothing to do except lie in bed; loiter about the room; or, as David and his new acquaintance, Yura, did, sit on the wide sill of the south window and look outside in expectation that one of their parents might appear on the horizon. Yura was the same age as David; his mother came to see him every other day. David's father came to see him daily, usually in the early evening. To see his son more closely, he used a ledge of the wall. When he climbed up on it, the top of his head was level with the windowsill.

On the fourth day of David's "incarceration," in the room where life was dull, gloomy, and depressing, two young women, each with a male child—four and five years old—were admitted to the ward. Following the common practice, the children shared the same bed with their mothers. The children's mothers were beautiful and, unlike other inhabitants of the ward, were dressed in fine imported gowns. Alas, the natural good looks of these women sharply contrasted with their mean spirits. Maybe they acted so because of the boredom, but their main entertainment was to offend and frighten the children and adults on the floor. As one of the objects of their nastiness, they chose David, who tried to stay away from these mean women as much as possible. However, whenever David, who they correctly determined was a sensitive child, appeared in their field of vision, they enjoyed themselves by scaring and embarrassing him. Somehow, these women figured out David's Jewish heritage and on several occasions with joyful laughter told him in the morning that the previous night, while he slept, they had removed his blanket and looked at and touched an intimate part of his body. As if that was not enough, they painfully embarrassed him by describing the anatomy of his sexual organ in detail. At other times, in sweet, dripping-with-honey voices, they told David that at night big rats were running on his face while he slept. As his bed was next to those of his torturers, David could not avoid contact with these women, and there was nobody around him to complain to.

At nine years of age, David was smart enough to understand that his female tormentors were taking advantage of him and lying to him; nevertheless, it was impossible for him to remain indifferent to the women's evil nonsense. Most of all, David was wounded when his abusers told him that they heard from the nurses that he would be discharged three days later than planned.

One day, out of nowhere, an old issue of the newspaper *Pravda* appeared in David's hospital room. For David this newspaper provided huge entertainment, and though he hardly understood what was written there, he read and reread the newspaper many times.

Samuel visited David almost every day. They communicated through a double window and yelled to each other in order to be heard. His father comforted David, told him about things at home and about his mother's health. Nevertheless, the main part of their conversation was dedicated to David's discharge from the hospital. On the fifth day of David's hospital stay, Samuel told David that he had met Dr. Reznik in the city and threatened him with physical violence if he did not allow David to go home as soon as possible.

According to Samuel, Dr. Reznik was so scared that he promised to follow Samuel's request without delay. David, who from previous experience knew that his father could exaggerate facts to please him and torn between the positive news and the possibility that his dad was just trying to reassure him, began to cry as bitterly as he ever had in his life. It was a Niagara Falls of tears. He sobbed unceasingly as if everything was lost. Nobody paid attention to David's tears except his father, who could not do much, separated from his son by a double window.

David was discharged from the hospital on the ninth day after admission, on a Monday morning. A custodian returned David's clothes. David did not forget to say goodbye to Yuri, who cried at their parting. Finally, David was out of hospital where he was not only neglected but also abused.

On the way home, Samuel first took David to the bookstore, where he allowed David to buy any book of his choice. As usual, there were not too many interesting children books in the store, so he bought the famous *In the Stalingrad's Trenches* by Victor Nekrasov. To make David feel better, Samuel took his son to a bakery where David ordered two of his favorite custard cakes.

The next day, David returned to school. Life went into the usual channel, but he never was able to erase from his memory the nine days of his hospital stay in the scarlet fever ward, where he was placed only because of a symptom that had nothing to do with scarlet fever. Nothing surprising: It is well known that the road to hell is paved with good intentions.

—

Marc Gordon, a short, stocky, intelligent boy, was David's classmate and neighbor. He lived at the south end of the block while David lived in the middle. During summer vacations, the neighbors read books and played soccer, volleyball, chess, and checkers while during the academic year, they frequently did their homework and prepared for tests together. Marc was not David's first choice as a friend, but they were neighbors, and they could not avoid meeting each other daily. Their superficially friendly relations from time to time broke down. Being envious of David, Marc did not hide unpleasant words about him. He did not like that David's house and backyard were larger than his, that—according to him—the teacher gave David higher grades, that David's father made more money than his.

Among other classes in school, there was also a singing class. This class always took place at the end of the school day. On the way home, David and Marc, still inspired by the patriotic and life-asserting songs they had practiced in class, loudly sang their favorite newly learned songs.

On a pleasant sunny October day, David and Marc, then third-class students, were walking home in the shade of trees singing their favorite songs. Suddenly, a stranger, a man who was walking behind them, addressed them. The man was in his sixties, of average height with shiny gray hair. He had kind, friendly, almond-shaped brown eyes; a straight nose; and a rounded jaw.

"You are singing really beautifully. I admire you kids," he said to the boys, giving them both a radiant smile.

Fifty years later. the former friends met in the United States. They were exchanging old memories, and one of them was about the stranger who had praised them both. They never forgot this very short episode because a kind word, though it cost nothing, stays with us forever. It is in the nature of normal human beings to be motivated by positive compliments rather than by boring criticism.

A month after the stranger's praise, when the weather continued to be nice and warm, the classmates walked through the backyard of a three-story school on the way home. In this building two years before, David had been dangled from a window on the highest floor, held by his feet by the tenth graders who decided to have "a little fun" using him as a prop.

Passing the now-empty backyard, Marc and David decided to spend their energy jumping and running. When they got tired of their activities, they had a good time walking and running on a low barrier in front of the several window wells of the school basement. The window wells were five feet deep; their walls and the floor were covered with cement. Standing on the barrier around the window well and looking up, David became distracted. A minute later, he lost consciousness. When his consciousness returned, he initially did not have any idea why and for how long he was lying on the bottom of the window well. The impact of the fall was probably not too powerful because his consciousness was gradually returning. Marc was nowhere around, and there was not a single person in the yard. David examined the walls surrounding him and realized that he could climb out of the window well by himself.

Shortly after, when David was out of the window well, he began to understand what had happened. It was obvious that when he was standing at the edge of the well, his "friend" and classmate Marc had pushed him down from behind. Obviously, when Marc saw his victim lying motionless on the floor of the window well, he got scared and decided that the best thing for him to do was to run away from the scene of the crime.

David had a headache; he was confused, feeling as if in a fog, not quite remembering what had happened recently. He wanted to go home, but he could not find his briefcase. He looked into the window well and noticed it lying there. Feeling a sense of nausea and dizziness, he managed to get back into the window well and pick up his briefcase. Again, he climbed out to the barrier and, appearing dazed, went home. While David was walking on the familiar path, he saw people, buildings, and trees in a dimension yet unknown to him, as if he saw what was going on around him from a deep cave. Despite its being a sunny day, everything, even the sky, appeared to him fuzzy and darker than usual. To pedestrians he looked like a normal child, but he was disoriented and confused.

David did not remember how he got home. All he could tell his mother was that he fell in the window well. Ilana put him to bed, he fell asleep, and to the surprise of his parents he woke up twenty-four hours later. He spent four days at home before returning to the school. During his home stay, his favorite teacher, Zoya Kondratevna, visited him to encourage him and to keep him abreast of the homework. She came voluntarily, just because she was a dedicated teacher who was proud of her profession.

Marc never was confronted for his misdeed, and he never apologized. David and Marc studied together another seven years in the same class and never discussed what had happened when they were in grammar school. In life, many things do not happen as they do in movies and books.

—

During summer school vacation, David, who was eight years old, could not find anything more interesting to do than first jumping on a bouncy spring mesh mattress, then hopping on two chairs, and concluding with a jump to the floor. Enjoying such amusement, he fell on the floor and hit his head against the back of the bed's metal frame. There was no pain, but instantly blood began running from his forehead. His mother, to whom David ran with blood dripping on the floor, put a piece of gauze on his forehead to stop the bleeding and took him to *Скорая Помощь*, the urgent care center located not far from the Lamms' house.

In the urgent care center, a physician, a woman with a hearty face and professional manners, asked David to lie down on a procedure table. She injected local anesthetic and then applied eight stitches to the gash on David's forehead. Instead of crying or complaining of pain during the procedure, David smiled widely and tried to make jokes, for which he received praise from the physician who took care of him.

Finishing her job, the physician asked David why instead of crying, he was smiling.

"I don't know," David answered.

Not until three years later, when he went for a visit to a dentist, did he understand why instead of suffering pain at the urgent care center, he had smiled happily.

When David was eleven, all his baby teeth dropped out except one, which stubbornly remained in his upper gum. His permanent teeth were coming in on time, and one of them now grew at an angle outside the gum and above the baby tooth that "refused" to drop out. The misplaced permanent tooth annoyed David to such a degree that he developed the habit of involuntary touching the new growing tooth with the tip of his tongue. Eventually, Ilana could not stand to see her son persistently moving his tongue under his cheek and took him to a dentist.

The dentist's office was located in the city's children ambulatory in quite a dilapidated building near the *Родильный Дом* (maternity ward). Air conditioning at that time was a totally unknown entity; not a single city building, including medical institutions, had it. Therefore, in the summer, when the windows of the maternity hospital were wide open, people who were passing by could hear the loud moaning, yelling, and crying of women who were in the state of labor and delivery of their babies.

Next to the old children's ambulatory building was a notable landmark: a building under construction. When Ilana brought David to the children's clinic for the first time—he was seven years old then—she brought to his attention the foundation of a future structure.

"Look carefully, David," Ilana told him excitedly. "What you see is the foundation of the future new children ambulatory. I read in our local newspaper that in a year or two, you'll be able to be taken care in this modern building!"

Ilana was too optimistic: the ambulatory clinic was built at a turtle's speed. Year after year, when David visited the children ambulatory, he saw minimal changes in the construction of the building. Needless to say, ten years later, when David had already graduated high school and was accepted to Kishinev Medical School, he was passing by the site of the future children's ambulatory and noticed that construction workers were in the process of putting a roof on the recently finished walls of the building.

On a winter day in 1952, when David was eleven years old, accompanied by Ilana, he visited the children's ambulatory for the removal of the tooth from his upper gum. His mother stayed in the waiting room when he was summoned to the dentist's office.

David was not a coward; he was not afraid of the upcoming procedure. The dentist, Dr. Shpaner, was an energetic man in his late thirties. Tall and well built, he moved through the dental office as if he was a king. His movements were accompanied by comments directed toward his young assistant, a dental student. A nurse helped David to take a seat in the dental chair and advised him to relax. Dr. Shpaner approached him and asked David to open his mouth. When David followed his request, the doctor quickly injected anesthetic into the gum where the additional tooth was growing. When the gum became numb, he picked up large forceps and began to shake David's protruding extra tooth. As luck would have it, this tooth was quite stubborn, and the dentist had to work hard to extract it. Overall, the procedure lasted about twenty-five minutes. At the end of the procedure, Dr. Shpaner showed David the tooth he just extracted and then looked into his eyes.

"Hey, kid, why did you smile during the entire procedure?" he asked, not hiding his surprise. David could not answer him right away, but on the way home, he realized that the answer was very simple, the same as when he had lacerated his forehead two years before. He had smiled during both these procedures for a simple reason: because the pain he experienced was not as strong as he expected it to be. A good definition of such an attitude is "positive thinking."

—

During the Second World War, Officer Lamm served as quartermaster of a special pontoon engineering battalion. He was the serviceman in charge of the food supply and the military economy, including providing the battalion with quarters, food rations, clothing, and other needs. During the last months of the war, Officer Lamm's battalion was located not far from Leningrad, which he visited on regular basis to bring the necessary supplies to the soldiers and officers. He traveled there by truck in a company of three soldiers who helped him. Due to the poor condition of the roads, the travel took a significant amount of time. It was quartermaster's personal responsibility to provide his battalion with food without delay, which made each trip to Leningrad a stressful experience.

In the beginning of 1945, he went with a team of soldiers to Leningrad for food supplies. Unfortunately, on that day, the military warehouse where he received the goods opened late, and he had to wait longer than usual to get the ordered cargo. His team had to leave the city a bit later than usual but still had enough time to return to their unit. Everything was in order until the truck broke down halfway to his unit. To avoid punishment for being late, Samuel Abramovich had to do something unusual. In search of a solution, he asked one of the soldiers to climb a tree and look around. From the top of the tree, the soldier informed Samuel that not too far away, he saw a railway station, and a freight train had just passed there. Samuel and the rest of the team realized that if they could get on this train, then they could be in their military unit on time.

However, how would it be possible to stop the train?

After a short consideration, Samuel came up with a possible solution to the problem. He gave each of the soldiers a link of hard sausage—a highly valuable food product during the war—and instructed them to take a position along the railway track with a distance of about two hundred and fifty feet between them.

To stop a train without a serious reason was considered a state crime, but stomach urges are stronger than severe punishment. The machinist and his assistant noticed the soldiers who were waving the precious bribe and stopped the train. Samuel and the soldiers shifted their cargo to one of the open freight cars, and three hours later, the machinist—against official rules—again stopped the train. The operation was successful, and the battalion had their hot meals on time.

During longer stays in Leningrad in wartime, Samuel used the hospitality of the Aksyonov family. This was an older couple who survived the Leningrad blockade, when citizens of that heroic city were dying of starvation in the streets. Wartime friendship continued in peacetime, and from time to time, Samuel and Ilana were guests at the Aksyonovs' apartment.

Once, when the Lamm family lived in Moldova, Ilana wrote the Aksyonovs a letter in which she mentioned that she and David, who was at that time nine years old, planned to visit Leningrad. In a week, she received a reply in which the Aksyonovs persuasively invited her and her son to be guests in their spacious apartment.

In three weeks—it was during David's winter school vacation—Ilana and her son arrived at the Aksyonovs' apartment, where they received a warm welcome. The owners of the apartment took good care of their guests and went with them to different world-famous Leningrad museums.

On the third day of the Lamms' visit, their hosts told them that they were going to attend a long-planned symphony orchestra concert of the Leningrad Philharmonic, which would end late at night.

The Aksyonovs had a house dog, a large German shepherd. This beautiful and strong dog minded her own business, completely ignoring Ilana and her son as if they did not exist. The hosts went to the concert, and the guests were left alone in the apartment with the dog, who slept in the kitchen, continuing to ignore the guests. Later in the evening, Ilana and David went to sleep to their separate beds. Before going to bed, David put on his favorite pajamas. Everything was going nicely until they both took to their beds and covered themselves with blankets. What happened then was an unpleasant surprise. At the slightest attempt of one of them to change their body position, they could hear the dog's malicious growl. This experience paralyzed Ilana and David to such a degree that they were afraid to take a deep breath. Eventually, the guests fell asleep. They woke up in the morning when it was already light outside. David, who had been toilet trained at an early age, realized to his horror that his pajamas pants were wet. He had been afraid even to think about using the washroom. As a result, his bladder overfilled and eventually, when he was deeply asleep, the accident happened. Only his mother knew of that fiasco, and she did not tell anybody about it. As a child, David was ashamed about that wet night for a long time.

As for the German shepherd, it continued to ignore the guests for the rest of the visit. When Ilana told the hosts how terrified she was on that unforgettable night, they refused to believe her: "Our peaceful dog? No way!"

—

Except for the first four years of the war, David was a healthy child. In his early teens, his body was strong and full of life energy. He ran as if he was almost flying, his legs asking for perpetual motion. However, when he was twelve years old, he learned that his body was not made from a magic material.

Anatoliy Kondratyevich Yar, his geography teacher, was a man in love with his profession. As a talented teacher, he was able to make geography one of the most important subjects in the class curriculum. He loved to teach his students and to answer their questions. Though astronomy was not the subject he taught, he loved to bring a large globe to the classroom and demonstrate to his students different cosmic phenomena that affected geography and life on earth. Thanks to his energy and influence, the school bought a meteorological station manned by the students of the sixth grade.

In early November, it was David's turn to read the data from the meteorological instruments, to write them down in a logbook, and then to transmit the findings to the local meteorological service by phone. David was on his way to the booth with the equipment when he felt unpleasant feelings: his usually healthy and strong body all of a sudden transformed into a heavy, awkward, and painful structure. Not ready for such a drastic transformation in his health, David resisted it as much as he could. Climbing up the ladder with difficulty and opening the booth, David managed to perform the required tasks, but he was too weak to call the meteorological service with the data.

The trip home from school was torturous; he was taking frequent rests, which was not typical for him, and was breathing heavily. Eventually, he reached his home, where his mother realized that her son was sick and—judging by the appearance of the rash on his body—most probably had a case of the measles.

What happened after that, David did not remember: he lost consciousness. He did not know how long he was unconscious—probably several hours—because when he came to, he realized that he was lying on his parents' bed. Behind the windows, it was night, and the large family alarm clock showed it was four o'clock in the morning. Without warning, David felt the light touch of a wet cloth against his forehead. He turned in direction of the touch and saw his mother; she was using wet cloths on his forehead to try to bring his temperature down.

Since David was a child, he did not take the help he received for granted. At twelve years of age, he felt a deep appreciation of his mother, who at this late hour was taking care for him. A warm instinctive feeling of gratitude flared in his chest.

"Mom, why aren't you asleep? It's very late," David asked quietly.

"Oh, thank God you woke up, my dear sonny," Ilana said. "You were so sick; your temperature was very high. We were all very worried about you."

"But it's so late, Mom. You're probably tired. Go to bed. You see I'm getting better."

"Stop worrying about me, silly one," Ilana answered naturally and without pretense. "That's what the mothers are for. To be with their sick children."

—

In a week, David was on the road to recovery. On the third day of recuperation, in the late morning, he was lying in bed reading a book. There was nobody at home except him: his father was at work, and his mother had gone shopping at the grocery store. At noon David heard the front door open; it was his father. When Samuel entered the room, he asked David about his health and was pleased when David answered that he felt better.

"Listen, David," Samuel said. "I didn't come only to hear about your health. I came to tell you that today I have an interview on the city radio. Keep it in your mind that when the time comes for me to name the best workers in my production plant, I will mention the name of David Pasternak. David Pasternak doesn't work in my plant; when you hear the name *Pasternak*, it means I'm thinking about you. Turn on the radio at six o'clock in the evening. Don't forget!"

David and his mother turned on the state network radio at the appropriate time and waited until Samuel was interviewed regarding his plant. In the second part of the interview, the newscaster asked Samuel to name the best workers in his plant, and, as promised, he mentioned the name of nonexistent worker David Pasternak. David was very pleased that his father once more demonstrated his love for him. Happy are children who have somebody who loves them.

—

David's measles infection coincided with winter school vacation and with his introduction to the English language. Fully recovered, he went to school to pick up his briefcase, which he had left in the teachers' lounge when he fell ill. On the second floor, he met his English teacher, Raisa Chaimovna Yusim, a fair, slightly overweight woman in her late thirties with strong character. Her plain face was freckled, and her hair was fire red. She was a good teacher, but the system of teaching of foreign languages in the Soviet Union was such that grammar was the prime goal, and conversational English was on a far periphery, so the efforts of even the best teachers resulted in poor outcomes.

"Where are you running?" she asked David when he was passing by.

"To the teachers' lounge and then to the library. I want to pick up a book there to read."

"Wait, David. Wait for me here."

She disappeared and soon returned with a little paperback illustrated with black-and-white pictures on the cover and showed it David. The book contained a few tales from *One Thousand and One Arabian Nights*, abridged and adapted for easy reading.

"Try to read it, David," she suggested.

"Not bad, not bad at all," she praised him when he finished reading a paragraph. On her face was a mysterious smile. "Learn the English language, David. One of these days, it might turn out to be very useful for you."

Did she know that at that moment David thought that, sometimes in the far future, he would be able to escape the Communist authoritarian regime and that his knowledge of the English language would help him to start a new life in a new land? It might be that she thought so as well, because years later she, along with her family, moved to the state of Israel.

—

David had a good reason to associate a stubborn cough with a Chinese circus. This episode took place when he was thirteen years old: his mother received a telegram saying that her aunt was very sick and needed Ilana's help, and she left the next day. The aunt's health was so bad that David and his father were alone for the next four weeks. David was an independent child, and he took adequate care of himself. A neighbor across the street prepared food for the father and son. Samuel was too busy to clean the house, and David did not take cleanliness too seriously.

Time was flying fast. David enjoyed his vacation: he read books, played with his friends, went swimming in the lake, went to movies, and played the violin. Life would have been ideal if David had not begun to cough. First, it was an episodic dry cough, and later it became a persistent one. Gradually, the cough began to manifest the entire day, especially when he was at home.

Eventually, on his father's advice, David went to the ambulatory to see a doctor. After signing in at the reception desk, he was soon called to the office of the doctor of his district. In the Soviet medical system, the urban territory was divided into districts. A patient did not choose a doctor but used the medical services of his district physician.

David's district doctor was an old man with rich practical experience. As was universal in the Soviet medical system, a nurse sat at the opposite desk, facing the doctor. Her function was to prepare David for examination, and, if necessary, to give injections and write prescriptions.

Checking David's lungs, the doctor told him that he could not find anything abnormal and prescribed him extracts from medicinal plants and a sulfa drug. David returned to his physician for a follow-up visit three days later. The medicinal plant extracts did not help him. His cough progressed; it became more persistent and began to interfere with his daily activities. As he had during the previous visit, his district physician listened carefully to his lungs and once more could not find anything abnormal.

On David's fourth visit, the doctor recognized him when he entered the room.

"Young man, you are a difficult patient," he said when David "awarded" him with a long and stubborn bout of coughing. "Your X-ray is normal; your lungs are clear on auscultation. I don't understand why you're still coughing. During your last visit, I prescribed a strong expectorant for cough with codeine and a sulfa drug, and it didn't help you. I'm inclined to think that you have some kind of exotic bronchitis. Continue to use the medications I already prescribed, and take them four times a day instead of three. Come to me in two days if the cough continues, OK?"

"But, Doctor," interjected the nurse, "you forgot to prescribe calcium chloride for him."

"Oh yes. Sorry, I forgot. Yes, young man, starting today, you'll come to the procedure room, and the nurse there will give you injections of calcium chloride. These injections will help you get rid of your cough. See you tomorrow."

Calcium chloride solution occupied a special place in the armaments of Soviet medicine and is still used in the former Soviet Union. One of the qualities of this solution is that with intravenous administration, the patient feels a sensation of intense heat starting from the oral cavity and then spreading to the entire body. Not-too-conscientious doctors used this remarkable effect in order to provide their unsophisticated patients with the impression that they had received first-class treatment.

Naturally, David did not have any idea what to expect from the injection when his doctor sent him to the treatment room. Without warning him about possible effect of the injection, humming a popular song under her breath, Flora, a young nurse, broke the ampoule of calcium chloride, sucked its contents into a ten-millimeter syringe, planted on its end a long and thick needle, put a tourniquet tightly around David's upper arm, placed the needle into the vein, and injected the solution with considerable speed.

"Wait, wait. I'm hot; I'm very hot," David complained, feeling terrible heat first in his throat and then throughout the entire body.

"Don't worry, kid. It's calcium chloride," the nurse joyfully reassured him. "You just react to the medicine. If you feel heat, that means that you aren't in bad shape."

Altogether, David received four injections of calcium chloride during the week. The fourth time, Flora partially missed his vein, and as a result, the medicine produced strong pain in his elbow. When David returned home after that unsuccessful injection, he sat in the gazebo, coughing and pressing a cold compress to the spot of the ill-fated injection. Arkady Melman, a neighbor who passed by a gazebo, noticed him. Son of Yankel and Manya Melman, Arkady—a kind and caring individual by nature—lived with his wife, Raya, in a separate apartment of his parents' home. He was in his thirties and worked as a weaver.

"What's your problem, David?" he asked.

Before answering, David produced a new bout of a dry cough. "For some reason, I can't stop coughing, Uncle Arkady," he eventually answered.

"Since when?"

"I don't know. Maybe a couple of weeks. I take medications and receive some kind of hot injections that my doctor prescribed, but nothing helps me."

Arkady scratched his head, thought for a while, and went back to his house.

In the evening, David, periodically coughing, was sitting in the gazebo reading a book when he saw Arkady and his wife at the gazebo entrance.

"You see, Raya, I told you. David can't stop coughing. What do you think we could do for him?"

"I don't know," Raya answered.

"But I know," Arkady said, slapping his forehead. "We will follow the saying 'Change of place, change of happiness.' We will take David to our apartment and see what happens. Right, Raya?"

Raya agreed with his suggestion.

With Samuel's permission, David spent the next week at Arkady and Raya's apartment. The apartment consisted of a midsize room and an unheated kitchen. David slept in a corner of the room that was separated by a sheet.

Simple people sometimes have a better understanding of what is going on with a patient than doctors. On the second day of his stay in Arkady's apartment, David's cough significantly decreased, and on Arkady suggestion, David stopped taking medicine. No more calcium chloride injections, no more codeine, no more visits to doctors. The reason for the David's persistent cough was nothing more than the dust in his house, which usually was taken care by his mother. Ilana was absent, and the presence of dust in David's house had an allergic effect on him.

David's father was delighted to hear about his son's improvement.

"I'm so happy you stopped coughing, David. I have to do something in honor of it. I must give you a present. You're lucky. You don't know it yet, but in four days, a real Chinese circus is arriving in our city. I'm going to buy you a ticket to attend the show at the City Theater. I would have bought you a ticket earlier, but you were constantly coughing, and I was afraid you wouldn't be able to attend the performance."

David, whose cough by this time had ceased completely as if he had never had it, was pleasurably excited to see his first circus, which came to his city all the way from faraway China.

Meanwhile his mother returned from the visit to her aunt. She asked Arkady and his wife to let David stay one night more with them as she organized a thorough cleaning of her house. When David returned home, everything inside was shining with cleanliness.

That same evening, David learned that his father had kept his promise: on the dining table lay the ticket—a little rectangular piece of blue paper—to the Chinese circus. Not spoiled by entertainment in his provincial town and eager to see something new, David could not wait to see the performance. Meanwhile, he needed to figure out where to store his ticket. With a little reflection, David decided to keep the ticket between the pages of a book. He walked up to his bookcase, chose a suitable book from the shelf, and put his ticket between its pages.

That was in the morning, but in the afternoon, when David decided to make sure his ticket was still in place, he pulled out the book in which he thought he had hidden his ticket and, to his amazement, could not find the ticket there. One after another, he checked all the books on the shelf, but the ticket was not there. Where could it be? He was going through the books for the third time to find the small ticket he had hidden when his father entered the room. He had come home for lunch.

"Dad, I'm so sorry. I can't find the ticket you gave me to the Chinese circus. I thought I put in one of the books, but I've already spent an hour, and it's nowhere to be found," David said, ready for his father's reprimand.

"Don't waste your time, David. It will take forever to find this little piece of paper. Don't you worry. I'll buy you a new ticket. After all you went through with your bad cough, you deserve it," he said and stroked his son's head.

That same day, Samuel came back from work late in the evening when David was already in bed.

"Here, David," he said with a tender smile on his face. Without other comments or lecturing, he handed David a new precious ticket to the Chinese circus.

This time David decided to be more serious in storing the ticket. He went to the family closet, pulled a pair of his pants from a hanger, and carefully hid the ticket in its pocket. He studied the pants where he hid his ticket to remember. The next morning David had another reason to be upset and ashamed with his absentmindedness. The ticket to the Chinese circus had disappeared from the pants pocket where he clearly remembered putting it.

David could give up everything but not the Chinese circus. That was why, that evening when his father returned from work, David had no other choice but to swallow his young pride and share the bad news with his father.

"Dad, I'm very sorry. Please don't be upset with me," he said, beginning to cough. (This time, the cough was probably due to his nerves.) "I lost my ticket again, Dad."

"Where did you put it this time, son?"

"In a pair of pants. I don't remember which pants I put it in exactly. I checked each pair of them, but the ticket is not there. Dad, I feel so bad. Honest. The ticket has disappeared. It's like it dematerialized."

"No problem," Samuel said, unperturbed. "The main thing is that you are healthy and that your cough practically gone, son."

On the third day, Samuel brought with him brand-new third ticket to the Chinese circus. This time David wrote down in a new notebook that he had stored his third ticket in the top drawer of his desk. He locked the drawer with a key, hung the key around his neck, and checked its presence many times.

This time the system worked: several times David took the key from around his neck and opened the drawer of his desk with it. To his pleasant satisfaction, the third ticket was exactly where it was supposed to be.

On the day of the performance, David dressed neatly, and to make sure he was not going to lose the ill-fated ticket, he clenched it in his fist. Keeping in his mind what had happened with the previous two tickets, he did not part with the third one until he arrived at the theater. He climbed the theater stairs, approached the usher at the door, and opened his fist to show her his ticket. His ticket was there, as it supposed to be, but, to his unpleasant surprise, David found that the third ticket was not only rumpled and wet but also torn exactly in half. How it happened he had no idea. A state of panic related to all that had happened with tickets to the circus again seized David. He began to cough, worried that the usher would not accept his torn ticket. At this moment, David noticed that his father, as if out of nowhere, miraculously appeared next to him.

"What's the problem, sonny?" he asked calmly and with tenderness in his voice.

"Oh, Dad, it's you! Look at my ticket, Dad. It's torn," David said, having another bout of coughing. "Let's go home, Dad. I guess the usher won't let me in."

Samuel took David by the hand, approached the usher with him, and signaled David to show his ticket. David opened his fist and handed the usher the two halves of the ticket with a history.

"What is this?" the usher asked, first looking at David and then at his father.

"Never mind," Samuel answered. "My son accidentally tore the ticket. It happens to everyone."

The usher shrugged her shoulders and allowed David to enter. At last, David's dream came true. He waved goodbye to his father, and soon he took his legitimate seat in the first row in the main theater hall. The Chinese circus, especially teams of magicians and acrobats, was outstanding.

Most of all David remembered when a magician, an old Chinese man dressed in traditional clothes, invited a volunteer to the stage. David, who seemed to be just waiting for this moment, immediately jumped in. The trick was that the magician asked David to bend his neck and then began to snatch from David's back coin after coin, a whole small bag of coins. Leaving the circus David felt that the delight that he had gotten there was worth going through the unpleasant experience that had preceded it. In addition, David never forgot that despite the lost tickets, his father had never rebuked him.

As could have been predicted, with time David found the lost two tickets. They were exactly where he had left them. David's state of panic had been responsible for his state of confusion.

In conclusion, it's worth saying that it's good when a child has a dad and when there are good neighbors who are ready to take care of somebody in need.

—

David's parents were busy people. His father was in charge of a knitting and weaving manufacturing plant, and his mother was busy with numerous household and community obligations. They hardly ever checked David's school performance and did not monitor his presence or absence at home, trusting their son's ability to make the right choices.

In the warm season, two or three times a month, thirteen-year-old David and his friend Arseny went all the way to the edge of the city just to hang around. Arseny was a Moldovan boy from a simple family. He was of average height with swarthy and smooth skin, brown narrow eyes, and dark hair. He had an oval face, a straight nose, and a cleft chin.

In the city outskirts, among hills and groves, the friends enjoyed all that nature offered them: fresh air, the aroma of field plants, the blue sky, and the sounds of birds' talk. At these moments David had a feeling that he existed in two worlds: one of strict order and rules and another the world of simple life where people feel happy and satisfied with what little life can offer. Outside the busy city, where trees murmur their eternal tales, where birds sing their countless musical masterpieces, where plush grass invites a wayfarer for a rest, where the sky is adorned with clouds of quaint shapes and colors—in this reality time dissolves, concerns and worries disappear, and the invisible human soul floats high above heads like a halo on a picture of saints. Both children loved nature. This is an innate feeling that people are born with.

Once, in the beginning of June, misfortune visited David's friend. The boys were wandering through the hills, part of which were overgrown with all kinds of wildflowers. In the middle of the hill, they went in different directions. After about twenty minutes, David heard his friend's heart-rending cries.

"I was bitten by wasps! By wasps! Help! Help!" Arseny shouted.

"David, David, I was bitten by several wasps," Arseny yelled when David ran up to him. "It hurts badly. Quickly, pick up a leaf of a plantain and give it to me."

Plantain was considered to be a healing herb that people believed was a good remedy for various skin problems. The name *plantain* is shared with the unrelated cooking plantain, a kind of banana. Fortunately, the leaves of the plantain with a characteristic pattern formed by large veins could be easily found on the hill.

Arseny stood in front of David, pale, his lips gradually developing a bluish hue. David now could clearly see several points of stings on the skin of his arms. From Arseny, David learned that while he was looking at the flowers, he had seen a strange small gray ball, which he had the imprudence to move out of its place. The moment he touched it, he felt as if burning needles were piercing his arms and legs. Looking closer, he saw that the small wasps that lived in the ground under the ball had attacked him. The wasps were thin with black-and-yellow coloring and long dark wings. He also saw small holes in the ground, from which new wasps flew out to attack him. Distracted from this spectacle, he looked at his arms and saw how two wasps angrily waving their tiny wings sat on his forearm and having formed a back part of their bodies pierced their sting to his skin. Other wasps circled angrily over Arseny's head, preparing for attack. Arseny thought that at least fifteen wasps had stung him. He decided on the best thing to do: to run as quickly as he could from the nest that he had disturbed.

While Arseny talked, his condition became worse.

"David, David, I'm so afraid. These damn wasps bit me once before, but then I didn't feel so bad," Arseny muttered, and with his eyes closed, he slowly slipped to the ground.

David did not have any idea what to do. They were at the edge of town; no phone, no one was near them for a couple of miles.

Meanwhile, Arseny regained his consciousness for a short time. Still lying on the ground, he opened his eyes and looked around in surprise.

"What's going on, David?" he asked in a weak voice, trying to keep his eyes open. "Why it is so dark all around? Why everything is so dark?"

"It's not dark," David answered, trying to hide his panic as well as he could. "Do you want me to run for help, or do you want me to be with you?"

"No, no, no. Don't leave me for a second, whatever happens," Arseny whispered and again closed his eyes.

After David gave him water from a metal flask, a terrible thing happened: Arseny stopped breathing. Life was leaving him.

Fear paralyzed David; he could neither move nor speak. It cost him a great effort to get himself out of this state. He remembered a documentary about first aid he had seen on TV a month before. Placing his hands on Arseny's chest, he assumed the position to start CPR when he noticed that his friend took a deep breath and then resumed breathing on his own. David took Arseny by his shoulders, pulled him under a shade of an acacia tree, and elevated his legs using his friend's backpack that lay on the ground.

"Don't leave me" was the phrase that Arseny uttered for the umpteenth time.

Long minutes passed before Arseny's blood pressure raised enough for the darkness surrounding him to transform to the bright sunny day. His skin assumed its normal color, and he began to complain of a burning sensation at the sites where the wasps had stung him. Using his jacket, David elevated Arseny's legs even higher. Then he again gave him water from a flask and covered his skin with more plantain leaves.

What David had prayed for had happened. Arseny, who had almost died twenty minutes before, was able to stand up and walk on his own. The worst was over. Decades later, David became a doctor, and on that day, Arseny was his first patient.

The friends said goodbye, and David was on his way home—earlier than he usually was when he was returning from his nature trips. Normally, trusting his maturity, his parents did not control his coming and going. Being in a heightened state of mind after the successful conclusion of the incident with the wasps and not expecting any surprises, with a briefcase in his hand, he opened the gate to his backyard and entered. To his surprise, he saw his parents standing in the middle of the pathway. Their faces were red with anger, and their eyes were fixed on him.

"Why are you so late?" Samuel yelled at David. "I came home to pick up my wallet, and you weren't at home. Your mother and I are losing our minds here. Where have you been?"

"Nowhere special; I was with a friend of mine. I've come home later than this many times, and you never paid any attention . . . I was with—"

Before David finished the sentence, Samuel came up to him and gave him a strong slap in the face. After that he let David loose and went back to work.

Was David upset? Yes! Was he mad at his father? Not at all. It was the first slap David had ever received from him. How could he be mad at his father, whom he would not exchange for any other father in the world? He was not mad, but he was deeply offended. He was upset that Samuel and Ilana did not want to listen to his explanations. Besides, if his parents had told him to come home earlier, he would have returned at the exact time, thus avoiding the humiliation he had just experienced.

In any case, it was the first and the last slap in his face he experienced from his father, and though David knew that it was unfair, he never stopped loving his dad. What was that slap in his face in comparison with Samuel's presence in his life and all the love and devotion he gave him? David's philosophy was that before becoming upset with somebody, it was necessary to remember all the good deeds and words that this person did for you.

CHAPTER 10

Introduction to Vice

To help Ilana with unusual household chores, such as painting the house inside and outside or other extra household activities, the Lamms used to hire a woman whose name was Praskoviya. She was a pleasant woman in her thirties. Praskoviya did not use makeup and wore a clean white apron over an inexpensive worn-out brown dress with long sleeves. She wore a kerchief tied around her head. Not educated, she was an unusually sweet and intelligent person.

Since Victor was studying in a textile institute in Leningrad, David was the only child in the Lamm family. Praskoviya never failed to ask David what he studied and read. After David's answer, she clattered her tongue, lamenting that she had only graduated grammar school and always added that she would do her best to see that her two young children received a good education.

During the annual Passover and Easter exchanges of food presents, Praskoviya never failed to mention that Easter cakes and painted eggs tasted much more delicious than Jewish matzos.

Sometimes, Praskoviya's husband, Semyon, who was a handyman, helped the Lamms with outside jobs. Semyon was a simple man, pleasant and hospitable like his wife. One day his job was to dig a garbage pit in the backyard. Into such simple dug-out pits—without any additional constructive details—millions of housewives in the country poured the slop that they accumulated in their kitchen buckets. While Ilana and Praskoviya were inside the house, David was playing in the backyard where Semyon was digging the pit. Eventually, after hard work, Semyon took a break. Driving his shovel into the freshly dug earth, he sat down on the ground at the edge of the pit with his feet dangling. Enjoying his rest, he pulled a pack of cheap cigarettes out of his pocket, took one out, and lit it with a match. Catching David's curious glance, while thick smoke came out from his mouth, with a gesture, Semyon invited him to join him.

"So how are things?" he asked when David sat next to him.

"OK," the child answered.

"How about a cigarette?" Uncle Semyon asked eleven-year-old David naturally, as if he was not a child. In David's family, nobody smoked, and the unusual invitation produced mixed feelings in the boy. On one hand, he was brought up to be polite and had not been taught how to refuse from things he did not want, but on the other hand, he did not want to offend the hospitality of the giver, whom he liked. Imitating adults, he took the cigarette from Uncle Semyon's hands and put it in his mouth. Uncle Semyon struck a match, held it to his cigarette, and lit it.

"I see you don't know how to inhale, kid," Semyon said, peering at David. "Let me teach you how it should be done."

Semyon demonstrated to David how to inhale tobacco smoke, and David tried to imitate him. His first three inhalations were not successful and were followed with bouts of coughing, which made Semyon laugh. On the fourth attempt, David was successful. While he felt bad dizziness and lightheadedness, Semyon was generously praising him. David did not like the taste of the cigarette or the way it affected him at all.

David did not blame Semyon for teaching him how to smoke at his young age. Semyon lived in a world where smoking was an indelible part of communal culture. For him, treating David to a cigarette was a welcoming gesture; he did not think he was doing something inappropriate. As for millions of uneducated (and educated) people, smoking was a benevolent luxury for him.

—

Neither David nor his older brother, Victor, was attracted to alcohol. In their city, they saw plenty of examples of the ugly effects of its use. They frequently saw severe degrees of alcoholism when the drunkards were lying on the sidewalks in their own waste. However, life is complex. There are sometimes circumstances so propitious for alcohol use that it is difficult to avoid its consumption. David was eleven years old when the knitting manufacturing plant of which Samuel was the head had a party to celebrate the new year 1952. Many guests at the party came with their children of different ages; eleven-year-old Victor was among the oldest. In a midsize, relatively narrow hall stood several rectangular tables covered with tablecloths. On the tables, which were bursting with all kinds of food, stood many bottles of vodka, white and red wine, and beer.

Having had enough to drink and eat, the adults were involved in conversations while their children were on autopilot. Those children who did not fall asleep were entertaining themselves by running chaotically around the hall, pushing and kicking each other, shouting, laughing, and screaming.

On the table stood small, faceted glasses of wine and vodka left unfinished by guests. Having nothing else to do, David took one of the glasses of red wine and drank a little from it. He did not like the taste of red wine and tried muscatel, a sweet white wine with a nice heady aroma. Muscatel David liked. As an unselfish boy, he shared his opinion with other children who, like locusts, attacked the unfinished sweet wine, not having any idea of the possible consequences of its use. The children drank the wine mostly to quench their thirst, but small quantities added up, and soon the alcohol affected the kids. Some children became more boisterous and noisy, some became sleepy and lay in different corners of the hall, puffing and snoring. Their parents, excited from the jovial party, thought that their poor children were becoming tired and were happy that they took a little rest. David took alcohol well and functioned surprisingly normally.

After three hours of the party, Samuel announced to everybody that those who had tickets for the play *Platon Kretchet* should go to the theater, as the performance would start soon. David's parents were among the ticket holders, and along with David, they hurried to the theater.

Despite the fact that it was the end of December, the night was cool and pleasant. David remained sober as if he had not drunk at all. The Lamms were late for the play but on this New Year's night, the usher was kind and let the family take their seats in the middle of the hall, next to the aisle. After the family took their seats, David found out that the people sitting in front of him were tall and completely obstructed his view of the stage. Because they believed that their son was "unusually advanced and self-sustainable for his age," Samuel and Ilana did not mind when David said that he wanted to find a better place in the hall to sit.

While the performance continued, David went to look for empty seats in the front rows. Not finding empty seats at the oversold play, he went up the aisle between the two main sections of seats and sat down on the carpet. Now David was fully satisfied: he was able to see everything that was going on onstage. However, his triumph was spoiled because by that time, the level of alcohol in his blood had reached its peak; despite David's best efforts, his eyelids became heavy and tired. Eventually, David capitulated and plunged into a deep sleep. An usher brought him out of this blissful condition. Unceremoniously shaking David by his shoulder, she brought him back from the kingdom of Morpheus to the world of reality and ordered him to go back to his assigned seat. Swaying from side to side with an unsteady gait, David returned to the seat next to his parents, who welcomed him, not realizing that their beloved child was drunk. After settling in comfortably, David again fell deeply asleep.

The next morning when our hero woke up and recalled what had happened the day before, he decided that he would never drink alcohol again on his will. He tried to keep his word for the rest of his life. Thinking of alcohol, David never could understand why people who drank heavily voluntarily took themselves out of the relatively short stream of human life.

—

Growing up in fifties of the last century—like almost all the other boys on his block—David periodically experimented with smoking. In Russia, until now, besides regular cigarettes, people smoke *папиросы,* cigarettes with cardboard tips and without filters. None of the street boys among whom David grew up had enough money to buy cigarettes. Smoking among men was common, and on the streets of the city cigarette and *папиросы* stubs lay all around. All that was necessary for a boy on the street to begin smoking was to pick up a (supposedly) clean stub with a satisfactory amount of tobacco and then to get a light from an adult passerby. Like adults, teenagers had heard that tobacco was not good for your health (the official propaganda line said "Two drops of nicotine kills a horse"), but who pays attention to that when adolescents are strong and healthy? The fact that it was possible to catch a disease from a cigarette or a *papirosa* that was previously in the mouth of a possibly sick person some members of the butt-collecting community solved by rolling the end of the stub in a clean piece of a paper.

David was in his thirteenth year when, on the way to a friend's house close to his home, he found a "nice" stub of expensive Kazbek *папиросы*. Happy to find higher-quality tobacco product, David returned home, wiped the cigarette tip with a piece of clean paper, rolled the end of it in a small piece of the clean paper, put the cigarette in his mouth, and lit it on a gas stove burner in the kitchen. Still with the *papirosa* in his mouth, he left his house and went to see his friend. To shorten the distance, David chose a path between buildings in the middle of the block. One of the problems with this path was that it required passing an outhouse communal latrine with its generous stinking side effects. The home construction workers who lived in the nearby dormitory used this latrine. To overcome the strong stench coming out of the latrine, David usually ran through the area, but today, a *papirosa* in his mouth served as a reliable deodorant.

Though David had been using the unofficial path next to dormitory for a long time, he did not know anybody who lived there well. After safely passing the communal latrine area, he resumed inhaling his *papirosa,* letting out a thick cloud of tobacco smoke from his mouth. He was enjoying smoking until suddenly, he heard an angry female voice behind him. Ignoring it, he continued to walk until he was grabbed by his collar. Turning his head, he saw a woman in her thirties, accurately dressed in cheap clothing, typical for the residents of the dormitory. She was fair skinned and of average height, her eyes were blue, and a white kerchief covered her brown hair.

David knew well how poor the people who lived in the dormitory were. A year ago, when he was passing the dormitory, he had heard heartrending female cries. Struck and not knowing what to do, he stopped.

A man, a construction worker, came out of the building and, seeing David's reaction, stopped close to him and shook his head.

"Don't worry, boy," he said. "This woman lost fifty rubles, and now she can't stop crying as if her crying might return her money. She's been crying for an hour already."

For families like David's, fifty rubles was not such a large amount of money that it was worth a bout of crying an hour or longer, but the loss of this sum of money to the victim was very traumatic. David had not imagined that people could be so poor as to experience such a deep despair.

He remembered this episode when the unknown woman from the dormitory stopped him. Could it be she was so poor that she wanted to ask him to give her money, which, by the way, he did not have?

While he was thinking, the woman grabbed David's cigarette from his mouth and trampled it under her feet.

"Don't you dare to smoke, boy," she screamed at David angrily. "Don't you know that the nicotine in tobacco is very dangerous for your young health? I'm sure that if your parents knew you smoked, they would punish you. Don't you dare to smoke; do you hear me?"

Not knowing what to do, David looked at his lecturer with fright as she continued.

"Don't pretend you don't know that smoking ruins your health, boy! My only two brothers were smokers, and they both died of lung cancer! Both! I asked them a thousand times to stop smoking, but these asses didn't pay attention to my warning. It hurts me to see you, a young boy, shorten your precious life like a fool!"

Standing before the woman, David cast down his eyes.

"Do you understand what I'm telling you, kid?" the woman asked David, bringing her face close to him and looking straight into his eyes with a hypnotic look. As strange as it might sound, in the depths of her blue eyes, David could see rays of a pure human kindness.

"Yes, I do," David muttered in response.

For a moment, the woman gave David a short hug, then pushed him back, turned around, and resolutely walked toward the dormitory.

Following a famous maxim that raising a child takes a village, this woman affected David for the rest of his life. David forever remembered her words and arguments.

It is interesting that countless lawsuits were brought against tobacco companies all over the world. The main premise of these lawsuits was that the victims did not have any idea about the deleterious effects of smoking. If that was so, then why, so many years ago, did a poor and noble provincial woman know this plain truth?

CHAPTER 11

Lessons in Psychology

When David's older brother, Victor, who studied in Leningrad, arrived for summer vacation, he brought a present for his younger brother: a shiny chromium-plated toy gun that fired paper-roll caps, precious at that time. Shooting paper-roll caps while walking around the block where he lived, David tried to share his excitement with one of his friends and acquaintances, but none of them was around. At last, not far from his house, he met a boy unknown to him whose name was Boris. He was nice looking, taller and bigger than David and a couple of years older. David was streetwise enough to know whom to trust, but nothing in Boris's guise aroused suspicion. When after ten minutes of acquaintance, Boris—with a wide, friendly smile—first highly praised the toy gun and then asked David to give it to him to shoot a little, David did so without hesitation. Boris carefully took the shiny toy in his hands, shot couple of paper-roll caps, and then ran about ten meters from David and shot the gun again. Then he turned the gun toward David, pretending he was aiming to shoot at him.

"I like your toy, David," he said, looking at him with a treacherous smile.

A nightmare started. David first asked then begged Boris to return the gun. Boris pretended he was ready to return it, but the minute David approached him, Boris immediately ran a safe distance away from him. He was stronger and quicker than David was. All that remained for David was to continue to implore Boris to return his property. Without doubt, David would have stopped this humiliating experience long before, had not his tormentor each time created the impression that he was ready to return the toy gun. However, each time David approached him, Boris ran away, looking at David with his honest eyes. In his cat-and-mouse play, Boris was excellent. The play soon brought tears to David's eyes. While David was beseeching Boris to return his toy, Boris listened to him attentively, looking at him with an expression of sincere compassion and a benevolent sweet smile as if he was ready to return the toy to David. Then the running resumed. When, exhausted and humiliated, David finally realized what was going on, he left his tormentor with his gun and paper-roll caps. "Poor" Boris was quite disappointed: he had enjoyed the cat-and-mouse game he played with David.

Later, when David was older, he realized that he had dealt with a young sadist who enjoyed inflicting pain. He understood that negotiations with any kind of villain are counterproductive. Sadists like when their victims are asking for their understanding and sympathy; it flatters them, but it does not change their behavior for the better. Very important lesson, indeed.

—

In the eighth grade, David Lamm's school principal was a Communist named Eduard Fillipovich Gradobic. He was slightly above average height, neatly built, with inquisitive eyes and a pale face. Eduard Fillipovich, a pleasant man, taught the constitution of the Soviet Union. The main purpose of the class on the constitution was to teach students that, thanks to the efforts of the Communist Party, they lived in the best country in the world. Once, the lesson was about the role of the constitution in the regulation of the national question in the Soviet Union. Explaining this issue, Eduard Fillipovich stated that all nationalities in the Soviet Union were equal—and here he sounded like George Orwell in *Animal Farm*—but the Russians should be considered "more equal" than those of any other nationality because proportionally they were majority, which overthrew the tsarist regime. Moreover, Russians were a decisive majority, which had built socialism and lately defeated fascism.

Maxim Gradobic, Eduard Fillipovich's son, studied in the tenth grade at the same school where his father was principal. Maxim Gradobic was a rather tall, solidly build adolescent with an oblong face covered with active juvenile acne. He had narrow watery blue eyes with short eyelids. His lips were always dry and chapped.

David never understood why Maxim chose him for his "special attention." From the beginning of the school year, whenever he saw David, he did not miss an opportunity to bully him, verbally abusing him, calling him names, and periodically "rewarding" him with painful punches. It was practically impossible for David to avoid encounters with his nemesis in the corridors of the school. Maxim was much stronger than David was, but even if they had been of equal strength, David never forgot who Maxim's father was. Besides that, being a proud boy, David did not want to show Maxim that he was afraid of him. It was not in his character to complain to anybody, his parents included. Since birth, his credo had always been to solve his problems by himself. Knowing beforehand that he would be subject to bullying meeting Maxim at different places in the school, David clenched his teeth and did not say a word.

Once David's cousin Yefim came from Moscow for a visit. Yefim was a strong and brave twenty-two-year-old man. Once, when David went with him to watch a movie, Yefim observed David's facial expression when he saw Maxim.

"Why did you become so pale and tense, David?" Yefim asked. "I see that your fists are clenched. Is something going on between you and this pimply idiot?"

"You're right. I have frequent conflicts with this guy. He spoils my life."

"Let me beat him up so that he never harms you. Do you want me to do it right away? He'll forget what his name is!"

"No, I don't want that. I'm not looking for revenge; all I want is to be left alone. You might be too rough, Yefim, and then this fight might have consequences for me. You're leaving for home in three days, but I will remain here, vulnerable to retribution not only from Maxim, but also from his father, who is my school's principal."

Soon Cousin Yefim left for Moscow, and Maxim continued to bully David physically and emotionally. David was busy enough with his life, which helped him not pay much attention to his enemy. Yet everything has its limit, and the day came when David felt that his patience was exhausted.

He was walking on the school's second floor when he saw Maxim, who was stepping out on the floor from the stairs. At the sight of his enemy, David was overwhelmed with rage, and instead of waiting for the bully to approach him, he resolutely walked toward Maxim and pulled him by his sleeve. His move was a surprise to his adversary.

Not understanding what was going on, he turned around and looked at David questioningly.

"Now, you listen to me," David said without introduction. "Listen to my warning, pal: if you ever bother me again with your garbage, I will kill you. Do you understand that? If I don't succeed, than my friends will let your stinking guts out. I was patient enough with your stupidity, but if you open your mouth again or touch me with your finger, you might be decorated with a broken skull."

David stopped exhausting his imagination. Maxim was looking at him, not knowing what to say. David was bluffing, but he did not have anything to lose: it was not possible for him to live with the humiliation of his human dignity any longer. He felt a great relief and did not worry about the consequences. Whatever happened.

To his satisfaction, Maxim had a strange reaction. His face became paler than usual; he shrugged his shoulders, turned around, and went away without saying a word. After this, Maxim never again came close to David. For David it proved that, with rare exceptions, the majority of bullies of all ages were pitiful cowards who tried to prove to themselves that they were not miserable cowards by attacking other people.

—

Before the new year 1958, the future graduates of the tenth grade in the city of Beltsy learned that they were going to have a masquerade ball in one of the large city halls. The only condition for participation in the festivity was to register on time and to arrive at the ball in fancy character dress.

The minute David and his friend Yegor Tchufarov learned about the ball, they decided to attend. Naturally, the main reason for their decision was an expectation of meeting students of the opposite sex there.

David, at his mature adolescent age, had accumulated a lot of knowledge, but he still could not understand what attracted girls to boys, why some of the boys he knew were so popular with girls, and why pretty good boys (including himself and his friend Yegor Tchufarov) were ignored by them. He hoped that the upcoming masquerade ball might help him get at least a partial answer to the unresolved question.

After David registered his name for participation in the ball, he turned to his mother with a request for a big favor—he asked her to saw him a fancy masquerade costume. Sewing was Ilana's favorite hobby, and David knew she would not refuse his request.

"I'll be glad to sew it for you," Ilana told him. "The only problem is that we don't have enough money to buy a good fabric. But I know what I'll do; I'll use several layers of a good-quality wide cheesecloth. I'll dye it green, red, and white, and then I'll generously starch it. It will be a great outfit. And I'll make a clown mask from papier-mâché."

The masquerade ball happened only once during the school year. Anticipating the upcoming festivity, David and his registered friends were excited, expecting something very special from it.

Spending plenty of time sewing David's outfit, Ilana finished it a week before the ball. The multicolored clown costume looked pretty decent. David thanked his mother not only for the outfit, but also for the mask she made for him. The most remarkable feature of the mask was the clown's ironic and condescending smile.

Though David had a nice personality, he was not spoiled by girls' attention. Sometimes he thought the reason was that he was not super athletic, like the guys who enjoyed great success among the girls. Not being a good dancer either, David did not expect any personal success at the masquerade ball. All he hoped for was that at least one or two girls from his class would agree to dance with him if he ventured to ask them. As for the girls from neighboring schools, well . . . it was an impossible dream.

Before changing into his masquerade clothes, David Lamm and his friend Yegor entered the dance hall to see what was going on there. They saw that dancing was in full swing to the sounds of a military brass band. There were so many dancers on the dance floor that those who were not dancing stood or sat along a narrow perimeter of the hall.

The friends left the dance hall, went out into the corridor, found a secluded place, and dressed in their fancy masquerade costumes. Yegor's costume was a knight; he had borrowed it from his neighbor.

In the past David had not missed a chance to attend school dances, which took place every three or four months. The main lesson he learned at school dances was that he did not have a good approach to girls: when he asked one of his female classmates to dance, she usually refused his request. David did not to show that these rejections upset him and refused to give up. As for the ladies' dance, when the girls asked the boys, it was a complete defeat for him. Once in a blue moon, he would be asked by one of the girls who had a vision problem and who was too shy to wear her glasses. Timid and shy in his relations with girls, David was close to giving up his dream of being popular among them. Today, during the ball, he planned to continue his futile efforts to attract the attention of the beautiful sex.

With these thoughts, in his clown masquerade costume, David entered the dance hall with Yegor. They stood in the corner of the hall where they were difficult to notice. The friends began to discuss the situation when all of a sudden, a pretty girl ran up to David and cheerfully asked him to dance with her. David could not believe his success, but before he began to think about it, the girl he was dancing with tenderly cooed to him. "Who are you?"

David was shy, but he was not stupid. At once he understood that his partner was impressed not by him, by David, but by his fancy dress, and he promised himself that he would not let anybody know his name; he was going to keep his mouth shut to prevent anybody from recognizing him.

The dance with the girl was almost over when two pretty girls he knew from class who usually did not pay attention to him ran up—one faster than the other—with the next invitation for a dance. To be fair, David danced with the girl who ran up to him first. By this time, envious glances of girls in the hall accompanied the dancing couple. It appeared that David's dream was coming true: he had waited for such acceptance for a long time, and, finally, he had become popular. Naden'ka, his present partner, had always been an inaccessible princess in his eyes, but now she was openly flirting with David and eventually asked him a question he had heard several times before: "Who are you?"

David kept his word to himself; he did not answer. He suspected that as soon as Naden'ka learned who he was, the show would be over, and David again would become an invisible and prosaic figure in her eyes.

The girls did not give David a moment to rest. After Naden'ka, there were at least five new partners—each one more beautiful than the last—and each of them implored David to say what his name was and where he came from. Additionally, some of his dance partners enthusiastically offered closer acquaintance with them, but David's response consisted of a dead silence.

No doubt, David's fancy dress and the mask made by his mother won high popularity in the dance hall. Intrigued by the mystery of his appearance, the girls whispered among themselves and pointed their delicate fingers in his direction. David was at the peak of his success when two charming girls became involved in a fight for the right to dance with him. Eventually, they tried to solve their conflict by physical actions. Clutching each other's silky hair, they loudly challenged the other's right to dance with Mr. X. David wisely resolved this conflict by suggesting that he would take turns dancing with each of them. The unfamiliar ticklish feeling of being a favorite of the audience took possession of David, making him feel like the darling of fate and the king of the evening.

Alas, eventually all good and bad comes to an end. After an hour of David's stunning success came time for the sobering. Drunk on his success, David continued his butterfly-like dance when his new female partner, a tall brown-haired girl with determined features, loudly demanded that David identify himself. In response to his proud silence, violating from her point of view the rules of the engagement, she unceremoniously tried to take the mask off his face. David got away from his strong-minded partner and resumed dancing with a new partner, an innocent blonde maiden who danced gracefully, her eyes modestly lowered. In anticipation of a reprieve, David enjoyed her company, but in the third minute of the waltz, the humble creature became furious with David's silence and attacked him, jumping up and down like a wild sheep, trying to tear off her partner's mask.

David had had enough. He freed himself from the tenacious hands of his partner and ran to the corner where his friend Yegor stood, lonely. While Yegor hesitantly congratulated David on his success, a small flock of girls appeared before them unexpectedly. Without notice, producing high-frequency noise, they pounced on David trying to take off his mask and suit. There were too many of them to resist successfully. Instead of helping David, his friend, who was envious of David's recent success, openly chuckled at his attempts to resist the female assault.

When David's mask and costume were torn from him by the joint efforts of the girls, they had an opportunity to see who was hiding under the mystical attire. That resulted in the immediate and total collapse of David's reputation.

"Oh, but this is David Lamm," some cried in disappointment. "You are crazy! You are a fool! You screwed with our brains! Who needs you? Go home!"

Vanity of vanities; all is vanity. The girls who only recently were dancing around David and who gave him hundreds of smiles and compliments now looked contemptuously at him. David was not who they had expected to see, and that was, in their opinion, his fault. The moment David became who he was, the girls ignored him as if he had never been popular. At first, it upset him, but then he remembered that there is such a thing as the philosophic way of thinking, and he realized that only a select few could boast of such a grandiose, undivided success as had been his lot on this day. Since then, this memory belonged to him forever, and nobody could take it away from him. Besides, he received an important lesson: despite all assurances to the contrary, today he learned that people are judged not according to their character, but according to what plumage they presented outside. That partially answered his question why girls liked some boys more than they liked others. (To be fair, such a tendency worked both ways.)

—

To a newcomer a provincial city could see like a boring place, but that is not true. People are emotional creatures everywhere, and conflicts among them happen as frequently in provincial cities as in large urban centers. David lived on a boring quiet street, but many times, when he was outside, he could hear the loud, passionate sounds of quarrels among residents coming from all sides.

One of David's friends on the street was Kolya or Kol'ka, who was three years older than he was and lived across the street from the Lamms' house. Kolya's mother, Vasilisa, worked as a janitor. She was a tall stooped woman with a natural dignity. In her midforties, full of energy, she looked at least ten years older. A hard life had left many deep wrinkles on her attractive face. Her husband, Afanasy, a construction worker, was an alcoholic, but she loved him. Vasilisa was the type of person who suffered silently—she never complained about her husband, and when her husband was killed by a car while crossing the street, she suffered and mourned his death.

Sometimes Kolya invited David to his home to have something to eat. Vasilisa treated friends in the house with the same food: tea and delicious hominy or mamaliga, which she cut with a thread. To the hominy, she added butter or milk on the side.

Once, fifteen-year-old David observed something he had never seen before. After finishing eating, Vasilisa began to clean the jammed pieces of food between her teeth with a strong thread that she rolled off a spool. David thought then that what he saw was a strange and backward procedure, but many years later, when he arrived in the West, he understood that Vasilisa was ahead of her time: she was flossing, a routine measure of modern oral care.

Once when Vasilisa and her son were absent from their home, David was outside and heard the sounds of angry voices coming from across the street. Curious, he went out into the street and saw that about twelve people from the Valutza family had gathered in front of Vasilisa's house. David joined a ring of onlookers. Sashika Valutza, his friend from earlier years, was not there. The Valutza family lived in the middle of the block and was involved in the shadow economy, manufacturing roofing materials in their backyard. They avoid punishment by paying generous bribes to the militia.

Though nobody was in Vasilisa's home, that did not prevent the Valutza family from being aggressive, angry, and hateful. Nobody in the little crowd that gathered around them knew the reason for the attack. Each member of the group of assailants was yelling a stream of curses and profanities in Moldovan and Russian. The main instigator of the attack was the Valutza family matriarch, grandmother Pelagea, a short woman in rural dress: a dress and an apron in dark tones, a kerchief of the same color on her head. Like a storm, Pelagea's rage was gaining strength, and when it reached its crescendo, she bent down, picked up a large stone, and threw it through one of Vasilisa's windows. Her action served as a sign for the entire family to join her in the expression of their hatred. Now the whole Valutza family enthusiastically was knocking out the windows of Vasilisa's residence. The silence of a quiet street was filled with the sound of breaking glass.

David hated to see the scene of human depravity around him; violence was against his nature. Calling the police was not possible because there were no public phones, and nobody in the community had phones. Besides, because of a lack of cars, the militia—if informed about the riot—would have come too late. David left the mob and returned home.

David did not know how this pogrom ended. Thinking about mob mentality, he thought that if circumstances had been different, the Valutza family, headed by its matriarch, would have burned Vasilisa's house and killed its inhabitants. David had read in books about pogroms, and today he had witnessed a pogrom in action; in this case, it happened at a Christian house. Any native inhabitant of the city knew that behind the visible calm simmered human violence. Periodically, David witnessed a mob of people running after a single person, ready to inflict on him the worst cruelty.

A year later, when David was in tenth grade, the last at his school, he observed another episode of blind human hatred. In the city where he lived was a youth club. It had a drama and performance class in which David participated. Thanks to talented students who were involved in high-quality drama and concert performances, the club was popular among the city youth. It was difficult for outsiders to enter the club: close to ten volunteers guarded the door. There was always a group of young people outside the entrance to the club hoping to get in. When members of the club wanted to enter, they shouted their names, the doors opened, and the volunteers at the door let them in. The mob of outsiders was so tight that it was sometimes necessary to drag the body of a legitimate spectator out of the crowd.

Once when entering the club, David noticed that an outsider snuck through the door with him. Trying to merge with the crowd, the happy young man began to run into the hall, but the volunteers caught up with him. Instead of taking him outside, they grabbed him and dragged him into the basement, which was located not far from the entrance. Curious to know what would happen to the uninvited guest, David followed the volunteers and with his own eyes saw how the students from nice and respectable families knocked down their outnumbered victim and mercilessly beat him up with their hands and feet. Vainly, David asked the participants in the violence, whom he knew personally, to stop the cruel beating of an innocent man, but no one wanted to listen. Future worthy members of society calmed down only when the stranger was close to losing consciousness. Only then, happy they could commit crime without a punishment, they picked the stranger up from the floor and pushed him out through the entrance.

Observing similar fights on streets and in public places, David learned that people could be divided into three categories: angels, devils, and the intermediates between them. The intermediate category was the majority.

CHAPTER 12

Power of Alcohol

The environment in which David was growing up was rough. One evening, when he was eight years old, he stood with his mother in a line at a taxicab stop at the railway station. Meanwhile, a group of World War II veterans with different disabilities, who were standing in a circle next to the cabstand, became involved in a loud argument. This particular group, most of them alcoholics, could be encountered at different public places in town: at the food market, next to liquor stores, or at a bus stop. Some of them were on crutches, some had canes or eye patches. They were permanently drunk and loud. When somebody objected to their profanities or tried to stop their hooliganism or when they fought among themselves, their main defense was, "Don't touch me. I'm shell shocked."

While David and his mother were patiently waiting for their turn to take a cab, the argument among these drunken veterans was becoming hotter each second, voices were raised, and some of those present began to show their fists. David, who already knew many profanities, was not paying attention to them, but now there was a torrent of uninterrupted swear words from which he could not escape. As David did not know a meaning of these colorful expressions and nothing could exceed power of Russian profanities, he asked Ilana to explain their meaning.

"Those are not good words," Ilana answered. "Never use them."

Despite his mother's demand, in the future, David learned the meanings of dirty words too well.

Ilana, holding David by hand, left the cabstand and went to the bus station.

—

The railway station was the last bus stop, and at the beginning of the route, only six people were in the bus. From time to time, the bus made stops to let passengers on and off. Gradually, the number of commuters increased.

The peaceful environment that Ilana and David enjoyed after the recent quarrel at the cabstand did not last long. At the next stop, when in the pitch-dark doors of the bus opened widely, the passengers heard a man's loud scream next to the bus. The next minute a drunken, disheveled, and shirtless man with his belt unbuckled burst into the bus through the back door. He carried a kitchen knife in his hand. Saliva flowed from his mouth, and on his scalp and face were signs of recent bleeding. With bulging bloodshot eyes, he looked for his enemy on the bus and, not finding him, ran through the bus and jumped out the open front door.

That was not the end of the show on wheels. As passengers sighed with relief, five seconds later, they heard the loud screams of the man the previous hooligan had been chasing. This thug looked like a twin of the original intruder, and he was also very drunk. The only difference between them was that the second man's knife was twice as large. The criminal action was in progress.

"Where is that son of a bitch?" the hooligan yelled, swinging his knife. Everybody was silent, and when the thug was finally convinced that his adversary was not on the bus, he jumped out the door and dissolved into the darkness. The bus driver used this moment to close the doors. The potentially dangerous episode passed so quickly that no one was really scared; the passengers perceived what they just saw as free entertainment.

—

As for drinking, David experienced it in his own house, where alcohol was always present. His father drank in small amounts but frequently. Samuel's "passion" for alcohol continued until he reached his early sixties. After that age, he developed a peptic ulcer and liver problems, which made the use of alcohol physically impossible for him.

From time to time, alcohol made Samuel angry and aggressive. When this happened, he could initiate long and ugly arguments with Ilana, during which he used words that David by was no means supposed to know. At other times, a drunken Samuel could become mellow and emotional. In these moments, he asked his younger son to come closer to him so he could give him a wet kiss. David hated both the wet kisses and the smell of vodka fumes that accompanied them. The main reason Samuel could not stop drinking—even if he sincerely wanted to—was because, as the head of the company, he could not avoid the mandatory drinking parties with his numerous bosses. Drinking was an integral part of the business culture in the socialist economy. Practically all Samuel's bosses were drunks. Thus, it could be said that alcohol was a lubricant of the Soviet economy.

With all his capacity to drink, Samuel was not able to drink as much as many of his overseers, auditors, and inspectors. In order to drink less—whenever he was able to do it—he resorted to various popular tricks. For example, in the summertime, when he drank with his bosses outside, his trick was well choreographed. The drinking usually took place behind small street food stalls, called *ларьки*, where sellers kept illegal alcohol under the counter for such occasions. For the sake of privacy, restaurants were ignored. While Samuel and one of his bosses or inspectors sat opposite each other behind a small square table covered with a tablecloth, the stall operator served them alcohol and light snacks. Guided by considerations of a sick psyche, the bosses universally demanded that their drinking companions poison themselves equally with alcohol. When the time came for endless toasts and the drinking companions were ready to clink their glasses, the goal of the stall operator was to distract Samuel's superior with some innocent remark or gesture, which allowed Samuel, with a sharp movement, to spill his alcohol over his shoulder onto the ground behind him. In the cold times of the year, the performance of similar tricks depended on the skill of the waiter in the restaurant, who was supposed to add water surreptitiously to Samuel's glass of alcohol. When such tricks were discovered, the results were lamentable; the main outcome was that Samuel drank an amount of alcohol that he could not handle.

One such case happened when David was eleven years old. His older brother, Victor, was at home as well; he had arrived for summer vacation from his study in Leningrad. On that day, Samuel came home drunk as a fish. His appearance was horrible: his face was as pale as paper, he could not say a single word, and when he got close to his bed, he fell on it without taking his shoes off. Ilana and her sons watched with fear as Samuel's breathing gradually became more and more shallow.

Like the majority of families in the city, the Lamms did not have a phone. But even if a phone had been available, paramedics would take at least an hour to arrive, and even if they arrived sooner, there was a chance that, instead of a hospital, Samuel would be brought to a *вытрезвитель,* a local detoxification facility, where medical personnel were absent and where a contemptuous attitude to its clients reigned. It was a common knowledge that in some cases a drunken person taken to the detoxification facility died there.

Fortunately, at this time, Ilana's friend, a nurse, had come for a visit. While Ilana wrung her hands, her friend examined Samuel and told Viktor to run to the closest drugstore for ammonia. Liquid ammonia, which stimulates the respiratory and vasomotor centers of the brain and causes stimulation of breathing, was widely used in Russia in fainting episodes. David joined Victor, and after running a few blocks, the brothers reached the pharmacy where Victor told the druggist, an older man with the appearance of professor of medicine, what he had come for.

"Why do you need ammonia?" asked the pharmacist with a serious air.

"To save my father; he drank too much vodka," Victor answered.

"Aha. Everything is clear to me," the pharmacist said. He knew well about these kinds of situations. While both brothers were literally shaking with impatience, the pharmacist solemnly and slowly walked, shuffling his feet, in the direction of the shelves where all kinds of medical preparations stood. There he found the necessary bottle and shuffled back to the counter with it in his hands. Though the pharmacist certainly knew how precious each second was, he spent time fiddling with the label until he had carefully glued it on the bottle. To ask him to hurry up was not advisable; he might get annoyed, and that could only prolong the process.

"Take this receipt, pay the cashier a ruble and twenty kopecks, and come back to pick up the medication," he said eventually.

After receiving the medication, brothers rushed home at full speed. Fortunately, by the time they got home, the concentration of alcohol in Samuel's blood had decreased enough for him to improve, and there was no longer need for the medicine.

—

In Beltsy, where David lived, many different industries existed, including a large distillery. The school in which David studied in the ninth grade could not have chosen a better place for the students' educational tour than the distillery. Two teachers were appointed in charge of the tour: Alexander Onufrievich Peretyatko and Iosif Napoleonovich Mudrik. Alexander Onufrievich was a teacher of Moldovan language, and Iosif Napoleonovich taught mathematics. Both of them were middle aged and of average height. Alexander Onufrievich had a light build. He had brown eyes, brown hair, and a mustache on his oblong face. In general, he was a friendly person, and the poor knowledge of Moldovan among the students in David's class was not his fault: the system of education in foreign and local languages was focused on grammar rather than conversational skills. Alexander Onufrievich's subject was not a part of the final examinations, which resulted in the students' lack of motivation to study it.

Alexander Onufrievich pretended that he was teaching, and the students were pretending that they were learning.

Unlike him, Iosif Napoleonovich, a thin, energetic, and polite man with an olive complexion, was a responsible teacher: he was doing his best to help students with different issues in mathematics and was fair in his appreciation of their efforts.

On the appointed day in late October, students in the A and B classes, under the supervision of their mentors, were ready to make the two-mile walk to the distillery. When the classes reached the distillery, ninth grade A went with Mr. Mudrik and ninth grade B with Mr. Peretyatko. David was with Mr. Mudrik.

The distillery produced ethyl-rectified vodka, alcoholic beverages, and fruit wine. The source of the alcohol was grain and sugar beets. The distillery had three main sections: a department for the preparation of the alcoholic beverages and two bottling stations. Many students were sincerely interested in the technology of alcohol manufacturing. Several production stages when grain or sugar beets became alcohol were a discovery for them. During the visit to the production stage of the distillery, David noticed that Iosif Napoleonovich had disappeared from the group.

When the tour was over, David's group went out of the building into the yard, where they joined the other group of students, who were already there. Before starting their walk back to school, they patiently waited for the teachers in charge.

At last, the front doors of the distillery slowly opened, and the teachers came out, or rather crept out. Their appearance was pathetic. Always sober, now they were shamelessly drunk.

"You guys, you guys, excuse us. You see, they forced us to taste the alcohol. You know vodka, wine. Too much, too much," the Moldovan teacher stuttered, in Moldovan and in Russian.

Holding each other by the waist and the shoulder, swaying and almost falling, both teachers led the students back to school.

Alexander Onufrievich gradually became wasted. His face was flushed, his eyelids were almost closed, and his clothing was disheveled. He was restless and disoriented and made irrational statements. On top of this disgrace, his pants were wet in front.

Iosif Napoleonovich was not as drunk as his colleague was. He made desperate but unsuccessful attempts to pull himself out of his alcoholic stupor. He mumbled something about binomial theorem and logarithms and was constantly thanking the students who helped him and the other teacher walk more or less steadily toward the school.

Not a single student made rude remarks, and nobody laughed at them. On the way back to the school, both teachers vomited two or three times, and each time, their guides patiently wiped their faces and clothes with handkerchiefs. Both teachers looked like helpless infants. Eventually, both groups successfully arrived at the school. By now, the teachers had begun to sober up. They were late: when the students tried to open the door, it was locked. They loudly knocked, and the school custodian appeared and unlocked the door. The custodian understood right away what was going on and without delay led the latecomers to the teachers' office.

The next school day, the teachers came to the school as if nothing had happened. Students who would usually ridicule people, especially their teachers, about their shortcomings never did it with Mr. Peretyatko and Mr. Mudrik. Not a single pupil ever informed the school administration about them. The main reason for that was simple: both teachers were respected fatherlike figures.

—

After studying for ten years, David graduated high school in 1958. For two years prior to graduation, his best friend was Yegor Tchufarov. Though the friends lived two kilometers apart, this did not prevent them from seeing each other frequently. Like many urban inhabitants, the Tchufarov family lived in a state-owned apartment. Yegor had two sisters, both younger than he was. Yegor Tchufarov's mother, Maria Fedoseevna, a slightly overweight woman in her forties with a kind face and pleasant manners, was busy with her homemaking duties, which she combined with employment at the local military factory. She was a very hospitable and caring woman. Maria Fedoseevna's husband, a militia (police) captain, occupied an important position but never bragged about it. Like the majority of Soviet citizens, the Tchufarov family lived from paycheck to paycheck.

Maria Fedoseevna loved to feed both friends. She treated them to simple but always delicious food. In the warm season, her treats included her signature spring salad, which consisted of tomatoes, cucumbers, radishes, and young onions dressed with sunflower oil. When the friends reached the age of seventeen, a small bottle with vodka also appeared on the table, which Yegor and David used in minimal amounts.

Both friends appreciated their friendship and enjoyed time together. For David, spending time with Yegor was easy and interesting. His friend minded his own business and, like the rest of his family, was not affected by popular community virus of anti-Semitism.

Yegor was a neat person. One Saturday, before going to a city dance, the friends were in David's backyard gazebo. Yegor was dressed in a white shirt and new dark-color pants with carefully ironed longitudinal creases. During their conversation, David noticed that while he sat, Yegor remained standing, refusing to sit down despite David's repeated invitation. Eventually, David inquired why his friend refused to sit down. Yegor was silent. Finally, after intense questioning, David understood that the reason his friend kept standing was that he was afraid if he sat down, it would ruin the crease in his cheap pants.

The friends studied in the same year in parallel classes, which did not prevent them from doing their homework together. They spent a lot of time in the library, at sports activities, at the lake, or just chatting. In the warm seasons, they spent (or, better to say, wasted) their time in the vain courtship of nice-looking girls. The main places for courting were dances at city schools and, more frequently, at the city dance pavilion. Though the friends were nice looking and smart, they were unsuccessful in their courting, which by no means discouraged their efforts to follow their rich hormonal instincts. They could not understand why, despite their efforts to start relationships with the opposite sex, the opposite sex was not interested in them.

Open, peaceful, and easygoing, David and Yegor understood each other with half a word. The friends got along well and never had any conflicts, except for those inevitable cases when they could not decide who was going to court his next choice of romantic (and unsuccessful) encounter.

David and Yegor liked to bicycle, but Yegor was a much better cyclist than David was. Once—for the fun of it—he pedaled eighty-three miles on a hilly road all the way to Kishinev, the capital of

Moldova, in one day, and after returning in the late afternoon, he went with David to a school dance.

Once, the friends were following two beautiful girls about whom they were optimistic. They were carried away with their pursuit to such a degree that they did not notice that they found themselves far suburb that was unknown to them. It seemed that the girls were ready to start a conversation with them when a local gang of teenagers them appeared before them, the leader unhappy that the suitors were courting the girls from his neighborhood. Right away, the friends forgot about the girls they hardly knew; they quickly got away, but the gang caught up with them and left superficial scars on their faces as a reminder of the unsuccessful courting.

One early morning in July, during the summer vacation after the friends graduated from ninth grade, they decided that they needed extra money, and they wanted to earn it. Yegor had a plan. Somewhere he knew that was not too far from the city, there was a kolkhoz with a vineyard. That vineyard was always in need of day workers for grape harvesting. Not thinking much, the friends took their bicycles and were on the way to their destination. Though this July morning was cool, later it promised to be hot and humid. Therefore, the friends dressed lightly and filled their canteens with water.

They reached the kolkhoz's vineyard at ten o'clock in the morning. After a fifteen-mile bicycle trip, David and Yegor were not tired; just the opposite, they were full of energy and the desire to make money to buy books or records. Actually, more than anything else, they wanted to prove to themselves that, at their young age, they were able to earn their own money.

They introduced themselves to the supervisor, a short man with a red face and a low, wrinkled forehead, who explained to them what was expected of them, and they joined the other people in the vineyard. Some of them were city dwellers, but the majority were local peasants. All of them were working hard, and none of them paid any attention to the newcomers. The energetic teenagers began enthusiastically collecting grapes into wooden boxes and then hauled the load away to a horse-driven cart at the entrance to the vineyard. Meanwhile, the burning sun rose high. In heat and stuffy air, with the high humidity, it was very difficult to work. In the past, passing by the countryside, David had frequently seen the kolkhozniks who worked in the agricultural fields. Only now did David understand how difficult and monotonous the manual work was.

David and Yegor could not wait for their break. It was already two o'clock. By that time, they had worked about four hours. Sweaty, dirty, and very tired, they approached the supervisor and told him that they are leaving. Not saying a word, the supervisor pulled a ten-ruble banknote from the breast pocket of his crumpled gray jacket for "the great workers."

"Is that all?" Yegor, who had expected a small bonanza for his hard work, asked.

"And how much you were expecting for your lousy work, boy?" retorted the supervisor, who was prepared for this kind of protest.

"Listen, I never realized that it was so difficult to earn money in agriculture," Yegor complained to his friend on the way home from the vineyard. "You know, David, my parents are right when they tell me that to live normally, I need to get a good education."

The friends had gone a couple of kilometers on their bicycles when Yegor asked David to stop. "Listen, David, I'm so tired. I heard they have a kolkhoz water pool somewhere around here. Let's ride and have a swim there to refresh a little. Before we return home, we need a short rest anyway."

David readily agreed, and after consultation with a passerby about the direction, the friends easily found the kolkhoz pool. Nobody supervised the pool. Besides David and Yegor, there were three men at the pool: two of them in their late twenties and the third one, quite overweight, closer to his thirties. Judging by their appearance and their clothing that lay in a pile next to them, they were peasants from the kolkhoz.

David and Yegor settled on the other side of the pool and jumped into the water. The water in the pool as a greenish color and smelled of algae, but it did not bother them at all. The Propaganda and Agitation Department had taught the Soviet citizens that they lived in the best (but not perfect) country in the world. Soviet citizens were not supposed to be fastidious and had to be grateful and thank the Communist Party for anything it offered them, especially "the free stuff."

After the heat and humidity the friends had experienced on this summer's day, the color and smell of the water was insignificant: most important was that the water helped them get rid of the heat of the day. Swimming in the pool, the friends were surprised to discover that the unsupervised pool on the opposite side was very deep—at least eight feet.

After a quarter of an hour of swimming, David and Yegor got out of the pool; it was necessary to return home on time. Without towels, they waited for the water to evaporate from their bodies. The friends were ready to depart when they noticed that instead of three men on the opposite side of the pool, there were only two of them. These two men, before they entered the water, were sitting on the pool's edge washing their bodies with a bar of laundry soap.

David and Yegor picked up their bicycles and looked around to make sure they hadn't forgotten anything. Suddenly, they heard one of the two remaining pool visitors yell, "Hey, where is Radu? I haven't see him for a while. What happened to him?"

"I saw with my own eyes that he dove in the pool," his companion responded, looking in vain at the pool with wide-open eyes. The water in the pool was too muddy and green to see anything below its surface.

"Wow, oh, then he probably drowned. *Dumnezeu,* [Oh God], today is his birthday, and he drank too much wine. You're the witness, Dumitry. I warned him not to swim, but he didn't listen to me."

"Stop talking," Dumitru yelled. "We've got to pull him out of the water. He might still be alive."

The peasants, David, and Yegor jumped into the water and began to dive again and again, trying to find the drowned man on the bottom of the deep side of the pool. It took ten long minutes before Yegor found the drowned man. The rest of those present helped him pull the bluish body from the green pool water. The group put the motionless body on the grass and tried to resuscitate him. Judging from how bluish his entire body was and how swollen his face was, nobody present expected the resuscitation to succeed. After ten minutes, it became clear that the man was dead, and the group stopped resuscitation. One of his companions dressed and ran to the village to find transportation to bring the drowned man home.

Depressed after what they had seen, David and Yegor mounted their bicycles and rode toward the city. "You know, David," Yegor said while he was riding next to his friend. "I'm just thinking. I read many books where the heroes die, and their friends—at least one of them—go berserk after learning the bad news. People are crying, pulling their hair, moaning, tears are running like a stream, everybody talks about the dead person, but look at us and at those two peasants. In my mind, I understand that we witnessed a tragedy, but otherwise I feel nothing special. Is it abnormal?"

"Calm down, Yegor. I feel the same way. We're only human. We have our limitations and should not forget that death is a part of human life," David answered.

Later the same day, the friends spent their honestly earned money on a book, ice cream, and tickets to the city's dance pavilion.

—

After David became a student in the Kishinev Medical School and Yegor entered Moscow Polytechnic University, the friends met once or twice a year in their native city during summer or winter vacations.

In the beginning of August 1960, they met once again. At that time, they were on the third year of their graduate education. Yegor had matured and become a handsome young man with an athletic build. As in the good old times, the friends enjoyed each other's company. However, after a couple of weeks had passed, Yegor told David that he was bored in the city and that he had one of his "brilliant" ideas. He had a phone conversation with one of his friends who told him that a group of girls from his university had recently come to Moldova's capital, Kishinev, where they were taking a summer internship at one of the local factories. According to Yegor, all the girls from his university were outstandingly beautiful and were not too strict in their attitude toward friendly relations. Yegor promised that they were both going to have a great time in the company of his fellow students.

For a healthy young man of David's age, such an offer sounded tempting, especially because he was studying at Kishinev Medical School, where he lived in a dormitory. Anticipating an experience worthy of remembering, David compromised with his conscience and told his parents that he needed to return to his medical school in order to retake a test in his medical statistics course. His trusting parents believed the shameless lie and provided him with a modest allowance.

Two days later, early in the morning, the friends bought the cheapest tickets to Kishinev. At this time of year, Kishinev was beautiful. The weather was excellent. In a great mood, the young adventurers in the sphere of love affairs went straight to David's dormitory, hoping that despite the fact that it was summer vacation, they would be able to stay in the David's room and save money.

When they got to the dormitory, a big summer repair was underway. The air smelled of fresh paint; in the corridors, where chaos reigned, stood ladders, buckets of paint, and brushes. Because of the painting, a thick layer of sawdust covered the floor—a local method of preventing floors from being spotted with paint.

In the lobby behind a table, Anna Afanasevna Sokolovskaya, the warden of the dormitory, sat. Over her blouse and skirt, she wore a long leather jacket. On her head she had a kerchief and on her legs tarpaulin boots. The warden was strict but also just and effective in her capacity. Seeing David, she smiled at him, and while they had a short talk, Yegor, imperceptibly, made his way from the lobby to the dormitory corridor. After David joined him, the friends went to the room where David lived during the school year. David used his key to open the door, and they found five unoccupied beds inside. To David's delight, the sixth bed was occupied by his friend Ion Popa, who was sleeping peacefully when they came in. Like everywhere else in the dormitory, the room was covered with a thick layer of sawdust.

Medical student Ion was two years older than David. For additional income, he worked as an evening nurse in one of the city hospitals. David had shared the same room in the dormitory with him since he arrived at medical school. The arrival of the friends awoke him. David introduced Ion to his companion and received Ion's permission to have Yegor to share the room with them.

Yegor, who had never been in Kishinev before, decided to look around. Agreeing to meet in the evening, the friends parted ways. David spent the day in the medical school library, while Yegor went to visit the city's museums. When the friends met in the evening, Yegor, who was slightly inebriated and in a great mood, told David that besides visiting the museums, he had managed to spend time with his fellow female students.

The next morning, before he went about his business, Yegor gave David the address of the party and told him that he expected to see him there at seven o'clock in the evening.

"Don't forget to bring a bottle of vodka and a snack with you," Yegor said when they parted.

The party was being held on Youth Boulevard, which was about three kilometers from the dormitory. David took the trolley and arrived at the party at the appointed time. Entering the room, David understood that Yegor's friends—there were five of them—lived in a private house, where they rented a room. After Yegor's description of his university classmates, David expected a chorus of cheers and sweet girls' laughter on his arrival, but this did not happen; no one paid any attention to him when he entered the room. Yegor was involved in a conversation with a nice-looking girl while the rest of the company was preoccupied with their own business. On the table next to them stood bottles of vodka, wine, and beer and clean glasses. Seeing David, Yegor took the bottle of vodka that he had brought with him and then introduced his friend to his female companions. There was not too much enthusiasm in their response.

After that, Yegor lifted his glass and invited David to join him and his girl for snacks, which they washed down with alcohol. Soon David became bored with small talk about things that were not of interest to him. Meanwhile, Yegor became more and more drunk. All of a sudden, David saw a Yegor he never knew before. Alcohol made him garrulous and playful; he was making stupid jokes at which his female companion loudly laughed with him. He reeked of alcohol; his face was sweaty and flushed while his eyes were bloodshot and watery.

Soon Yegor decided that it was time for the party to begin. He asked for snacks, and the students brought to the table bread, cheese, sausages, vegetables, and opened cans of food. Previously known to David as modest and shy, Yegor entertained the audience that encircled the table. While the girls were filling their plates with food, Yegor, the leader of the party, was pouring alcohol into the glasses. All who so desired ate and drank as they wished.

Yegor picked up a bottle with vodka and asked David to come closer.

"Listen, David, before I pour you vodka, I want to introduce you to my friend Katya. She told me she wants to get acquainted with you," Yegor said, taking Katya by the hand. Katya, a young woman of David's age, was quite attractive; her face, from which her cheekbones protruded slightly, was a perfect oval. Smiling at David with a full mouth and showing her snowy teeth, Katya slightly squeezed his hand.

So far, everything was going well: David had a nice female companion for the evening and next to him stood his proven and reliable friend.

"Where is your glass?" Yegor asked. "Let's drink to our good company."

Without hesitation, David approached his friend, who knew well that he did not drink. To David, even moderate drinking was an unforgivable waste of time; life for him was too interesting and too intriguing to shut himself from it with alcohol. In his life, in his own family, he had observed enough of the destructive influence of alcohol on the psyche to be disgusted with its excessive consumption.

With a cunning smile, Yegor grabbed a bottle with vodka from the table and poured more than three quarters of its volume into his friend's glass.

"Yegor, are you crazy? What are you doing?" David protested.

Yegor did not hear him. By this time, he was sufficiently drunk.

"Bottoms up!" he ordered abruptly. With bloodshot, watery eyes, Yegor looked at his friend. The peaceful and mellow tone of his friend's voice, so familiar to David, now changed to aggressive, not tolerating objections, an order issued by a commander.

David protested. "Yegor, you know well that I don't drink vodka. Do you want me to fall asleep or faint?"

However, his trusted true friend was now transformed into a stranger. "You better stop arguing, David. As long as you are here, drink! Nobody forced you to come to the party. I won't let you leave the table until you drink your glass. Drink!"

"I will not drink," David answered him decisively, "and stop trying to force me."

"No, you will," Yegor said. He grabbed a glass of vodka and brought it to David's mouth. He did not hide his anger that someone would contradict him.

Now the eyes of all present in the room were focused on the former friends.

"OK, if you insist," David said. "But remember, Yegor, you will be responsible for the consequences."

David drank all the vodka in the cup in one gulp and then, trying to show his bullying friend that he was his own master, poured himself a glass of wine and drank it as well.

"That's a boy!" Yegor praised David. With a shaking hand, he poured him half a glass of beer, which David gulped as well.

Meanwhile, alcohol loosened the tongues in the room. Katya, who stood next to David, told him that she liked Kishinev, and David readily agreed with her. She appeared to him to be a pleasant young woman, and he was grateful to Yegor for introducing her to him. For a while, it appeared that David could hold alcohol well. After socializing for a while, David felt he was making a certain progress in his relations with Katya, whose eyes were becoming more beautiful with each minute. The modest amount of wine she drank made her lively and cheerful. The room was getting warm, and Katya asked if David would like to go for a little walk.

Holding hands, they walked a couple of blocks toward an area where several standard five-story residential buildings, all similar to one another, stood. Next to most of them, which were recently built, were buildings in the process of construction. Around them were all kinds of construction machines: excavators, bulldozers, cement mixers, and graders. By the time David reached the area where the new buildings had been constructed, he realized that he was getting drunk. His tongue, his legs, his whole body refused to obey his will. Tongue tied, he asked if Katya wanted to sit down, to which she readily agreed.

The best place the couple could find for a rest was a low barrier that served as a perimeter of a window well for the basement floor. By this time, in David's eyes, his female companion had transformed into a beauty queen. A strong magnetic force attracted him to Katya. Holding hands, the couple had a pleasant conversation, but, unfortunately, the queen complained that she was cold. As a real gentleman, David took off his light beige wool jacket and reverentially put it on her girlish shoulders. He embraced Katya's waist, and their faces were close to each other.

This divine moment was broken in the most prosaic way. David's bladder demanded immediate emptying, and there was no way to escape this feeling. It was necessary to solve this problem immediately. Otherwise . . .

Embarrassed, David explained to his companion that he had to retire for a very short moment. Katya nodded knowingly, and David happily ran behind one of the bulldozers and did something that was not allowed in a public place. At least his pants remained dry.

Physically relieved, with an unsteady gait, the embarrassed David returned to the place where he had left Katya minutes ago, and to his foggy surprise, he realized that she had disappeared without a trace. By this time, David's alcohol intoxication was approaching its peak, but he still was able to more or less control himself. Concentrating as much as he could, David went first toward the house he had come from. Passing through the path, which was covered with weeds on both sides, he was getting lost and realized that he must return to the dormitory. His legs felt as if they were made of cotton; they moved of their own will. David turned toward Youth Boulevard, from where he had come hours before. It was supposed to be in front of him, but as his vision was affected as well, he was unable to see it. Not knowing where to go, he stood hesitantly until he heard the voices of children; to his right, a group of young teenagers was playing soccer. Observing the older children beside the small playing field stood a little boy in drawers and a T-shirt, seven or eight years old. Not to scare him with his lamentable countenance, David came closer to the boy.

"Excuse me, little boy, can you take me to Youth Boulevard?" he asked, moving his tongue with difficulty.

"But it's right in front of you," said the boy, who did not appear to be scared. Just the opposite: he looked at David with his angelic unforgettable trusting glance, and David could see in this child's bottomless eyes compassion for his deplorable state. The boy responded to David's request with a nod of his head, took him by his hand, tightly squeezed it, and brought him to Youth Boulevard. The moment the boy let go of David's hand, consciousness abandoned him.

Consciousness returned to the drunken medical student about nine hours later, at five o'clock the next morning. David was lying in the dormitory bed, and somebody was shaking him by his arm. Not having any idea how he got into his bed and who was shaking his arm, he opened his eyes and, to his amazement, saw the face of Anna Afanasevna Sokolovskaya, the dormitory's warden. Seeing that he was awake, she stopped shaking his arm.

"Get up, Lamm," she said. "I can't understand what happened to you. You, who were always such a quiet and polite student, came in the middle of night like a real drunkard. I didn't recognize you. I tried to speak with you, but you didn't say a word. Tell me, what mess were you in yesterday?"

"I honestly don't have any idea," David answered.

"Sure you don't know, as if I believe you. In any case, Lamm, it looks as if you are in a serious trouble. They called me from the local militia station and requested that you go there right away."

"How can they know my name? What have I done?"

"I know nothing," answered Anna Afanasevna. "I'm telling you what they told me on the phone. That's all."

Anxiety and fear took over David. For any conflict with the law, the administration could expel him from medical school. What happened to him after he entered Youth Boulevard was a total mystery to him.

The warden of the dormitory left, and David began to dress go to the militia station. He looked around, and to his sheer amazement, besides Ion Popa, he noticed Yegor, who was sleeping on the bed next to his. Previously drunk and noisy, Yegor now was peacefully breathing in his sleep, as if nothing had happened.

When it was time to put on his jacket, David could not find it. If he lost it yesterday, it would be a serious blow for him because in the pockets of the jacket he carried his passport, student ID, and money.

Before leaving the room, David decided that he had a moral right to wake up Yegor and to ask him to accompany his friend on the intimidating visit to the militia station. But before David could wake up Yegor, Ion woke up.

"What was the problem was you last night, Lamm? I never knew you to be drunk, but you behaved like a real drunkard," he told David, not hiding his displeasure and contempt. "You were totally out of it when you came in last night. I tried to speak with you, but you behaved as if you were deaf and mute. You undressed yourself as if you were a robot, but before you fell asleep, you puked twice. Do you think it's pleasant when somebody vomits next to you?

"Then your friend came back. I tried to make him clean up the mess you made on the floor, but he was as drunk and unresponsive as you were. So you owe me—I cleaned up all your vomit. The only good thing is that we have this sawdust on the floor; that made my work much easier. Shame on you, and shame on your friend!"

David tried to explain to Ion that he was ashamed himself for what had happened and that it was not his fault but Yegor's, but Ion did not want to hear. He'd had enough.

Finally, Yegor woke up. Now he was the Yegor David had known for many years: warm, understanding, and sympathetic. Without a word of objection, he quickly dressed, and they went to the militia station.

The summer morning was magnificent. The clean streets were lit by the bright rays of the rising sun, the air was fresh and crisp, birds were performing their masterpiece performances, and among this grandeur, betrayed by his friend yesterday, David needed to go to militia station for who knew what purpose. The worst of all would happen if the militia contacted his medical school; then nothing would help him.

David and Yegor went by foot to the militia station located a couple of miles from the dormitory. When they entered the station, the only person there at this early hour was a middle-aged officer who was working with papers. Leaving Yegor in the waiting area, David approached the officer with a worried heart and introduced himself.

The officer looked at him, right away understanding whom he was dealing with.

"Ah, so that's you," he said dryly and without any intimidation in his attitude. "Go to the waiting area. I'll call you."

David joined Yegor immensely relieved; it appeared to him that he had not committed any crime.

"What was the problem with you? Why did you leave the party? We had such a great time," Yegor said. "Was something wrong with the girls? I looked for you everywhere."

David remained silent. He did not want to remind Yegor how aggressive he had been, forcing him to drunk against his will. To start such a conversation meant bringing a long-term friendship to an end once and for all.

The sergeant came out to the visitors.

"OK, young man. Did you lose your jacket today?" he asked.

"Yes, I did," David confirmed.

"So, the jacket with your documents that you forgot in front of a building on a barrier around a window well yesterday was found by nobody else but the chief prosecutor of the Moldovan Republic. You're lucky; he called me and ordered me to find you. Here's his address. Go there; they're waiting for you."

A load had been taken off David's mind. He did not break the law, his medical school would not be notified about his drinking episode, and soon he would have his jacket and documents back.

David and Yegor went to the address provided to them at the militia station. Indeed, the chief prosecutor lived in the building next to the one in front of which yesterday, in anticipation of unearthly pleasures, David was embracing the beautiful Katya. While Yegor waited for him downstairs, David went up to the third floor of the building. When he reached the apartment he was looking for, he rang the bell. A minute or two later, the door slowly opened, and a woman, most probably the prosecutor's wife, emerged. In her hands, she carried David's jacket, in which breast pocket, to his incredible relief, he found his wallet with all his documents. For some reason, the prosecutor's wife frowned when David profusely thanked her. She just silently handed David his jacket and immediately returned to the apartment, slamming the door behind her.

Going down the stairs and checking the contents of his jacket's pockets, David understood the squeamish reaction of the chief prosecutor's wife. In the breast pocket, he found a condom of domestic production. After all Yegor's promises, as a responsible young man, David had carried the rubber device to ensure the safety of intimate relations. It seemed that the prosecutor's wife did not share with him such an enlightened attitude.

That same day, Yegor and David took a bus to their native city. David's parents never learned how their son had been drunk and how without consciousness he had been able to walk almost three kilometers.

On the way home, David spoke with Yegor about many things, but not what had happened the day before. David felt sorry for his long-term friend, whom he liked so much: he realized that his previously reliable friend had sold his soul to the Spirit of Alcohol. Very delicately, he tried to start a conversation with Yegor about the danger of alcohol, but his friend became angry and refused to hear a word.

—

A year passed and David and Yegor met again during summer vacation in Beltsy. This time Yegor came to the native city not alone but with his twenty-one-year-old bride. The friends met by chance in the town square. David was on his way to the library when he heard a familiar voice. It was Yegor; he was with a girl. The young adults held each other's hands tightly.

"I'm so glad you're here on vacation, too. Meet Julia!" Yegor said, smiling.

Julia, a beautiful woman, slightly shorter than Yegor with an attractive face and lush blonde hair, exchanged greetings with David.

"It's so good I met you," Yegor continued. "As a matter of fact I was going to visit your parents to tell them my great news, but now I met you. Congratulate us! Julia is my wife. Yesterday we signed up at the registrar's office, and, remember, the day after tomorrow, we're having a wedding at my house. So you are officially invited to come at four o'clock in the afternoon. We will celebrate, David."

"Yes, please come," Julia confirmed in a sweet voice.

The next day David, dressed in his best suit and a new tie, arrived at the Tchufarovs' apartment at the appointed hour. Entering Yegor's house, David expected to see a lot of guests. Instead, in the living room, he saw only Yegor's parents and sisters and the Tchufarovs' neighbors' family. Nobody represented the bride's family. All present in the room were sober and retained serious expressions on their faces. Only the bride and the groom were moderately drunk; they did not express much joy, either. Yegor was dressed in a shirt and pants, without a jacket or tie. Julia wore a nice beautiful white dress, but because she was drunk, she looked neither accurate nor well groomed. Alcohol took away the bride's beauty.

Half an hour later, Yegor invited David to go outside with him for a smoke. When they left the house, Yegor took David to the alley that led to the backyard shed. On a primitive ladder, the friends climbed up to the flat shoddy roof of the shed. When they got there, Yegor lit a cigarette and offered one to David. To keep him company, David did not refuse. While standing and smoking, David tried to start conversation with Yegor, but Yegor was too drunk to maintain it. Looking at David with glassy eyes and droopy eyelids, he answered in simple flat phrases.

Soon, the bride appeared in the alley. The bride probably already knew about her groom's favorite place because she walked straight to the shed. With her white bridal attire stained with wine and a white corolla on her disheveled head, she approached the shed with an uncertain gait. Affected by episodes of alcohol-induced crying, her face was smeared with makeup.

"Hey, Julia, come up and join us," her groom magnanimously suggested from the roof. Julia was able to climb up a couple of steps on the ladder; then Yegor and David dragged her up onto the roof. She joined the men, lit a cigarette, and was looking intently at the horizon as if the Messiah was on his way to her wedding.

The newlyweds did not speak and deliberately or unintentionally did not show interest in each other's company. A few more minutes passed, and the neglected bride resumed her sobbing. While his bride cried, Yegor paid no attention to her and continued to live in his own world.

The wedding, for which the Russian expression is "a dog's wedding," ended as boringly as it began.

—

A year later, David again visited his town to spend his last vacation there—this time, it was after his graduation from medical school. On the second day of his visit, he went to Yegor Tchufarov's home on Shchusev Street. Yegor's mother, Maria Fedoseevna, opened the door. At the sight of David, she burst into bitter tears.

"David, my dear boy, come to me. I will embrace you. Don't you know, dear, that my Yegor is not alive any longer? My Yegor is not alive. Can you imagine?"

"What happened? I know nothing," David answered, shocked by the terrible news.

"Come in, David. I'll tell you what happened."

David went into the house that was so familiar to him, where he spent many happy hours with his best friend, Yegor Tchufarov.

The story was a tragic but unfortunately a very typical one. Yegor had lived with his wife, Julia, only two months before they divorced. Last year, as a bachelor, he had attended a New Year's party in one of the Moscow restaurants with his new girlfriend. Against his girlfriend's protests, Yegor's friends insisted he drink more and more until he passed out. His girlfriend called for emergency medical help, and when they arrived, Yegor was still alive. But instead of taking him to the hospital, the medics took him to *вытрезвитель*—the city detoxification center. While he was deeply asleep there, they placed him in the room without medical examination. In two hours, an agent from the center found him dead. He lay on the bed in an fetal position.

Such is the true and sad story of a nice man. Yegor was born into a good family and had the potential to have a nice and decent life. He was an exemplary young man until he became a slave to alcohol. Nobody forced him to drink. It was his own decision. Such a pity. In the future, no one could replace David's friend Vladimir Tchufarov. Alcohol took him away.

CHAPTER 13

Encounters with Anti-Semitism

After service in Karelo-Finn Province, Samuel was transferred to serve in Pontonnaya Station and later in Vyborg, both in Leningrad Province.

In Pontonnaya Station, a town located next to a railway station, the Lamms lived in a traditional Russian wooden house not far from the military unit where Samuel was stationed.

In Pontonnaya Station, five-year-old David learned for the first time in his life that he belonged to an ethnic group that was subject to prejudice and humiliation.

One day in August, Ilana, humming some Ukrainian song, comfortably settled herself in the middle of the yard, cut a big bar of soap into pieces, put them into a large tub, filled it with hot water from a pail, and began doing laundry.

Dressed in childish pants with narrow breast bands, in a splendid mood, David hung around next to her, trying to do whatever she asked him to do for her. Suddenly the peace and quiet was disturbed by a thin teasing voice.

About thirty meters away, a ten-year-old girl was standing on the pavement and, pointing her small finger at David and his mother, singing loudly: "*Zhid*, *zhid*, *zhid*, hangs on the little rope…"

By the cocky tone in which she sang, David could understand that it was supposed to be an insult.

After repeating the song from the repertoire of anti-Semitic "folk art" several times, the girl stuck out her tongue, turned around, and ran down the street.

Before that, David had never heard the word *zhid*.

"Mummy, what does the word *zhid* [*kike* in English] mean?" he asked Ilana who, looking sad and pale, was mopping soapy foam from her hands.

"This is a very ugly word," she answered as she stroked David's head and looked away. "Don't ever repeat it, and please don't pay attention to those who say this word in the future..."

"Why is this word ugly, Mom?

"Because... When the time comes, you will know about it well yourself." David's mother answered in a soft muffled voice while angrily waving her fist in the direction the offender had disappeared and soon went back to her laundry.

—

David's brother, Victor, graduated from the Textile Institute in Leningrad in 1953 and, by official assignment as a mechanical engineer, was sent to work at a broadcloth plant in Boguslav, a picturesque city on the Ross River located in the Kiev Province of Ukraine. Boguslav is translated as *Glory to God*.

Victor liked his place of work and sent regular uplifting letters to his family. He was a great lover of Jewish culture and never missed an opportunity to remind his family that he worked in the town where, at the end of nineteenth century, his idol, the famous Yiddish writer

Sholom Aleichem, who called Boguslav "an entirely Yiddish shtetl," lived.

The year after Victor arrived in Boguslav, at the beginning of June, Ilana and David, who was thirteen years old at the time, paid Victor a ten-day visit. First, they went to Mironovka Station in Ukraine, and from there they went to Boguslav on a narrow-gauge train. The narrow-gauge railroad had existed from the tsarist time. It consisted of locomotive and railroad cars that looked like a documentary showing life at the beginning of the century. The distance from Mironovka to Boguslav was not far, but the train moved slowly, and it took a long time to reach their destination.

There were many empty seats in their railway car. Besides Ilana and her son, there were no other passengers in their own compartment or in the compartment to their right. The compartment to their left was occupied by two well-dressed women in their midthirties, who sat on either side of a small table that was fixed to the floor. One of them was dressed in a red sweater and a wool skirt. Her face was attractive, with clean skin and a dime-size birthmark on her right cheek. Long, straight, well-groomed hair framed her face. Her eyes were brown, and her lips were thin. Her companion wore a blue dress and a business jacket. Her narrow oblong face with angular cheekbones and pointed cheeks had a pleasant, prepossessing appearance as well.

As soon as the train began to run, Ilana and David opened their books and began to read. The slow speed of the train allowed ample time to admire the scenic views. Periodically looking throw the window, David admired the wide Ukrainian landscapes, fields of wheat and corn, rivers, woods, forests, and groves. Soon, listening to scraps of conversation under the accompaniment of the moving train, David realized that his neighbors frequently mentioned "the Jews" in their conversation, along with the repugnant word *zhid*. Actually, it was not a discussion but rather a monologue by the woman in the red sweater. The second woman was silently agreeing with her, nodding her head approvingly and periodically inserting her own supportive comments. These two representatives of the intelligentsia could find nothing else to brighten up their three-hour trip but a popular verbal sport called anti-Semitism. According to their assertions, the Jews were source of all the evil in the world. At his age, David had gotten used to anti-Semitic rhetoric, but what he heard from his travel companions was exceptional. The woman in the red sweater was a "champion" in the field of hatred. There was no problem in the world for which she would not blame the Jews. According to her, the Jews were responsible for passivity and for violence, for bad manners and for elitism, for perfidy and for stupidity, for the subjugation of non-Jews, for discrediting innocent people, for slander, and for secrecy. The Jews—according to her—were greedy and dirty, and their main wish was to own the world. She could easily prove the inferiority of "the Jew race" because its representatives needed medical help when they were sick, had long noses, were lop eared, and spoke with a burr.

When Ilana woke up from her nap, she also had the opportunity to hear the poisonous rhetoric of a maniac.

"Say nothing, David. It's impossible to do anything with them," she said to her son quietly. "In this country, we are a minority, and if we say something here, most possibly, nobody will support us. They could even accuse us. Get used to life as it is. Remember: you live in a country where in practice you have only limited civil rights. We're lucky this woman doesn't know we're Jews. She represents those who participated in horrible pogroms, which happened in my own shtetl when I was young and during the recent world war."

"You just wait, Olga," the woman in red sweater continued loudly. "I see we have only a half hour before we reach Boguslav, so let me entertain you." She pulled a small thick notebook from her bag. "See this notebook, Olga?" she continued. "I spent plenty of time collecting a lot of funny jokes about Sarahs and Abrams on its pages."

She began to read her slanderous collection of nasty, hateful, tasteless jokes, which portrayed Jews in subhuman mode. Listening to her, David did not recognize his fellow Jews, whom he knew well and whose only fault was that they tried to live decent, secure, and civilized lives.

Meanwhile, the train was approaching the city of Boguslav.

"Well, well, Olechka," the woman in the red sweater said, putting the notebook next to her. "We're almost home. Let's go to the washroom to freshen up a little."

The woman in the jacket agreed with her companion, and they went to the back of the railway car.

As soon as they disappeared from sight, David stood up from his berth and entered the one that had been occupied by the two women.

"David, come back here immediately. What are you trying to do?" Ilana yelled, but he ignored her words. Coming closer to the place the women had occupied, David noticed on the berth the notebook dedicated to numerous insulting jokes about the Jews. With the notebook in his hand, he went to the back of the railroad car, where he opened the door and threw the notebook out onto the escarpment. Then he slammed the door and returned to his compartment where his mother met him with anxious looks.

"What did you do with the book?" Ilana asked him quietly.

"I threw it out. She'll never find it," David answered.

"OK, David. You did the right thing," Ilana said. "Now pretend that you never left your seat. These monsters might return any time."

The two women returned to their compartment only when the train had almost arrived in Boguslav's railroad station. They picked up their luggage in a hurry and went to the door to be among the first to leave the railway car. David would have loved to see the moment when the woman in the red sweater discovered that she lost her "priceless" collection of bigotry. In this case, she would not be mistaken if she blamed the Jews for her loss.

When Ilana and David arrived at the Boguslav station Victor met them there. On a city bus, the family rode to Victor's rented apartment in a house located not far from the city center on the embankment of the Ross River. The house's owners, a widow and her sister, both close to their fifties, warmly met the guests. They fed and entertained them well. After the meal, David went outside and, standing on a cliff near the house, admired the picturesque Ross River, which flew below among the large granite boulders.

In the daytime, many locals swam and splashed in that river. Friendly local boys accepted David as one of their own, and he had a great time swimming and splashing with them in the crystal-clean and pleasantly warm water of the river.

Among others, he became acquainted with a young teenager whose name was Karandash (Pencil.) Such a nickname was deservedly awarded to him because, being tall and thin, he reminded people of a pencil. One day Karandash had visited his dentist, who told him that if he did not want his teeth to be yellow—as the boy complained of—he should use a toothbrush and toothpaste to brush them on a regular basis. The best way to do it, the dentist said, would be with the crystal-clear water from the Ross River. Karandash took this recommendation very seriously, and since then, he visited the Ross River on a regular basis to brush his teeth. This he did with real zeal, each time spending at least twenty minutes performing this procedure. The result was stunning: his teeth now looked like a collection of precious pearls. Even a Hollywood superstar would be proud to have such snow-white shiny teeth as he had.

When television was introduced in Boguslav for the first time, the population met it with great interest. David himself had never before had an opportunity to watch television. One day Victor told him that every early evening at the local Weavers' Club downtown, a group of people watched a television program. David could not wait to see the new marvel of technology. After a day of swimming and tanning, he went to the Weavers' Club and there, for the first time in his life, had the opportunity to watch a program on a real TV. The brilliant invention of the human mind fascinated him. Who could dream that it was possible to transmit both sound and picture wirelessly through the air? In the room with David were more than twenty other spectators. The television screen was as big as an ashtray, but that did not prevent the listeners from looking at the display without taking their eyes off it. Only one TV channel was available. As could be easily predicted, the main content of this state channel was ideological material dedicated to the incredible achievements of the Soviet economy. The audience in the room watched the program silently, acting as if they were in a movie theater. David, like many of the other spectators, was interested mostly in the technical side of the show.

On his fifth day in Boguslav, a beautiful sunny day, David left his brother's house earlier than usual, when the sun was still quite high on the horizon, to see a promised interesting show. As on the previous days, he began his walk on the main city street, Lenin Street. He admired the lush vegetation and the nice houses on the street. Soon he reached the top of the hill and was ready to turn toward the Weavers' Club. The sun that at this time of the day was low on the horizon and shone in his eyes, blinding him. He did not even notice a teenager, seventeen or eighteen years old, appear before him. The stranger looked intently at him as if David was an alien from another planet. Not understanding what was going on, David looked at the teenager questioningly. His face became pale in an instant, his chin was literally shaking, and his eyes bulged out of their sockets.

"Look at him," the teenager said loudly as people passed by. "Look at him. A Jew! Go back where you came from, Jew! Get out of here! Go to the ovens, kike. You're dead!"

The murderous anger and malevolent hate in the voice of the stranger shocked David. He thought that the anti-Semite he just encountered was a soul mate of the morally depraved female monster he had met in the train. They were united by the hatred they cultivated in their hearts.

Taken by surprise, David was silent: he was not on his own turf, his adversary was much bigger than he was, and some pedestrians might take the side of a person they knew. Not saying a word, David turned toward the Weavers' Club and went there trying to forget about the incident.

In the Weavers' Club, while he was watching a TV program dedicated to the international friendship among Soviet nationalities, he could not help but recollect a joke popular in the Soviet Union at that time: "A listener of Armenian Radio asked what word *international* meant. Armenian Radio answered, '*International* is when

Russians takes the hand of Ukrainians, Ukrainians take the hand of Armenians, Armenians take the hand of Moldovans, and all they go . . . to beat the Jews.'"

Actually, the joke was tragic and meaningful. The irrational attitude toward the Jews was the reason for the exodus of more than two million Jews from the USSR starting in 1971.

Paradoxically, those who disseminated the ideology of hate themselves become its victims. Hate destroys human hearts. It spreads like an oil spot on paper, eventually leading to the demoralization of the nation with tragic consequences.

—

David's involvement with amateur art activities began when he was in high school. Initially he had terrible stage fright, which he resolved by persuading himself that he was no worse than those who had performed on the stage for a long time and that overcoming stage fright was a challenge that he should meet. With practice, he was able to perform onstage without feeling butterflies in his stomach. Since then, he had enjoyed performing on the stage of his school and in other places. Eventually, he became a master of ceremonies, a performer, a reader of short poems, and a participant in the students' theatrical circle. In addition, he played the accordion and was a part of his school orchestra.

Among other players in his orchestra was young accordionist Aliosha Makarov, a student in the eighth grade. Despite their difference in age—David was two years older than Aliosha—they always had something to talk about: music, soccer, movies, books, and recent concerts. Like David, Aliosha loved reading, and they enjoyed discussing what they had recently read. During rehearsals, David and Aliosha sat next to each other and exchanged jokes.

Sometimes during performances, Aliosha's parents, nice and friendly people, were present in the audience. Aliosha was a diligent student in many subjects and was good in mathematics.

During the second quarter of the academic year, a talented girl, Rita, joined their school musical group. She was in the sixth grade and had a natural talent for singing and playing the violin as if she was born on the stage. Her nice clothes further emphasized her artistic personality. Onstage, she was charming and assertive; otherwise, Rita was humble, never put on airs, and behaved with dignity. David never communicated with her directly, as the age difference separated them by light years.

One day, in the hall of the school's second floor, David and Aliosha were discussing the previous day's soccer game. They were alone there when Rita, in a beautiful dress, her violin case on her back, passed by Aliosha and David and went about her business. At the sight of her, Aliosha stopped in the middle of a sentence and, frowning, focused his flaming glance on Rita. His face twisted in anger, his eyes blazed, and his hands shook with excitement. A disgust unknown to David was shining in his eyes. Now, Alyosha reminded David of an attacking dog that was ready to bite.

"Aliosha, what's the problem with you? Calm down. Rita didn't do anything bad to you. She's a very good girl," David said, putting hand on his interlocutor's shoulder. David's words did not affect Aliosha, who now was in the hands of a blind hate. He ran closer to the little girl, who was much shorter than he was, and growled in her face: "Kike, kike, kike."

David was utterly shocked. How could it be that such a humble, handsome, and good-natured boy on the turn of the screw turned into a rabid anti-Semite, attacking a defenseless girl?

Rita tried to pass the attacker, but Aliosha followed her, blocking her path, pushing her and shouting the same offensive word. David ran up to the raging Aliosha, grabbed him from behind with one hand, and began striking him with the other one. At first, David was hitting him with strong single blows, expecting that Aliosha would stop the flow of dirty insults from his mouth, but that did not help. Paradoxically, the harder David beat him, the louder and fiercer Aliosha become, bellowing "Kike" with all the strength in his lungs.

Rita stood next to the boys and looked with astonishment at her defender; she was too young to understand that David was defending not only her but also the human dignity of himself and of his people. In the empty hall of the second floor, nobody could prevent David from beating Aliosha as long as he wanted, but then, suddenly, David understood that he could win the battle but he could not win the war.

He realized—remembering the many previous episodes of that kind he had encountered—that in the country where he was born, there were people, young and old, who grew up and lived with hatred and that for them hatred was an oxygen that allowed them to breathe. He realized that there were no arguments and no force in the world that could change people for whom hatred was an indelible a part of their character. Such people were always present in human society, and their incurable anti-Semitism could withstand only the law and order of a civilized society, preventing the society from violence, pogroms, and murder.

David let go of Aliosha and pushed him toward the exit where he disappeared, continuing to repeat the slogan of immemorial bigotry.

Rita also went her own way. David never learned what this little girl could do to produce the reaction of destructive half madness that he had just observed.

David remembered the episode with Aliosha five years later, in 1963, when he was a student at the Kishinev Medical School. A clinical practice in psychiatry he was in was held at the psychiatric hospital located in a suburb of Kostjuzhen.

In addition to the floors where patients with severe psychiatric illnesses were kept in huge wards and treated with medieval methods, there were floors with patients who suffered from less severe manifestations of mental disorders. There were endless patterns of manifestation of the deformation of human mind, but David noticed a symptom common in many patients: the tendency of such patients to use anti-Semitic lexicon with or without the presence of Jews in their environment. Anti-Semitism served as a lightning rod of human frustration for these people.

One of his teachers was Jewish. One day David entered his office and told him about his observation.

"Forget about it, student Lamm," answered the instructor. "Nothing can be done about this. These people are crazy by definition. Don't pay attention to this."

David disagreed. He understood that these mentally challenged people, united in their anti-Semitism, reflected an incurable mental disorder of the society at large.

CHAPTER 14

David in the Soviet System

Only people who lack the ability for criticism—and there are many of them—could not see all the absurdity of the socialist system. For David, the main catalyst of his critical attitude was his father, "a communist by necessity." Without belonging to the Communist Party, he, a Jew, would never have been able to manage numerous administrative posts during his working life.

Samuel was born nine years before the Russian Revolution. His father was a teacher of Judaism, a melamed. There were thirteen children in the family. To earn money, Samuel's father, who was killed during the Holocaust, traveled to the villages surrounding Proskurov, now Khmelnitsky, and earned money teaching Jewish children how to read, write, and pray in Hebrew.

Samuel's family was very poor, and when Soviet power arrived, only three children were still alive; the rest had died because of poverty and various childhood infections.

Samuel went to Cheder, a Jewish primary school. After that, he went to the local public school but never finished it; he needed to earn money for the family. At twelve years of age, he worked as a roofer, then as a glazier, then as a painter, and then as a seller of newspapers and cigarettes.

The great October Revolution was a huge boon for Samuel. He moved to a larger city where nobody knew him and presented himself to the authorities as the son of a worker. That opened for him all the doors to social ascent; while people of the so-called bourgeoisie and clergy class were subject to merciless purges and repressions, he—a representative of the working class—became a loyal and respectable member of the new society. Without graduating high school, he was admitted to the Commodity College in Polonne in Ukraine, where, as a Komsomol organizer, he had a great undeserved authority over the teaching process. In those early post-revolutionary times, colleges were using methods of collective education. In practice that meant that the one or two most capable students could pass exams and different educational tests for the entire group. As a rule, in the first years of Soviet power, teachers of proletarian origin were a rare commodity, and almost all teachers were considered representatives of the former bourgeoisie who could be easily intimidated by their proletarian students. These teachers were subjects to whims of their "privileged class" poor students. The list of possible reprimands of teachers was long, which made them afraid of their pupils, including the Komsomol leader, Samuel Abramovich Lamm.

After graduating college, Samuel became a business specialist and headed state-owned stores of different profiles. At the age of twenty-two, he became a member of the Communist Party. Without such a step, he would not have been able to be in charge of a large store or a midsize plant. In the same year, 1930, he met Ilana Lvovna Fikhman and married her. Two years later, when their first child, Victor, was born, the couple moved to the newly organized Jewish town of Stalindorf in the Dnepropetrovsk Province. Jewish towns were created in the Soviet Union in order to prove to the West how successful the socialist national policy was.

In Stalindorf Samuel was appointed director of a bookstore, and Ilana became his official assistant. Life was stable until 1936, a year when Stalin ordered mass purges of all whom he considered disloyal to him. As paradoxical as it might sound, one of the largest groups of those repressed in mass purges in that period were members of the Communist Party. With this in mind, on the advice of his wife, Samuel burned his party ticket and moved with his family to Krivoy Rog in Ukraine. Fortunately, computers had not been invented then, and monitoring of people was limited. Now an ordinary nonparty citizen, Samuel Lamm found a job as a manager in one of the large city stores. His salary was small, but he felt secure in the new position.

In the years preceding World War II, young men in the Soviet Union were drafted for military personal training for a month or two once a year. Samuel proved himself to be a good army man, and in the third year of military training, he was offered the opportunity to become a career officer. Conditions were good, and he signed the papers.

After than he served in different geographic locations while his family accompanied him. As the reader of this book already knows, the Second World War found the Lamm family in the Moldovan city of Beltsy. During the war, Samuel was a quartermaster and participated in combat operations. In order to command a unit that was sent for reconnaissance, he was required to be a Communist. Simultaneously, this facilitated his promotion from lieutenant to senior lieutenant. That is how Samuel Lamm became a member of the Communist Party for a second time and stayed in it for the rest of his life.

The first time David learned about his father's anti-Communist views was when he was eleven years old. It happened when Victor, his brother, came home from the Textile Institute in Leningrad for summer vacation. The year was 1951 when the Lamms' household received a copy of the newspaper *Izvestiya* where the correspondence between an American farmer and Josef Stalin was published. One phrase impressed young David most. The American farmer stated that, despite all the shortcomings of American capitalism, he nevertheless felt happy that in his country, he was not afraid that in the middle of the night, someone would knock on his door in order to arrest him or other members of his family. In the published response to the farmer, Stalin reassured him that whatever he had heard in the media about purges in Russia, they were isolated episodes that were foreign to the Soviet Union reality.

Running back and forth between indoors and outdoors on this summer day, David overheard a conversation between his father and his twenty-year-old brother, which took place behind the door to the other room. They were discussing the correspondence between the farmer from Iowa and Joseph Stalin. Their discussion was loud, and the door was slightly ajar, so not a single word escaped curious David. Most of the time Samuel spoke, while twenty-one-year-old Victor objected strongly from time to time, refusing to agree with his father's arguments.

Over and over again, Samuel repeated about his many friends who had disappeared in the middle of the night and never returned home. He told Victor that, along with ordinary people, he knew about hundreds of people loyal to the Communist Party and to the country who suffered in Stalin's perpetual purges, about a population who was afraid to say a single word that could be interpreted by an informer as an insult to the Soviet regime. At the same time, Samuel told Victor to keep his mouth shut because KGB agents could put them in jail for the content of their conversation.

While listening to the conversation between his father and Victor, young David recalled that, indeed, on several occasions when he was playing with his friends in the neighborhood, he saw that some of the familiar houses were boarded up with fresh sheets of plywood for reasons unknown to him.

"What's going on?" he asked one of his older friends when this happened once again. "Only yesterday I saw the people who lived there, and today the house is uninhabited. What could have happened here?"

"Nothing special, David." Always the same answer. "*Их подняли*." (Literally, "They were raised [picked] up.") This euphemism meant that a truck with Ministry of State Security (MGB) or KGB agents had arrived the previous night at this house, where not one but all the members of the family, including children and old folks, were considered by the authorities to be "unreliable" or "disloyal" to the Soviet government. When the innocent residents of the house opened the door, the MGB or KGB agents gave the family an hour to gather their most necessary things and then transported the entire family to the railway station from which, under armed guard, they were sent to Siberia. David knew some of these families personally; they were simple people who did not appear to him at all to be dangerous enemies of the Soviet system.

David, who was a truth-seeker, believed his father when he told his older brother about daily purges of innocent people.

David was a child, and Samuel never told him directly about his contempt for the lies of the socialist system while he was young.

However, listening to his father's conversations with Ilana and Victor and comparing them with what he saw around him, David understood how deeply hypocritical the political system in the country where he lived was.

January 13, 1953, was a working day, a Tuesday, but for some reason David's father decided to leave for work later than he usually did. In the morning, David's parents were in bed, and as a big favor, they allowed him to lie between them in the master bed and read them Hans-Christian Andersen's tale "The Wild Geese." They were listening politely to the tale, but the magic of Andersen's story did not affect them as much as it did the reader. David had almost finished the abridged version of the tale when the famous radio speaker Yuri Levitan, the primary Soviet radio announcer, a Jew, in his characteristic, surprisingly unique solemn voice read a bombshell: a "horrible" Doctors' plot had been discovered by the KGB's security forces. During this presentation, hardly anybody in the country knew that the Doctors' plot, with its alleged "doctor-saboteurs" or "doctor-killers," opened a new page of anti-Semitism in the Soviet Union, this time a campaign organized by Stalin himself. According to the accusations, which citizens of the world heard coming from Yuri Levitan's mouth, a group of prominent Moscow doctors, mainly Jews, was accused of conspiring to assassinate the Soviet leaders.

On this Tuesday morning, none of the members of David's family, nor the rest of the millions of Jewish families living in the Soviet Union, could imagine that their personal destiny was dependent on a sinister criminal political play designed personally by Joseph Stalin. Samuel and Ilana listened to the news without saying a word. Only their faces expressed their fear for the future.

In the following days, all available media outlets of the country presented masked or open anti-Semitic material, which allegedly confirmed the "mortal threat of Zionism" and openly condemned many people whose names happened to be Jewish. Every day in the local or central newspapers, something threatening was written about the Jews. Never before had menacing materials of that kind originated from the highest spheres of the state. Throughout the country, there were rallies during which "doctors, the killers" were condemned. The focus on one ethnic group unquestionably belonged to racism.

On the local level, the most visible manifestations of the reaction to the invented Doctors' plot were in the media, in the medical sphere, and in transportation. In transportation, nasty remarks by random passengers addressed toward people with allegedly Semitic facial features increased in frequency and intensity. In the sphere of medicine, anti-Semitism grew like a big poisonous mushroom. All over the country, including in the city where David lived, in the clinics and hospitals, many patients were refusing to be treated by physicians with Jewish names, stating that they did not want to have anything to do with "killers in white gowns"—a term invented and repeated countless times by the media

The Jews of the Soviet Union tried to ignore what was going on and lived as if nothing had happened. This behavior had a reliable explanation: during the recent world war, fascism—among other things—had mercilessly destroyed millions of innocent Jewish lives. It was hard to believe that after such a catastrophe, anything of this kind might happen again, especially in the country that had saved the world from Hitlerism.

Three months later, on March 5, 1953, an ugly representative of the human race, Joseph Stalin, responsible for bloody political terror that took, according to different sources, at least twenty or thirty million human lives, a monster who for three decades consistently terrorized citizens of his own country, passed away. He'd had a bad stroke on March 1, but the media informed the Soviet citizens about his illness only a day prior to his death. Classical music by Beethoven, Tchaikovsky, Chopin, and Liszt was performed with interruptions every fifteen minutes for official reports on Stalin's deteriorating health. Stalin's condition paralyzed the entire country, which expected dramatic news.

Early in the morning of March 5, 1953, before waking up, David had a dream in which he saw an assembly of people sadly discussing Stalin's health. When he woke up, he heard on the radio the familiar "prophetic" voice of anchor Yuri Levitan, informing the country that Stalin had died.

David knew that, according to ideological norms, he was expected to cry, but he did not want to cry and instead thought of the possible outcomes of this historical event. Then he heard his parents, who had woken up earlier, enter the adjacent room. David left his bed and joined them to hear their reaction to the tragic news. To his surprise, their reaction was different than he expected it to be. His father did not even hide that he was on a peak of delight and triumph. While Ilana tried to keep him quiet, instead of expressing sorrow and emotional pain, David's father was . . . dancing. He danced because joy was overwhelming him.

"Samuel, stop dancing," Ilana pleaded with him in Yiddish. "Are you crazy? Stalin died, and you're dancing. Don't forget about your family. They'll put us all in jail for your dancing!"

"Eh, Ilanochka, [the diminutive of Ilana], it looks as if you understand nothing. The greatest murderer and bandit of all times finally croaked. A monster who destroyed countless people of his own country is dead. Now we have hope. Come, join me."

"Forget about your hopes," Ilana objected. "Just wait. Even before they appoint another villain as a dictator, you'll be in jail for your disloyalty. Don't be a fool!"

"You're very wrong, Ilanochka," Samuel retorted. "In the entire history of mankind, never there was and never will be such a horrible killer of millions of his own brothers and sisters."

"In any case, don't say your dangerous words in front of your son; he might say something wrong to his friends."

"My son isn't stupid. He'll be twelve years old soon, and if he's not smart enough to keep his mouth shut, then he's not worthy to be my son," Samuel said, looking sternly in David's direction.

Funeral music on the state radio was interrupted only by reports about further development in the funeral ceremony of "the greatest leader of all times and all people." David's classes began at two o'clock in afternoon that day. The first thing he learned at school was that the day's classes were canceled, and in an hour, a rally dedicated to Stalin's death would begin.

The meeting began at the appointed time in the school assembly hall, where all the teachers and students gathered in expectation of presentations. After David heard what his father had said, he did not have any desire to cry, and—to his surprise—he did not notice a single student around him who cried. The only difference from other days was that today nobody misbehaved, and all the students and teachers tried to glue solemn expressions on their faces. Some teachers were crying and wiping their tears with handkerchiefs. David's class teacher, Elizabeth Alexandrovna, did not just cry, she sobbed;

tears were running down her cheeks. Her mourning appeared to be sincere.

The audience was full of people. As inspirational as the principal wanted it to be, his speech nevertheless was long and boring, and soon the schoolchildren began to fool around as they would do on any regular day; Stalin's death did not affect their mood. Judging from the media, Soviet people were all in different degrees of trance after the loss of their beloved leader, but in reality, life was running its own course, and nothing had changed in the movements of the planets and stars.

David observed the same lack of mourning for "beloved leader" from the ordinary people on the streets and from those with whom he spoke on public transportation or in grocery stores. In contrast to the crying teachers David saw during the rally at the school, ordinary people did not show any signs of emotional tumult. Moreover, some of his friends and acquaintances whom he met were even making jokes as if nothing had happened.

Gradually, after two or three days of the manifestation of people's sorrow, Stalin's death stopped being the center of daily events. History went on its own course.

A month passed. Early in the morning on Friday, April 3, 1953, David and his parents were sitting around the dining table for breakfast, enjoying Ilana's delicious signature Russian-style pancakes. The regular program on the state radio was interrupted suddenly, and the Lamms heard the familiar voice of Yuri Levitan. He read a breaking news release. Not knowing what they were going to hear, the family stopped eating and waited in suspense. In his assertive and indisputable voice, unique in timbre and resolute, Yuri Levitan informed the citizens of the Soviet Union that the accusations against members of the "so-called Doctor's plot" were false, trumped up, and obtained under torture. The perpetrators of the crimes related to the Doctor's plot, Levitan stated, would be severely punished. Allegedly, the fault was with the MGB. A governmental commission under the leadership of Lavrentiy Beria (who was killed soon in a coup d'état without trial or investigation) was holding an inquiry into the crimes of Lieutenant-Colonel Mikhail Rumin and his deputies. The name of Stalin, the real culprit as it became known later, was not mentioned.

"What do you think about this news bulletin, David?" Samuel asked inquisitively.

"I don't know," David answered, "but everything is very strange. Only three months ago, they told us that Jewish doctors were guilty of unforgivable crimes, and now they say that nobody is guilty. Whom they deceive? Besides, did you notice that the same speaker, Yuri Levitan, informed us on two different occasions, both times solemnly and very, very convincingly, of opposite news. If this isn't a symbol of a supreme hypocrisy, than what is it?

"Your observations are outstanding for your age, David, but, please, keep them to yourself!" Samuel responded, wryly smiling. "Indeed, Yuri Levitan read the news in both cases as if he was an oracle. Let it teach you a good lesson, David. Never believe 'reliable' news. Believe only what your conscience and your instincts tell you. Don't trust anyone except those who really love you. The rest might betray you at any moment. Can you imagine: a country where you were born and that we all love, this country was ready to betray us only because we belong to an ethnic group chosen to be abused, insulted, and slandered. God knows what could have happened if Stalin had not died in time. We could all have become victims of a pogrom on a national scale. Remember, David: Jews in Russia are essentially without civil rights. Anti-Semitism is a national disease not only in Russia, but in almost all Eastern Europe, and we can't do anything to avoid it."

—

During the next state election in October of 1955, Communist Samuel Lamm—the Zorba the Greek-like figure in David's life—was appointed head of the local election committee.

On the morning of election day, Samuel offered to let his son accompany him to the polling place. David was happy to stay with his father until late at night when the election ended. He could easily do it because it was Saturday, and on Sunday, he could sleep as late as he wanted.

Samuel was at the polling place from the morning on, while David joined him at eight o'clock in the evening.

The spacious polling place was located in the same small plaza as one of the city's largest movie theaters. It had the more or less regular setup of a polling station: it was a rectangular room, at the back of which stood three tables with chairs for the election judges. Busts of Lenin and Stalin on stands covered with red cloth decorated the corners of the front wall. Between the busts were positioned booths for secret voting—two on each side—and in the middle was placed a big ballot box where electors could drop the ballots without even looking at what was written on them. The majority of people used this option: receiving their ballot, they carried it straight to the big urn, assuring those who might be observing them that they were loyal citizens. In other words, they did exactly what was expected of them in the socialist state: showed full confidence in the candidate whose uncontested name was printed on the ballot. A simple and effective way to assure that the candidate would win the election. Such are the tricks of socialism.

David, a typical teenager in casual clothes, was practically invisible to the public. His invisibility was helped by the harmonium, a large piano-like musical instrument before which he sat. The harmonium, or reed organ, generates sound as air flows past a thin, vibrating piece of metal, just like a regular organ. It was an old instrument, almost broken, but it still was able to produce sounds when David pumped air with his feet and pressed the keyboard keys. The majority of the keys on the harmonium were damaged, which did not discourage David. He enjoyed the instrument, pretending that he was playing a melody on it. Besides that, using his "invisibility," David could make interesting observations of the behavior of the electors.

Counting Samuel, there were four judges on the election commission. One of them had brought with him a lovely dog, a beagle, which sat under the table and did not depart from its owner for a moment. The judges were busy taking care of the flow of late voters and interacting with members of the mobile groups that were visiting with those voters who, for different reasons, could not come to the polling station to vote.

Besides "invisible" David, there was another "invisible" person in the precinct. This person, the third secretary of the district party committee, a man in a gray suit and pants with straight hair and a strong chin, sat next to Lenin's bust. With an impenetrable face and solemn appearance, mummy-like, chain-smoking, he sat on a chair and look intently in front of him.

From time to time, Samuel visited David to exchange a few words with him. On one of these visits, David asked him about the mummy-like man.

"Oh, that's Comrade Matvienko, David. He's a very important person. Please, don't dare to talk to him."

"OK, Father. I have one more question for you. Why do we call what is going on here an election? What kind of election is this if the people aren't electing anybody. All they're doing here is confirming a choice that was made for them by the authorities. There's only one candidate, Nikolai Zhiorzhiu, and nobody else. How can you explain this to me?"

"First of all, David, shut up, and stop asking stupid questions," Samuel answered in a cautionary tone. "You forget that when people receive their ballot, they can choose either to vote for Comrade Zhiorzhiu or to strike out his name."

"But, Dad, then it's not an election but some kind of a game; it's nothing more than a sham," David whispered to his father.

"You better stop your stupid philosophy, son. Remember that with your long tongue, our family, including you, might find ourselves in jail today. Is that what you want?"

"But, Dad, I only discuss this with you!"

"OK. Now just mind your business," Samuel said and left his son.

From his "invisible" place, David could see all that was going in the polling place. The majority of people obediently hauled their ballots to the central urn, but there were those who took the ballots to the individual booths for the secret vote, which could not be too secret: if the name of the candidate was crossed out, then the ballot was considered illegitimate and was not counted. To make the ballot legitimate and to make it count, the voter was supposed to write down the name of the suggested candidate. If the voters crossed out the candidate's name or wrote something inappropriate, they ran a serious risk that their handwriting might be analyzed by KGB services in the search of the author. Hardly anybody wanted to be in such a situation.

From his position, David was able to see how, on two occasions, voters took their ballots and, instead of dropping them in the urns, stuffed them surreptitiously in their pockets and left the polling place with them. David went right away to a window opposite the exit and saw one of these men pull the ballot from his pocket, look around to make sure nobody saw him, and then rip the ballot into small pieces.

It was getting late, and David was sleepy. He wanted to go home, but Samuel told him it was too late for him to go by himself.

The polling station was open until 10:30 p.m., after which the door was closed, all the urns in the precinct were collected on a large table, and the judges prepared to count the votes. Sealing-wax stamps were torn off them, and Samuel Lamm, as chairperson of the election committee, poured the contents of all the ballot boxes in the middle of the table, creating a big paper pile. All the judges got busy counting votes. Ballots with comments, remarks, and observation were registered in a logbook and placed in a separate pile.

The report of the election results was supposed to be submitted to the election committee no later than quarter to twelve. Now only the rustling of paper interrupted the silence in the room.

When the count started, the "invisible" district committee party representative came to life. He began to walk slowly around the main table where the counting took place. On one of these rounds, he reminded Samuel that the vote count must be completed as soon as possible. Another twenty minutes passed in complete silence. Sitting on a chair, David put his head on the lid of the harmonium and fell asleep.

The loud barking and squealing of a dog awakened him. It turned out that during one of his solemn rounds around the table, the party functionary had accidentally stepped on the tail of the judge's dog, which had been sleeping peacefully under the table next to its owner with a tip of its tail protruding from under the chair. Trying to escape, the beagle jumped first on an empty chair and from it onto the table where all the ballots lay. In vain, the judges, including the owner of the dog, tried to reason with the beagle, which was in a state of panic. As if that was not enough, the frightened dog lost control of her bladder and soiled a lot of the ballots that lay on the table. At last, the owner caught the animal, but by this time, the majority of the ballots were lying on the floor, and many of them were wet. When the beagle-related accident ended, only a quarter of an hour was left to report the election results to the commission.

"What are we going to do, Comrade Matvienko?" Samuel asked the party representative anxiously. "We don't have time to start our job from the beginning!"

"Don't worry," answered the representative. "Resume counting."

The judges shrugged their shoulders and, periodically wiping their hands with napkins, obediently resumed counting the ballots. When five minutes of vote counting had passed and only ten minutes were left to report the election results, Comrade Matvienko raised his hand, this time ordering the judges to stop the counting process.

"Comrade Judges," he began, "as you know, we did our best to be on time with the counting of the ballots, but as you saw with your own eyes, this politically irresponsible dog destroyed this process.

Therefore, in order to be on time, we must find an alternative way to report the election results in our district.

"Comrade Chairman of the Election Committee." Matvienko turned to Samuel. "Please bring us the reports of the election results of the last two years."

"Sorry, but we don't have these results, Comrade Matvienko," Samuel answered. "If we had known they would be needed, they would be here."

"OK, Comrade Lamm, I was ready for your fair response. You might not know these figures, but I'm not complaining about my memory, and I remember them well. Comrades, in the last two years, voter attendance was ninety-nine-point-six percent, and the percentage of those who voted for the candidate was ninety-nine-point-six as well. Taking into account that the dog created a state of emergency for us and correcting for a possible error, I suggest a compromise: we'll report to the commission that our voter attendance was ninety-nine-point-five percent, and the percentage of those who voted for the candidate was also ninety-nine-point-five. That will be only fair. Let's vote. Comrade Judges of the precinct, those who support my suggestion, please raise your hand."

"A hundred percent support," Comrade Matvienko commented solemnly, after all the judges obediently raised their hands.

The beagle added its endorsement of the suggestion by wagging its tail.

In half an hour, the polling place was closed. Samuel Abramovich was happy that the election was over, while David was satisfied to receive a lesson in the "unanimity" of the Soviet people.

—

The final blow to David's belief in the Soviet system happened in March of 1956, when David, a member of Komsomol, was in the eighth grade. On February 25 of that year, the leader of Communist Party of the Soviet Union, Nikita Khrushchev, made a special report to the Twentieth Congress of the Communist Party, "On the Cult of Personality and Its Consequences," that was devastatingly critical of the reign of deceased general secretary and premier Joseph Stalin. The main focus of the report was the mass purges against Soviet citizens organized by Stalin, which took the lives of millions of innocent people. Khrushchev charged Stalin with having fostered a cult of personality in spite of ostensibly maintaining support for the ideals of communism.

Half a month later, the Central Committee of the Communist Party forwarded a secret letter with Khrushchev's report to all party organizations in the Soviet Union to read its contents to communists and selected Komsomol members. David was one of those who were allowed to attend. The historic document was read in the local officers' house.

Prior to reading the letter, the city communist boss warned the audience that the content was a deep secret, and it was strictly forbidden to discuss it anywhere and with anyone beyond the auditory.

The contents of the letter were so shocking that the audience refused to believe that what was written there was true, but party discipline prevailed, and nobody in the audience dared to question the stated facts. At a time when anti-Soviet propaganda of any kind was considered to be a crime against the state and resulted in strict punishment, David heard the extreme degree of such propaganda. The irony of all of it was that the group responsible for distribution of such extreme anti-Soviet propaganda was the Communist Party itself.

The many-page report condemned Stalin's personality cult and mentioned secrets kept before Lenin's "Letter to the Congress" and notes by N. K. Krupskaya on the personality of Stalin. It also spoke about Stalin's use of the term "enemy of the people" as a weapon of political struggle and about Stalin's violation of the rules of collective leadership. The letter stated that most of the "old Bolsheviks" and delegates to the Seventeenth Communist Congress were killed; it described details of repression and torture against prominent party members and the deportation of Koreans, Germans, Finns, Karachais, Kalmyks, Chechens, Ingush, Balkars, Crimean Tatars, and Meskhetian Turks. It spoke about NKVD crimes; about mass falsification of cases, merely aimed at fulfilling "plans" for conviction of innocents; about Stalin's exaggerated role during World War II; and eventually about the Doctors' plot.

For those who wanted to come to the logical conclusion, Khrushchev's letter meant that Stalin was a tyrant, a despot, a dictator and the killer of millions of innocent people.

When David returned home, he tried to discuss report with his father, a Communist, but Samuel was not in the mood that day and only grunted, "All you heard today I knew well before, son, but you wouldn't believe me when I told you about my own experience."

The Khrushchev letter made the first powerful cracks in the foundation of the Soviet state. It would take another thirty-four years before it fell under the weight of all its lies and crimes. After listening to Khruschev's report, David read countless books on the subject of the crimes of Stalin's epoch, but there was no stronger indictment of the Soviet Communist Party as a whole than was presented in the report. Socialism concentrates enormous power in the hands of so-called "trusted people's servants." This creates conditions for infinite abuses of power by unelected state representatives.

—

Another memorable episode that helped David understand the profound hypocrisy of the Soviet system happened at the end of October 1957, when Marshal Georgy Zhukov, a great commander-in-chief, minister of defense, four-time hero of the Soviet Union, and a chevalier of two "Victory" orders, fell into disgrace with Khrushchev and was dismissed from the post of minister of defense of the USSR. David, who was in ninth grade at that time, learned this news from the radio before he went to school. He could not comprehend how the renowned hero of World War II, respected by millions of Soviet people, could all of a sudden be demoted to such a low status. Only yesterday, poets, writers, and composers sang about the glory of Zhukov, and today Zhukov was persona non grata. Children who, since birth, along with adults, knew well that talk was silver and silence gold, did not discuss Marshal Zhukov's downfall at David's school. During third period—math class—the teacher, Toyva Boruchovich Tubenschlyak, a Jew who had recently retired from the army as a captain and continued to come to school dressed as a military man in a military-style shirt and leather army boots, announced that instead of math, he would have a secret discussion with the entire class. Mr. Tubenschlyak was short and athletic, with a graying mop of hair. He was a good educator, though formal and with not a hint of a sense of humor.

When the students were ready for his presentation, he solemnly asked them if they had heard the news report about Marshal Zhukov. After receiving evasive responses from the students, he announced that Marshal Zhukov had been demoted because in recent years, he had not been good; did not respect his superiors, including Joseph Vissarionovich Stalin himself; and to those who were under his command, he was rude and thought of himself as if he was God incarnate. While listening to Toyva Boruchovich, David could not forget that on the preceding holiday dedicated to the Soviet army anniversary on January 23, he had made a special speech about Marshal Zhukov, during which he spoke very highly of him to the students of the entire school. He told then that without Joseph Stalin and Marshal Zhukov, World War II would not have been won. Toyva Boruchovich's speech on the anniversary of the Soviet army lasted a whole hour, and now, only four months later, he completely discredited his recent hero. It is impossible, David thought, for a human being like Marshal Zhukov to change so quickly. How could you believe in anybody, thought David, if today he was an idol and tomorrow he was the enemy of the people?

"Toyva Boruchovich, how could it be that Marshal Zhukov changed so badly in such a short time?" David asked in the tone of a naïve and innocent baby.

"I'm glad you asked that question, Lamm. The answer is simple: very unfortunately, during his residence in Berlin after the war, Marshal Zhukov became the subject of capitalist propaganda. I always suspected he was not a good communist, but it was only my feeling. Now that I know the facts, I must completely change my opinion about him."

The famous Abraham Lincoln maxim "You can fool all the people some of the time, and some of the people all the time, but you cannot fool all the people all the time" obviously could not be applied to Soviet Russia.

—

Ion Efimovich Shterental, a teacher of history, logic, and psychology, was in his midfifties. He was always neatly dressed in the same clean suit, which he wore with a solid blue tie. Ion Efimovich was popular among students. Early wrinkles covered his clean-shaven face. He was always formal and dignified, and despite good contact with the students, he knew how to keep a distance.

When Moldova was a part of Romania, Ion Efimovich had graduated from the Bucharest Law School and later became a lawyer. In 1940, Russia annexed Moldova from Romania, and Ion Efimovich, who was trained in Romanian law, could not be a lawyer and became a teacher. He spoke four languages and was good at explaining the material he presented to the students. Overall, Ion Efimovich was a well-qualified teacher who could easily impress the class with his knowledge and wide intelligence.

On some occasions, when Ion Efimovich arrived, the class was in a real mess. With the class logbook and couple of history books under his arm and a pointer in his hand, he patiently stood upright next to the lectern, the expression of a martyr on his face, waiting for the class to calm down. Standing in this pose without blinking, his eyes narrowed, he looked intently at the noisy class, which gradually calmed down under the compelling influence of his contemptuous glance.

Ultimately, when the class fell silent, Ion Efimovich, with an air of dignity, rose on the lectern's platform, and with his hand leaning on it, he made the same contemptuous pronouncement: "Lazy bums and hooligans, what are you doing here? What do you know? Let's face it, your 'rich' vocabulary is limited to words like *boots*, *borscht*, *sunflower seeds*, *potatoes*, and *lice*! Ignoramuses, do you want to remain on the stage of Neanderthalians, or maybe do you want to learn something?"

Impressed with such a standard monologue, the class calmed down for a while, but soon the students resumed their perpetual birds' talk. The art of schmoozing in the class consisted of ability to talk in such a manner that the teacher could not guess who was talking.

David was in the tenth grade when, during modern history class, Ion Efimovich announced that, following an order from the state Ministry of Education, instead of modern history, the class would temporarily study a course on "The General Crisis of Capitalism." As the textbook on this subject was not available yet, the teacher said that the students would have to write out word by word whatever he taught them. The material he was going to teach was important for them to know since, eventually, the class would have a special test on the subject.

Thus, in the year 1958 CE, twice a week the class learned from its illustrious teacher that the capitalists' economy was on the brink of destruction while the socialist economy would, in a short time, bury capitalism forever in the dustbin of the history. (The reader knows what really happened.)

The attitude of the students toward the "General Crisis of Capitalism" course was passive. Nobody in the class wanted to delve into the essence of what was being taught. On the other hand, the students liked the subject: it was easy and very predictable. To be prepared for the upcoming exam, there was no need to memorize or to learn material. All that was necessary to pass the test was to listen to the radio or read the newspapers.

The introduction of the "General Crisis of Capitalism" course coincided with another event: a local military infantry unit took patronage of David's school. The most generous contribution by the military unit to the school was an old military truck. In this truck, the soldiers from the military unit gave driving lessons to the students of the tenth grade. The students attended the lessons with real enthusiasm. Following the remnants of patriarchal ethics in the socialist society, the girls were excused from all military activities, including the driving class.

The noble intention of the program to make students into good drivers ended prematurely due to the sad fact that all four wheels, disks, and tires on the truck were stolen by unknown thieves in the third month of driver education. Well, where is it said that the Soviet army gives up? The soldiers placed the truck on a pair of sawhorses, and driving classes were offered in the truck without the wheels but with a real cab. Needless to say, such classes required the vivid imagination peculiar only to the young. Meanwhile, the military unit started to sponsor students at the school shooting range and offered a wrestling class.

The soldiers from the military unit used their presence at the school to increase their own level of education by attending selected classes. On January 21—the anniversary of the death of the leader of the world proletariat, Vladimir Ilyich Lenin—four soldiers and an officer from the patronage unit came to attend the class given by

Ion Efimovich. At the beginning of the class, the teacher announced that today's extraordinary lesson would be dedicated to the role of Vladimir Ilyich Lenin in the scientific discovery of the general crisis of capitalism.

David sat at the first desk in the center opposite Ion Efimovich, who stood next to him facing the class. The teacher's presentation was strong and inspired. In his narration, the word *Lenin* was repeated in some kind of a rhythm countless times.

Sitting close to the teacher, David—who had nothing else to do—entertained himself by softly mimicking his teacher's ardor and imitating the fanatical and piously loyal tribute to the worshipped leader. David was amusing himself very quietly, but he underappreciated the teacher's good hearing. When for the nth time within a short period, Ion Efimovich repeated "Lenin," and David parroted him in a singsong manner, howling "Lenin, Lenin, Lenin," the teacher abruptly interrupted his talk about the demise of capitalism and, piercing David with his eyes, sternly ordered him to stand up.

"Lamm, what's the problem with you? Why are you repeating the name of the greatest Communist leader of all time and of all people, venerable Comrade Lenin, like a parrot? Explain this to me and to everyone in the class: are you mocking me on the subject?"

There was a silence in the classroom; all eyes were fixed on the culprit. David at once realized how irresponsibly and ridiculously he had behaved. If he wanted to, his teacher could easily report his conduct to the appropriate authorities, and then David, along with his parents, could disappear into the Siberian taiga in a short time.

How unforgivably stupid it was to assume that the history teacher was intelligent and critical enough to understand his sense of humor. Caught by surprise, David had to somehow redeem himself.

But how? Fortunately, his brain was smarter than he thought; it was on top of the situation and provided David with the only possible correct answer.

"Sorry for interrupting you, Ion Efimovich. I worship the great Comrade Lenin's name like you do."

Ion Efimovich had no choice but to accept David's apology and explanation. Fortunately, he was not personally after David; his main objective was to save his own skin. He nodded his head, looked at his watch, and directed David to sit down.

David was lucky: the story did not have consequences.

The class on the general crisis of capitalism continued to the end of the semester, and the class on modern history, which was in the school curriculum, was never resumed. In the due time Ion Efimovich passed away peacefully at an advanced age while capitalism was still alive and well.

—

In 1957, the inhabitants of the city of Beltsy were excited about the arrival of a family from the capital of Peru, Lima. The parents of this family were Russians who had years ago somehow found themselves in Lima, Peru, where they spent many years. Their two daughters, who could hardly speak Russian, were born in Peru.

In the Soviet Union, shielded from the West by an Iron Curtain, each encounter with a foreigner was a special event, but in David's relatively small town it was a pure sensation. For the exotic family, which consisted of parents and two children, the local authorities provided outstandingly favorable conditions. The family received their own place to live, which would not have been available to many native residents, and nice positions in local businesses. Their children went to public schools, where they were provided with tutors to help them with the language barrier. Public organizations invited the head of the family to tell about life in capitalist Peru. The former Peruvian could not understand why, at the end of his speech, there was no reaction from the audience until somebody told him—in secret—that people in Russia are afraid to ask unnecessary questions.

The life of the family that had transplanted itself to the socialist paradise was under constant public attention. People wanted to know about the immigrants' impression of the "proletarian heaven." Many stories were passed by word of mouth, but one was especially popular. This story became a major source of entertainment among the city's inhabitants.

Once, in the presence of the head of the Peruvian family, his coworkers were brave enough to complain about their difficult work conditions and miserable salaries.

"I don't understand, Comrades," the immigrant from Latin America said. "If this is so, why don't you go on strike?"

The entire town was laughing at the naïveté of the foreigner who did not know that for participation in any kind of a strike, the workers would be immediately arrested and punished with deprivation of freedom. Even children knew it.

—

Many years later, in 1973, David had a rare opportunity to speak with a foreigner personally. It was during a time when this could still be dangerous, but his curiosity prevailed.

In the Soviet Union, having a phone at home was a privilege. In order to speak with a relative in Moscow, David went to the phone station in the Odessa railway building. While his turn was slowly approaching, he read the newspaper *Pravda*. Next to him on the bench sat a well-dressed man reading a magazine. It was this stranger who started a conversation with David. The stranger spoke Russian with a foreign accent, but he was easily understandable.

From the stranger David learned that, a year and a half before, he had arrived in Odessa from Detroit for permanent residence. In Detroit, he had worked for many years as an assembly worker at the Ford automobile manufacturing plant. Since he was young, he had sympathized with Marxist ideas, but he never was a convinced Communist. His uncle, who lived in Odessa, had sent him many uplifting letters describing how wonderful was life in Ukraine. David's new acquaintance was skeptical when he read similar assertions in the Soviet newspapers, which he received in Detroit; however, he trusted his own uncle. Most appealing to him were free health care and education and inexpensive food and appliances in the Soviet Union. A year ago, he had retired and moved with his wife to live in Odessa.

"So how is your life now?" David asked very carefully. There was a possibility that this American immigrant could be an informant.

"Oh, life is very good, believe me," he answered, winking at David. "All that I was looking for in the new place, I found here. The Soviet Union is such an outstanding country. You see—"

He did not finish the last sentence because the operator called him to the phone booth for a call to the United States. The stranger rose from the bench and went toward the phone. Halfway there, he turned around and quickly approached David, as if he had recalled something important.

"I want to be honest with you, young man," he said quietly but decisively. "What a fool I was to come here! What a bloody idiot I was!"

Saying that, he knocked his head with an index finger several times, turned around, and went toward the telephone booth.

How many more countries and human lives will socialism ruin before its theoretical admirers finally understand its insolvency? The temptation of heaven on earth is great, but the truth is harsh.

—

David's father, Samuel, had a steady job; he was in charge of a knitting and weaving plant. Like countless other representatives of small Soviet industries, both lower and higher in rank, he was an active participant in the "shadow" or "underground" or "parallel" economy. Most of the time, the shadow or underground economy was not a result of greed but simply a means of survival; it was a signature of the Soviet economy, where stealing from the government was considered noble. It was impossible for working people to live on their miserable salaries, and millions of them—whoever was smart enough to figure out how it could be done—were involved in this parallel economy.

Characteristically, in Samuel's knitting and weaving plant, practically all the workers participated in a well-known scheme to make extra money on the side. One essential feature of the Soviet underground or shadow economy was deals among the numerous heads of the Soviet economy. The other integral part of the relationship between administrators of the businesses and inspectors, state supervisors, and direct bosses of industry was bribes, mostly in the form of money, combined with the mutual consumption of alcohol.

Samuel Lamm's direct boss in the industrial cooperation network was Radu Ivanovich Frunze. Frunze was a typical Soviet proletarian aristocrat who suffered badly during Stalin's purges, spending several years in the Soviet gulag. In the 1950s, under the amnesty, he was released from the labor camp in Barnaul and became a high-level administrator. Radu Ivanovich's wife, Nadezhda Yakovlevna Frunze, a tall, beautiful, and respectable woman, a Russian beauty, mirrored the newly acquired aristocratic manners of her husband. The couple had only one son, whose name was Vadim.

One day David, standing behind the closed door to his parents' bedroom, accidentally overheard his father tell Ilana that Frunze had shared with him that, during the investigation of his case in the Kiev prison, in order to get him to sign a document admitting to crimes he did not commit, he had been tortured. One of the terrible tortures he endured was being placed in a bathtub filled with water into which the NKVD agents placed rats. The rats bit him until the torture ceased.

Samuel used to meet with Frunze once a month in Kishinev, where his boss lived with his family, or in Beltsy, where Samuel Abramovich lived and worked. The ritual was the same for each encounter: first was a one-to-one meeting with a meal and drinks in an expensive restaurant or a special outdoor food stall. At the conclusion of such a meeting, drunken Samuel gave drunken Frunze an envelope of money, for which he received a patronizing hug and a wet kiss on his lips from his boss. In turn, Comrade Frunze visited the Moldovan Communist Party building once a month, where he provided his own bribe (his contribution from the "revenue" from many small businesses like Samuel's) to the then–first secretary of the Communist Party of Moldova and future first secretary of the

Communist Party USSR, Leonid Ilyich Brezhnev. In a circle of trusted friends, Samuel boasted that he had the honor of providing bribes to Leonid Ilyich Brezhnev himself.

Like many students, David considered the long summer vacations to be the best time of the educational process. Many interesting things happened to David during summer breaks. One such memorable event happened during summer vacation in 1957, when he had recently graduated the ninth grade and become sixteen years old. On that occasion, which happened at the same time he discovered Giovanni Boccaccio's great book *The Decameron*, he had a rare opportunity to experience the scent of "high society."

It was hard to get *The Decameron* because of its erotic content, which contradicted the canons of socialist ideology. David periodically interrupted his reading with hysterical laughter over stories of close dealings between men and women. Unexpectedly, his father walked into the room and told David that he needed to speak with him.

"Listen, David, do me a favor. The family of my big boss Frunze is in Beltsy from Kishinev for a month-long visit. He has a son, Vadim, who's couple of years older than you are. His parents are worried that their son will be bored without friends in our city. To entertain him, they decided he would benefit from a trip to nature, preferably close to the water. With this in mind, Frunze gave Vadim his business car. Gennady Ivanovich's personal chauffeur, Fyodor, who also will supervise Vadim, will drive the car. For lack of other candidates, his parents asked me if you could keep him company. Tomorrow, he'll arrive here, and you'll help him have a good time."

David had no idea how to entertain Vadim, but he could not refuse his father's request. There were other reasons he did not refuse:

he wanted to ride in the personal car and to see with his own eyes how a teenager who belonged to a social level never attainable to him lived.

The next day, Ilana prepared David's swimming trunks for him, and at the appointed time—exactly ten thirty—a gorgeous Volga car with curtains on its windows arrived in front of Lamms' humble house on Svoboda Street. When David got in the back seat of the car, he found not only Vadim but also a young woman who was at least four years older than Vadim. No one in the car expressed interest in the new passenger when David introduced himself. Vadim and the young woman were busy flirting.

Vadim was a tall, attractive, and tanned teenager. His appearance was different from that of the other teenagers David knew. His face expressed self-assuredness and the complacent look of a young representative of a higher social stratum who feels he is entitled to societal privileges. His companion, Roxanne, looked like an ordinary provincial female in a state of excitement. Vadim had met Roxanne only yesterday, David learned, and today they were still adjusting to each other. Their communication consisted of loud, hot whispers and periodic explosions of laughter. Roxanne's laugh was a silvery kind, while Vadim's had a patronizing restrained quality. When laughing, Roxanne opened her painted eyes widely, while Vadim—a master of situation—did not miss a chance to touch different parts of her young body. Periodically, their vigorous communication was interrupted by quick kisses.

Previously, David had read feuilletons (articles) in newspapers about children of the ruling class who led privileged lives with the money of their highly placed parents. Such children were called *плесень* ("golden youth," or "mold"). Despite such a contemptuous official attitude, when these children grew up, they themselves became representatives of the ruling class (unless they had the misfortune of becoming clients of alcohol and drug rehabilitation centers). Now David had an opportunity to be in a company of one of these golden youth representatives and a female butterfly who was warming her wings in the rays of her benefactor. This benefactor, at his still-young age, had mature sexual desires.

David did not know what exactly his father had promised Comrade Frunze, but when the car reached the main city square, Vadim turned to him and asked where there was a nice place in the city to have a good time on that August day. David, who was not an expert in leisure and recreation, recommended the only one place he knew: the village of Kubolta, located not too far from the city.

"Listen, what's your name? Do you have a girlfriend?" Vadim asked David.

"My name is David, and I am only in the ninth grade," David answered. "I don't have girlfriends, and I don't think about them."

"OK, don't get excited, David. Is there a nice girl from your class who would like to come with us on the trip to this Kubolta village?"

David would have categorically answered no, but he loved his father and did not want to let him down. Making an effort to be polite and cooperative, he recalled that his schoolmate Nellie Kustovaya lived three hundred yards from the city square. She was a nice blonde girl from a Russian family, short, attractive, and—as far as he knew—modest. They had hardly ever spoken to each other, but she was quite friendly when they had the occasion for a very short conversation.

"Well, I'll try to speak with Nellie. I hope she agrees and her parents will let her come with us, but I doubt it."

"Don't worry. She'll agree," Vadim said confidently; he thought he was such a charmer that nobody could refuse his invitation.

As for David, he knew this plan would definitely fail. How could a nice girl from a nice family agree to spend time with her sixteen-year-old classmate in a car, in the company of people older than she was who wanted her to travel with them to an unknown place?

David and Vadim climbed to the third floor of the building and knocked at the door of the Kustovoi family. Nellie's mother opened the door.

"What do you want?" she asked David in a tone that proved to him that she would never allow her young daughter to leave home with unfamiliar people to who-knew-what destination.

"Good day. Can I talk with Nellie?" David asked.

"Who are you?"

"My name is David Lamm. I'm her classmate."

"All right. Wait a minute."

In a minute in the doorway appeared not only David's schoolmate Nellie but also her entire family: parents, two brothers, and the family dog. All of them looked at David and Vadim with great curiosity.

Nellie stood next to David in a cute house robe; with her wide gray eyes and slightly upturned nose, she was looking at him questioningly.

David's experience in communicating with girls was very limited; in an uncertain voice, stuttering and blushing, he asked Nellie, whose head was decorated with lovely silky brown hair, if she would like to go for a country ride in a personal car. Despite the entourage around Nellie, the strong no that David expected to hear did not ensue. Nellie looked first at her mother and then at the rest of the family and nodded her head in agreement.

"Are you sure?" David asked, his last hope of avoiding a female companion with whom he did not have any idea what to talk about.

"Sure." To David's great surprise, Nellie now answered without hesitation, and soon the state car took the company to Kubolta village.

During the trip, Nellie sat next to the driver, and the rest of the group was at the back seat. Nellie and David looked at the road while Vadim and Roxanne continued their bird talk, accompanied with periodic laughter, meaningful glances, and short kisses.

On several occasions, David tried to start a conversation, but nobody reacted to his attempts. When the car reached Kubolta village, David explained to the driver, Fyodor, how to drive up to the beach on the bank of the Kubolta River.

As it was a weekday, there were hardly any people on the beach. The shore where the car stopped was above the level of the river. When the group found a comfortable place on the elevation, Fyodor went to the car for provisions. As a rule, drivers of departmental cars were faithful servants—more precisely, lackeys—of the boss's entire family. While Fyodor was out, the young people exchanged their opinions about the weather.

Fyodor soon returned from the car. On a tablecloth that he spread on the grass, he placed different kinds of snacks, as well as bottles of expensive vodka and wine. Being experienced, he had not forgotten about glasses and napkins.

At the sight of the tasty food, the young generation revived.

In a socialist society, everybody is supposed to be equal. However, this is the illusion of naïve people. In the Soviet system, food was one of the criteria that distinguished different strata of the socialist society. Some of the appetizers that were now on the tablecloth David had never seen before; they were bought in stores for the privileged representatives of Soviet society, which were closed to ordinary citizens. Except for Vadim, for whom the food did not represent anything unusual, the company ate the offered delicacies heartily.

When Roxanne had had enough food, she joined Vadim in modest consumption of vodka. Not paying attention to the rest of the group, they were flirting and laughing nonstop. As for Nellie and David, natural embarrassment prevented them from communicating; instead, they attached emphatic importance to the consumption of exotic appetizers.

Fyodor was in a situation familiar to him; he was not passive, as could be expected from a driver, but an active participant in the group. It was obvious this was not the first time he had been present at parties where his Communist bosses fed and entertained themselves and their friends. He was not talkative and did not interfere in the conversation of the youth, but under his eyebrows, he attentively watched each participant in the party. For example, when Vadim poured too much vodka into his glass, Fyodor whispered to him in a low voice something like, "Vadim, dear, your mother would not be happy with so much vodka. That's enough."

Vadim, a disciplined family boy, obediently followed the requests.

After everyone had eaten enough, the group, except the driver, went down to the river. In the clean and cool water of the river, swimming was very pleasant. Vadim left the water first; he ran up to where Fyodor was waiting for him with widely unfolded towel to dry up his worker and peasant aristocracy body. Ten minutes later, the rest of the group joined them. While they were on the way up, Nellie asked Roxanne where she had met Vadim.

Roxanne looked at her and laughed. "Uncle Fyodor introduced us," she answered. "They know me well in the neighborhood. He told me about a nice, well-provided boy from a good family who was looking for company to join him, and that's how we met."

The sun was shining brightly, the weather was excellent, and the boys and girls were suntanning, when Fyodor, who reminded David of the resourceful comic hero of *The Barber of Seville* and *The Marriage of Figaro*" by Pierre-Augustin Beaumarchais, lifted his body on his elbow.

"Vadim, look at Roxanne; her back is getting red. I bet she needs a little break from the sun. Go to the car—here are the keys—and cool off there. There's a tube of lotion in the glove compartment. Lubricate Roxanne's skin with it. As for you, Roxanne, please, help Vadim relax. I don't need to explain how; you know it yourself."

Roxanne smiled shyly and waved goodbye to Nellie and David.

David did not lose hope of starting a conversation, but nothing meaningful came out of his mouth. As for Nellie, she did not have any desire to speak with him. Sitting around the tablecloth spread on the grass, Fyodor now treated them to desserts not available to simple mortals. David was concentrated on an exotic piece of chocolate cake when Nellie's wide gray eyes, concentrated on the car where Vadim and Roxanne now were, opened wider.

"Uncle Fyodor, what's going on?" she asked. "Your car is shaking!"

"Don't pay any attention, little girl," Fyodor comforted her, winking at David. "This car has such springs and shock absorbers that it rocks from minimal movement. Perhaps Vadim and Roxanne are listening to rhythmic music."

Visibly satisfied with this explanation, Nellie nodded her head and continued to munch on sweets. David laughed, remembering one of the stories from Boccaccio's immortal *The Decameron* that told of a situation very similar to the shaking automobile.

When Vadim and Roxanne returned to the group, Fyodor met them with a wide approving smile. "OK, kids, I hope you had a good time," he said. "Now it's time to return home. Your parents are waiting for you, Vadim."

If on the way to Kubolta village, Vadim and Roxanne could not stop flirting and laughing, on the way back home, they were silent, periodically touching each other's hands. The rest of the group was not talkative, either. Fyodor let David and Nellie out of the car downtown. Those who remained in the car hardly paid their attention to their disappearance.

David never met Vadim again. He never regretted this encounter. From it, he learned that the official propaganda statements about the "classless" Soviet society were nothing but a bunch of lies. He had an opportunity to see how a young privileged member of Soviet society, a future representative of the ruling class, was different from ordinary people his age in the so-called state of workers and peasants.

CHAPTER 15

Business, Soviet Style

Samuel would never have become the head of the weaving and knitting plant if he were not a member of the Communist Party and if he were not comfortable with drinking.

Since the formation of Soviet power, the main focus of the Soviet economy was heavy industry. Small businesses, which had status of the "second-class citizens" of the Soviet economy, nevertheless performed a large role for the society, supplying the population with the consumer goods that, since the October Revolution, were in chronic short supply. An important feature of such small businesses was their involvement in "underground" or "side" or "shadow" dealing. Underground business was the inevitable outcome of the miserable salaries of workers and administration. The other reason for the inevitability of the parallel economy was the perpetual necessity of the bribing higher officials who controlled and regulated small companies.

In 1947, when the Lamm family arrived in Beltsy, Samuel's plant did not exist, and when he approached local authorities in the search of job, they—taking into account his previous professional experience—entrusted him with the task of organizing a new weaving and knitting industry in Beltsy. In order to produce woven and knitted goods, it was necessary to equip the future enterprise with the appropriate machinery. After thorough research and negotiations, Samuel found a textile manufacturer in Orekhovo-Zuevo who was ready to sell secondhand equipment for his future enterprise. The Soviet financial system was at a primitive level, and instead of a check to pay for the equipment, Samuel received a large sum of money in his hand. Samuel carried this money in a field bag that had served him faithfully from the beginning of the war to the end. A field bag (or commander's bag or officer's bag), which was used for carrying and storing working documents and writing utensils, was rectangular and was carried on a leather strap over the shoulder.

Traveling on a train to Orekhovo-Zuevo for the equipment in the anticipation of the important business development, Samuel was full of expectations and hope. Getting there involved making three transfers. Already on the first leg of his long journey, Samuel was excited to meet in his compartment two inebriated passengers, who introduced themselves as entrepreneurs. They had a great time, accompanied by good food and vodka. Samuel, who had learned to drink during the war, enjoyed each minute of the excellent company.

After a nice talk and singing folk and war songs, Samuel went to sleep in the upper berth, taking with him the field bag full of money. The time was late, the light in the railway car was dimmed, and Samuel immediately fell sleep. Early in the morning, when he woke from his sweet industrial dreams, his realized that his recent drinking companions had disappeared. To his utter dismay, the huge amount of money was also gone, along with his field bag. All that was left of his bag was the pitiful leather strap, still hanging over his shoulder.

When the desperate Samuel reached Orekhovo-Zuevo, he was able to preliminarily arrange the purchases, after which he bought a ticket back home with the remaining money. When he arrived in Beltsy, he told the authorities of his shameful adventure. He was officially accused of major negligence, but after his previous military merits and his sincere admission of guilt were taken into account, along with a generous bribe given to the judge, Samuel was sentenced to repayment of the stolen money.

Only when David grew up did he learn what had happened to his father when he was robbed on the train. He never forgot the day when his father returned from court. It was late evening, and Ilana and David were sitting in the living room, each occupied with their own business. Suddenly there was a loud knock at the window. David ran to the window, opened the shutters, and in the twilight of the passing day, he saw his father, whose face glowed with joy. Never before or after did David see such expression of happiness on his father's face.

To obtain the large amount of money required, the following month, David's parents visited the local flea market, where they sold all they could from their home. Mostly it was clothing and some furniture that the spouses had bought when Samuel was demobilized from the army. After surviving the difficult years of war, Samuel and Ilana had gotten used to accepting life as it was. They never regretted what had happened, especially because, overall, Samuel's trip to Orekhovo-Zuevo had been a success.

The moment the Lamms repaid Samuel's debt to the state, the necessary knitting and weaving equipment arrived in Beltsy. Soon Samuel's new enterprise was producing products for satisfied consumers, who were happy to obtain items that once had been impossible to find in the stores. As dramatic as this episode was, it did not persuade Samuel to stop drinking.

—

David was in the eighth grade, fifteen years old, and his friendship with his father was at a high point. Samuel liked his son's company and took him to different work-related places. Ilana did not have anything against her husband's desire to expose David to the society.

Among Samuel Lamm's close circle of friends was Evgeny Fomich Zdravradinsky, a local newspaper correspondent, a tall, athletic, and nice-looking man. Though Evgeny Zdravradinsky, a very attractive man, looked like a conqueror of women's hearts, he was actually a faithful husband and a good family man. Once Evgeny had provided Samuel with unanticipated moral support, and since then, they had become friends.

The most advanced product of Samuel's weaving and knitting plant was Jacquard bedcovers, or, kilims, produced on a manual loom with a Jacquard head. Jacquard is a multi-patterned fabric whose rapport on the basis contains more than twenty-four mesh weave threads. A Frenchman named Joseph Marie Jacquard invented the Jacquard head in 1804, and it became the first programming device developed by the human mind. Through the Jacquard head runs a chain of programmed perforated cards (i.e., a number of punched cards laced together into a continuous sequence). By pressing the pins, the perforated cards programmed the types of patterns and the color on the resulting Jacquard fabric. The result of a complex weave, the original relief pattern resembles a tapestry. The thicker the threads used in the weave, the stronger the fabric becomes.

Workers at Samuel's manufacturing plant were proud of such a superior product and could not wait until customers would have the opportunity to appreciate and buy the beautiful bedcovers they produced. Unfortunately, movement of the product to the distribution network was not possible because of what appeared to be a petty thing: each of the bedcovers required a corresponding label, and these labels—such is the socialist economy—could be produced only by an outside printing house. The reason for this regulation was the Soviet Union's paranoia that an enemy could print incendiary leaflets again its "democratic" regime. Therefore, all printing enterprises in the country, including printing houses (typographies), belonged exclusively to the state. The problem was that because of this monopoly, all printing enterprises, including printing houses, were overwhelmed with work.

Months before the first Jacquard product was manufactured, Samuel Lamm placed an order at the printing house for labels with the specifications of the product: small pieces of paper or fabric to be attached to each produced unit. Five months had passed, but there were no labels yet. Thousand and more beautiful bedcovers could not be sent to the sales network without these small tags. Samuel tried different approaches to solving this critical situation, but nothing worked. There remained only one choice: to use the universal lubricant of the Soviet economy, a bribe.

With a couple of carefully wrapped Jacquard bedcovers under his arm, Samuel arrived at the printing house of the local newspaper *Communist*. In the shop, he found the manager who was responsible for printing labels. Samuel politely brought the issue of the labels to the manager's attention and asked him when they would be ready.

"I don't know. We're very busy with orders. In a month and a half or more, I guess. There are many of you, and I am alone" was the answer.

"Comrade Manager, you should agree that these labels are really a petty thing, and for now I need at least five hundred of them. Can it be done earlier, please?"

"We have our schedule and our plans, Comrade. Leave the premises; you're interfering with our work!"

"Comrade Manager, I'm not asking for myself. My entire facility, my employees, and also the local customers are dependent on these tiny labels. Without these labels, we can't sell our product to customers, and it will probably take minutes to produce them."

"It's none of your business how long it takes to produce the labels, Comrade. I repeat, leave the premises. You're trespassing."

"Before I leave, allow me to show you what we're producing, Comrade Manager," Samuel said, unfolding one of beautiful Jacquard bedcovers before the manager. "This is an item that customers are waiting for impatiently. By the way, this is a promotional sample, and on behalf of my business, I would be happy if you would take it for your business . . ."

"Aha, so you're offering me a bribe!" the manager screamed. "Don't you ever dare do that. I am going to tell our newspaper reporter Ivan Shmundyak about your improper behavior."

The manager kept his word, and in a week, the second half page of the city's four-page *Communist* newspaper was decorated with a feuilleton describing how Communist Lamm had tried to bribe the printing-house official.

The feuilleton—a short satirical article—was one of the most entertaining parts of an otherwise boring newspaper. The main targets of such feuilletons were frequently the Jews. The official national policy of the Communist Party did not allow a direct statement that the subject of an article was a Jewish individual. Instead, the publication repeated the name and patronymic of the culprit several times, from which it became clear to the reader about whom the article was talking. Correspondent Ivan Shmundyak supplied the feuilleton with a "cute" title: "The Bedcover Covered Samuel Abramovich Lamm." The patronymic *Abramovich* was repeated many times to let readers know that, without a doubt, Samuel Abramovich Lamm was a Jew.

When Samuel saw the feuilleton, he was upset and went to complain to the chief editor of *Communist* about exposing him on a mission that was beneficial for the business. In the corridor, he met the new chief newspaper reporter, Evgeny Zdravradinsky. They introduced themselves and started a conversation. Samuel, who needed to share his offended feelings, told the chief correspondent why he was upset, and the chief correspondent unexpectedly took his side, telling him that, actually, the feuilleton did not have teeth, and he should not worry about it.

"Don't get upset, Samuel Abramovich. Everybody understands that you wanted to facilitate your socialist business. It's clear you were doing it not for yourself but for your employees and for perspective customers. I like you, Samuel. You know what I'll do for you? I'll write a special article dedicated to your textile organization."

Indeed, a month later, in the same *Communist* newspaper, a commendable article dedicated to the enterprise headed by Samuel Lamm was published. By that time, Samuel and Evgeny Zdravradinsky had become bosom friends and drinking partners.

One day the Zdravradinskys invited Samuel Abramovich to a party at their house.

On the way to the party, another guest, the head of a construction company, joined the Lamms, who had brought David with them.

David walked next to his parents, minding his own business, when the companion who had joined them pointed a finger at him.

"Why did you bring your son with you?" he asked. "You surely know that most people at the party will be adults."

"We try to take our David with us whenever possible. Let him have the experience of being among adults," Samuel answered.

As the companion who had joined the family predicted, there were only two young children besides David at the party, and communication with them was impossible. Suffering from boredom, David walked from room to room in search of entertainment. In the corridor, he noticed a wooden cabinet with a tall glass door, behind which he saw a rifle. He was well acquainted with this weapon: Samuel, a former regular officer, had brought his personal rifle, a flare gun, and a couple of Finnish knives home with him after demobilization. They were openly displayed in his parents' bedroom. There was not a single bullet in the household, and David was allowed to play with the weapons at his leisure. The rifle was his favorite thing to play with. David knew all about it, including how to take apart and put together its bolt.

Seeing the rifle, which was exactly the same as the one in his house, not thinking twice, David opened the door of the cupboard, took out the rifle, and began to take it apart and reassemble it. He was so taken with playing with his favorite "toy," he did not even notice when he found himself in the room where all the guests were with the rifle assembled. The sight of the child with the weapon produced an indelible impression on the spectators. Except for his parents, accustomed to their son's fussing with a rifle, the rest of the guests—there were more than twenty people in the room—looked at David with wide-open and frightened eyes. David did not realize what was going on around him and continued to play with the rifle until Samuel took the rifle from his hands and showed him to the door.

After that, David's reputation at the party was completely ruined. Later, he received a strict lecture from the adults, who told him and his parents that he could have killed them because of his stupidity and their bad parenting. Nevertheless, David's action had one positive effect. Thanks to him, the people at the party revived and became united in their outrage against the boy who "you know, could have killed one of us."

Fortunately, David's misdeed did not discourage his parents from trusting their son. They knew David well and did not doubt that the episode with the rifle happened because, being naïve, he did not associate the rifle with killing people.

The friendship between Samuel and Evgeny continued for many years.

CHAPTER 16

Resort Sergeevka

In 1957, David's parents decided to spend the summer vacation at Sergeevka, a small picturesque resort located on the shore of the Black Sea. They took David, who was then sixteen years old, with them. Resort Sergeevka is located not far from the large city of Odessa in Ukraine, and it attracts many people with its therapeutic baths, flowers, and herbs, as well as with the sun and the sea. However, the special attraction is the resort's wonderful beach. The unique feature is the therapeutic mud that nature prepared in a giant laboratory—the Shabolatsky coastal salt lake (estuary, *liman*), which separates Sergeevka from the seacoast. Across the estuary is a pedestrian bridge, which leads to a hundred-and-fifty-meter-wide spit with pristine beaches. Small cruise boats are the other way to reach the spit. The shallow and sandy bottom of the sea creates excellent conditions for swimming.

David has interesting memories related to visiting this resort.

The Lamms traveled to Sergeevka by train; to save money on tickets, the family bought seats in the cheapest general railway car. The main problem with traveling in this car was not so much the lack of comfort but the large crowd of passengers, who consumed all available oxygen in the car. Samuel and Ilana sat during the entire trip while David was luckier: he climbed up on the third berth where the distance from his body to the ceiling was little more than the length of a lower arm. For a pillow, he used his jacket. Settling in his place, he began to read a book of Mark Twain's short stories.

The train departed late in the evening. In the air was a thick smell of sweaty unwashed bodies. Fortunately, the human being is a flexible creature, and with time, David's nose got used to the stink. In the dim light produced by a lamp on the car ceiling, he could not stop giggling reading Mark Twain's famous story in which a cowboy in a pub gives a pig such a blow that the poor animal flies faster than the squeal it produces while flying.

Meanwhile people were falling asleep, and gradually everything was quiet and peaceful in the car.

Also on the third berth, opposite David, slept a man, probably a peasant. His haggard face was covered with bristles, and he was dressed in cheap clothes. The man's five-year-old son was settled on the second birth under David, while his mother, along with three other people, was sitting on the lower berth. David finished reading and was ready to fall asleep when he heard a screaming cry, followed by the thump of a falling body. When he looked down, he was struck by what he saw. Lying on the floor was the man who had just occupied the berth opposite him. In his hands, he held his son, who had occupied the berth under David's. Doubtless, while the boy was falling from the second berth, his father jumped down from the third berth, miraculously got to the ground first, and was able to catch his son before he hit the floor. David smiled when he remembered the similar situation in Mark Twain's story, when a cowboy in a pub gave a pig such a blow with his foot that the poor animal flew faster than its squeal.

The family arrived at Sergeevka at noon, traveling there by bus from the railway station where they had arrived that morning. A remarkable feature of travel to Sergeevka was the road itself; the abundance of potholes created the impression that the road had recently been carpet-bombed.

At the bus station in Sergeevka, a woman promised to rent them a room on the main road. When the family came to the house where the room was located, they discovered that, actually, it was not a room but the attic of the house that was for rent. It was necessary to climb a ladder to get there. Samuel and Ilana rationalized that the price was good, and the entire attic was at their disposal; in any case, it was already too late to look for another room. During the day, when the sun heated up the attic, the Lamms would be outside anyway, so why worry? The main thing was that they were at the pinnacle of their dreams, in a real seaside resort.

Doubtless, the greatest showpiece of the residence was the hostess who met them at the bus station. She was a serious, mature woman who was constantly on the move. If she needed to get something for her husbandry, she did not ask her husband about it. Instead, she jumped on the family motorcycle and rushed to the store. She was an excellent chef. Everything she made with her own hands was always tasty. At the top of her menu was buckwheat porridge, the secret recipe for which she did not want to share with her guests.

The main entertainment for the Lamm family in Sergeevka was daily visits to the sand spit beach. In order to get there, they took a motorboat along with other tourists. David had read many books about the sea, but there in Sergeevka, he saw it with his own eyes for the first time. The view of the boundless sea space with high rolling waves made an indelible impression on him. There were no lifeguards on the beach: everyone was responsible for himself. While Samuel went about his business, David rushed to the water and began to swim away from the shore to have the feeling that he was in the open sea. Ilana, though she knew her son could swim well, rushed to the water screaming, demanding that David return to the shore. David was too far out to sea to hear her screams. He returned to the shore in three quarters of an hour; by that time, Ilana had lost her voice. When she calmed down, speaking in a whisper, she took David's word that in the future, he would never swim so far into the sea.

David was an obedient son and did not want to go back on his word, but two days later, something happened that made him break his promise. On that day, there were not too many people in the water because of an abundance of jellyfish. To avoid an encounter with a jellyfish, David swam along the shore. The sun was shining, a fresh breeze was blowing, and the sea waves were tenderly touching his skin when suddenly he heard a loud cry for help. He looked in the direction of the cry and saw a woman who was farther from the shore than he was. She was waving her arms wildly to attract attention.

Ignoring the promise he had given to his mother not to swim far from the shore, David swam in direction of the drowning woman as fast as he could. Soon he realized that he was not able to achieve his goal. In vain, he put maximum efforts in his arms and legs, but instead of moving, he remained at the same place. In another minute or two, he realized that instead of approaching the woman, he was moving away from her. Nobody had ever told David about the currents in the sea, and now, he had to learn about them by himself. Not knowing what was going on, David was very frightened: an invisible force was pulling him along the shore and toward the sea. Nobody knew what was happening to him, and nobody was around to help him.

David had no choice but to tell himself to remain cool and not to panic. The moment he turned around and began to swim perpendicular to the stream's direction, he felt a great deal of relief: the current that had prevented him from swimming before now let him out of its iron embrace, and suddenly, David could swim at will. Reaching a shallow place in the sea, he looked for the woman who had been yelling for help. Alas, he could not see her, and only a boundless sea was before him. The tragic fate of this woman eclipsed for David the joy of his own liberation from the recent grasping hands of the sea current.

Very tired, David returned to his parents. Not knowing what had just happened, they were sitting on beach towels, playing dominoes. They had no idea that only ten minutes before, they might have returned home from vacation without their son.

Samuel noticed that David was back.

"I'm glad you're here, sonny. Imagine, while you were swimming," he said, "a woman began to drown in the sea and screamed for help. Fortunately, an experienced swimmer swam to save her. Ilana and I saw how he approached her, grabbed her by the hair, put her on her back, and safely took her to the beach. Look to your left now. That's she. Now she acts like nothing happened to her. Such is the human being: when we're in trouble, we live in milliseconds; when we're not in danger, we live as if life never ends."

What a great day it was: David and the unknown woman had both avoided mortal danger. Furthermore, David had received a precious lesson about sea currents. A real trifecta, and the day was just beginning.

On the motorboat David and his parents took back to Sergeevka, he sat next to two young men in their early thirties who were convinced that they were the main resort features. Like cheap operetta actors, these small-town jerks repeated aloud with the air of experts the same refrain: they were deeply disappointed that they had come to this provincial resort. Instead of the beautiful women they had expected to encounter in Sergeevka, they complained, all of them were nothing but "old nags." David expected the women in the motorboat to protest these connoisseurs of their sex, but everybody was silent. No one reacted in any way to the insulting descriptions provided by two dummies.

The boat reached the pier, and using a narrow bridge without rails, the passengers were on their way to dry ground. When it was time for the disappointed critics to pass over the bridge, two average-age women approached the complainers, and with impenetrable expressions on their faces, amid the amicable laughter of the other passengers, they pushed the recent connoisseurs of women from the bridge into the water.

The next day, David awoke early in the morning when his parents were still asleep. It was a beautiful morning, and before his parents woke up, David decided to go for a walk to the shore of the Black Sea. He quickly dressed, went down from the attic on the ladder, and was soon on the edge of the cliff overlooking the sea. Before him was a narrow path that descended more or less smoothly down to the sea, which gleamed in the distance, about a kilometer away. David started his descent toward the sea.

At this early hour, the sun had just appeared on horizon, and its red disk was sending tender rays of reddish light. It was peaceful and quiet, and the blue-greenish water at the end of the cliff beckoned to David. Descending in the silence of the morning, he suddenly felt a light touch on his hair. David looked around but could not see anything that could have produced it. I probably imagined it, he thought. Ignoring what had just happened to him, he continued his way down. He had not passed another fifteen meters when again he felt a tap—this time stronger—on the top of his head. Now puzzled, David stubbornly kept going forward. Only after the fifth time did he understand what was happening to him. He saw a nest with eggs in it in front of him. This discovery coincided with a painful attack from the air by two seagulls; this time David was able to see both birds pecking his head. He was halfway to the sea, but not knowing what would happen next, he gave up and decided to return. As soon as he changed direction, the attacks from the air ceased, and soon he was back at the top of the cliff.

David was impressed with how the birds protected their unborn offspring. It reminded him of the recent episode in the train when the father, who was on the third berth, was able to catch his son who fell from the second berth. The seagulls that had attacked him protecting the eggs, their future offspring, were moved by the same universal law of nature, written in their genes, that moved the father on the train who was protecting his son.

The owners of the house where the Lamms were renting the attic left for a couple of days, and temporarily, the family had their meals at the only dining hall in Sergeevka. The dining hall offered food only for local residents. However, the young local woman who was in charge of the place, combining the responsibilities of manager and cashier, did the Lamms a favor: she allowed them to have dinner at her place. On the menu were four items: borsch, red-navy pilaf, buckwheat, and compote of dried fruits.

While David's parents were ordering food, David was making innocent jokes from time to time, which was typical for him. For some reason, the young woman disliked David. As there were no other customers in the dining hall except the Lamms, the woman used this opportunity to give Samuel and Ilana a long lecture, letting them know that their son, David, with his free manners, would wind up in jail when he grew up. In vain, Samuel and Ilana tried to insert a word into her monologue, which lasted more than a quarter of an hour. But they risked losing their lunch if they objected to her demagoguery. With a disturbed curiosity, David observed a complete stranger who was in love with teaching and giving advice to others. This was, of course, not the first time he had encountered an individual who, instead of minding her own business, was teaching other people how they were supposed to live.

After the family had their meal at the town's dining hall, the parents went home to rest while David went to the local library. In the Soviet Union, to buy or take out of the library an interesting book—not the omnipresent political trash—was always a difficult task, especially in cities, where the majority of potential readers lived. That was why avid readers traveled all the way to towns and villages, where in bookstores and libraries—because of lack the of a reading public—they had a chance of finding a book of interest. David went straight to the town library, where he hoped to find a recently published novel, *Не хлебом единым* (*Not by Bread Alone*) by Vladimir Dudintzev. From one of his adult friends, he had heard that such a book—because of its content—could never have been published during the recent Stalin era. However, in 1956, it was still the time of Khrushchev's thaw, and this book was a sign of a new time.

The book aroused great resonance and discussion among the Soviet intelligentsia. *Not by Bread Alone* was about an inventor, who, during Stalin's time, was struggling in vain with the dominance of not only bureaucrats but state authorities as well. In a fight with the ruling-class domination, he became a subject of libel. At the end, the hero is tried and sentenced to eight years in prison. This novel illustrated wide gap that existed in the USSR between the people and the state.

David had tried to find *Not by Bread Alone* in Beltsy, but it was unattainable. Since readers of this book could be accused of interest in anti-Soviet propaganda, David did not want to be accused of disloyalty to the Motherland, and he was careful not to express an excessive interest in the book. In Sergeevka Resort nobody knew him, so, hopefully, he could ask for the book without consequences.

The brick building in which Sergeevka's library was located was clean and quiet inside. David approached the counter behind which the librarian, a blonde woman in a nice dress, was vividly discussing a new book with three customers—all men—who stood on the other side of the counter. David waited patiently for the conversation to stop so he could ask for the book.

The usual policy at Soviet libraries was that the reader asked the librarian for the desired book, after which the librarian disappeared into the storage area and returned with the book if it was on the shelf. To prevent stolen books and to prevent readers from having access to semicensored material, free access to books was not available in public libraries.

In large libraries, especially the specialized ones, books were available only to a special contingent of people, such as researchers, journalists, or political functionaries. The staffs of such libraries included official censors who watched for those ordinary people who ordered uncensored "forbidden" literature. For example, the name of an ordinary person who too frequently ordered books by so-called "reactionary philosophers," such as Arthur Schopenhauer, Friedrich Nietzsche, or Nikolai Berdyaev, was included in a special list for further observation and could be shared with KGB. To have access to books that were stored in special funds, such as works by Trotsky or Bukharin, the reader needed to have a special access certificate provided by universities or by the party apparatus.

Finally, the librarian switched her attention to David and asked him what book he was interested in.

"Do you have by chance Dudintzev's book *Not by Bread Alone*?" David asked humbly and quietly, so the other customers could not hear his request.

"*Not by Bread Alone*?" the librarian asked in a regular voice. "Wait, I'll go to check if it's on the shelf."

After that, what David had been afraid of happened. One of the customers who stood next to David, a man in his thirties, looked at him and asked, "So, I heard you want to read Dudintzev's book. Is that so?"

David had no choice but to confirm the answer to the question reluctantly, after which he drew his head into shoulders, trying to be as invisible as possible, and waited for a new unpleasant question. He was mistaken. There were no more questions, but the man, whom David had never met before, unexpectedly began to tell David many details about Dudintzev's book. The stranger was careful in his explanation, but David understood well what he was hiding under his pauses and reticence. Like many people in the authoritarian regime, his interlocutor was thirsty to exchange his secret thoughts, even if it was only with a teenager like David. From this man, David learned in more detail about the hero of the book, an inventor whose fate clearly proved the shortcomings of socialist society. The conversation with the stranger only increased David's interest in the book.

Luckily, the librarian soon returned with it.

With the novel in his hand, David was on the way out of the library when another member of the same group to which the original stranger belonged approached David and told him about another book he might be interested in, as long as he was interested in Dudintzev's work.

David had a life-opening experience: he realized that even in such a provincial town as Sergeevka, despite the overwhelming cascade of official propaganda, there were people who understood the hypocrisy of the Soviet system and, moreover, wanted to enlighten their compatriots about it.

It took David three days to "swallow" Dudintzev's book. Many facts that he gleaned from the book widened his understanding of the country where he was born and lived. *Not by Bread Alone* was the first of many books that David was able to find legally and, later, from samizdat illegally, that allowed him to have a sober critical view of the utter pretense of the Soviet system. Thanks to his self-education, seventeen years later, he was one of the first who escaped with his family to the West.

Anti-Semitism was endemic to the country of "victorious internationalism" in which David lived, and it was not surprising to encounter it in the little town of Sergeevka. David was present when his father met an army colonel, Vladimir Stasovich Orlov, a tall man in civil clothes who had recently come to Sergeevka on vacation. The colonel had soft facial features and an overall friendly appearance. He used to serve in Viborg, where Samuel served as a military officer as well. Moreover, the colonel and Samuel had common acquaintances in Viborg.

Two acquaintances greeted each other cordially and got involved in conversation, during which Samuel casually asked the colonel what he had done the previous evening.

"Oh, yesterday, in the evening, my wife and I attended an excellent party. We had a great time there," the colonel answered, smiling. "The party was exclusively for military officers, and it was organized by a local veteran's family. We had a lot of fun."

"Congratulations, but why didn't you tell me about this party? I would have been happy to attend such a festivity," Samuel said.

"Well, at this party were only 'ours'," the colonel answered, intentionally stressing the word *ours*.

The last word angered Samuel.

"What do you mean 'ours'?" he reacted with indignation. "What makes you think that I am not one of 'ours'? I fought the entire Second World War, was wounded and awarded several decorations for combat operations, and now you imply that I am an outsider and a second-class citizen?"

"You should agree that some former officers feel more comfortable among those who share their heritage, Samuel *Abramovich*," the colonel answered, emphasizing the patronymic *Abramovich*. He was not showing any signs of inconvenience.

"I didn't expect you to be a dirty anti-Semite," Samuel said, looking into the serene eyes of the colonel. "As a Communist Party member, how do you dare to speak to me this way?"

The colonel was not affected at all by what Samuel said to him. He only smiled arrogantly and left to do his business.

Welcome to internationalism of the Soviet type.

David, a witness to the dialogue, was disturbed by what he saw—another reminder for him that he lived in a country where the contemptuous treatment of a representative of another ethnic group was a casual thing. He had many friends who were Russian and Ukrainian, but his overall experience was that, unfortunately, many of these friends let him know in different ways that "though you are a Jew, you are a good man." In other words, he was a person with an inherited defect, a second-class citizen.

"Why are you so upset, Dad?" David asked his father when they were alone.

"Because regardless of their devotion to the Soviet Union and regardless of their merits before the country, a Jew in this country is not considered to be a full-fledged citizen," he answered.

"Then what can we do, Dad?"

"I'll tell you what to do: the best this thing you can do is to survive in spite of your enemies. Get a good education so you'll be able to find a work in places where they need you more than you need them. Equip yourself with deep knowledge, be the best wherever you work, be a role model. Whatever somebody might try to reassure you, do not believe. You don't have full civil rights in this country. Being a Jew, you will be always under suspicion, and you will not be fully accepted. Be ready for challenges and have strong muscles and, better, a strong mind."

Paradoxically, instead of producing a depressing effect, his father's words helped David for years to come. He understood that he had to work hard in order to survive successfully. David did not have any illusions about the limitations of his place in society, and he knew that he had to be among the best. In addition, his father's words helped him decide to be among the first to leave the country where he was born.

He was working in Odessa's infection hospital in 1974 when he shared the news that he had decided to leave the Soviet Union with his very good Ukrainian friend, Dr. Archipenko, who provided him with the best justification for his decision.

"You're doing the right thing, David," Dr. Archipenko said. "The dog does not run away from a good master."

The unpleasant feeling after the episode with colonel faded from David's memory when late in the afternoon of the same day, saturated with many adventures, he had the opportunity to watch a vaudeville musical at the Sergeevka summer theatre in the open air, under the rustle of trees, the singing of birds, and the gentle touch of the summer breeze.

The next day, the Lamm family left Resort Sergeevka. As before, the family took the cheapest third-class railway car. This time there were not as many people in the car, and the Lamms had the opportunity to occupy desirable berths. It is a well-known fact that during railroad trips, people who are not destined to meet again open their hearts and entrust their intimate stories to strangers. Time passes quickly when people talk.

Among the other interlocutors in the car was a mature-looking man with coarse facial features, unshaven and with the hands of a working person. His clothing was of the cheapest possible kind. He was good at asking questions but did not talk much about himself; all he answered to Samuel's questions was that he was a bookkeeper and that he was traveling back to his family, who lived in Bendery, a city in Moldova. Recently, according to him, he had been a construction worker, and now he was traveling all the way from Siberia, where he had worked very hard. When he arrived home, he hoped to have several days of rest.

Soon it was night. To the uniform knocking of the wheels, the passengers went to sleep. After reading a few pages of a book, David fell asleep to the snoring of the other passengers. In the middle of the night, he and the other passengers in the compartment woke up to terrible blood-curdling screams from the man who was traveling from Siberia, who was asleep. Screams were followed with loud, heartrending cries.

"Stop beating me, stop beating me," the man was repeating in a loud, protesting tone, until he woke up and sharply sat up in his second berth, his legs dangling down.

Awakened by the man's screams, the passengers in the compartment looked at him with fear.

"Sorry, people," he apologized. "Understand me. I can't help myself. Only a week ago, they released me from prison. I haven't come to my senses yet," he added after a small pause.

"Dad, did this man tell you about himself?" David asked his father.

"No, and asking him was useless," Samuel answered. "When a prisoner is released from prison, he signs a nondisclosure statement. If he breaks this commitment, he could go back to prison. The prison system in the Soviet Union is enormous, and it's invisible because of the secrecy that surrounds it."

"Wait, Dad. In that case, any abuse in the prison could be concealed. Look at this poor man. It's clear that they beat him more than once in jail. Somebody should know about such horrible abuse . . ."

"Shut your mouth, son! It's dangerous."

"But it's not fair at all!"

"Welcome to the real world, son," Samuel answered. "Take life as it is; otherwise; life will sweep you away in its path. You are too young and too powerless to think about fighting injustice. When you grow up, we will talk about it, OK?"

CHAPTER 17

Instead of Epilogue

After graduation from high school, like the majority of his fellow Jewish tribesmen, David did not even think about what profession suited him most. Jewish youth in the Soviet Union did not choose a profession; their professions depended on their parents' or caregivers' ability to find a graduate institution where their children could be admitted not only for their educational achievements, but thanks to their ability to give a bribe or have a special connection. Though David graduated high school with high grades, that did not mean he would have privileges on admission. Throughout the European part of the USSR, there were official quotas for Jewish ethnic group education in the higher educational institutions that were not disclosed to the public. Many of David's Jewish classmates were traveling to the east of the Ural Mountains, where there was a higher chance of passing the entry exams. At the age of seventeen, David was ready to go anywhere to receive a graduate education, but his parents, especially his mother, could not imagine her son going to live as far away as Siberia.

Six months prior to David's graduation from high school, Ilana began to work intensively to find a place where he could receive his further education. She and Samuel asked everyone they knew about a possible connection that would help their son get accepted to a graduate program. Half a century ago, the famous Jewish writer Sholom Aleichem wrote in one of his stories that the good and highly regarded authority figure is the one who does takes bribes, not the opposite. David's parents were in search of a person responsible for admission to graduate school who took bribes and thus could open the gates for David's graduate education.

David would not have minded becoming a mechanical engineer or a teacher, an oilman or a specialist in the textile industry; he became a medical doctor simply because he had an opportunity to be accepted to medical school.

On the third day after the modest school prom, Ilana called David to the living room and solemnly introduced him to a Jewish woman, Raisa Nakhumovna Krasilnikova. She was a woman in her forties in a long gray jacket and dark skirt. Her face was covered with early wrinkles, although she was relatively young. There was no sense of personality in her appearance: a generic woman with a big vinyl matte purse in her hand. She was plump but not obese, of medium height, with narrow lips and brown eyes.

Raisa Nakhumovna was a resident of the city of Dneprodzerzhinsk in Ukraine. She had come to Beltsy to visit her cousin, an acquaintance of the Lamm family. Ilana had met her cousin at the market and learned that her visitor from Dneprodzerzhinsk had contacts at Kharkov Dental School and could help David become a dentist.

"David, Raisa Nakhumovna will help you to get into dental school in Kharkov. Together, you will go to Kharkov, where she'll introduce you to an important person who will help you become a dental student. Raisa Nakhumovna told your father and me that this person would give you detailed instruction regarding your preparation for exams. You leave in three days."

Ilana did not ask David if he wanted to accompany this unknown woman to a city located about six hundred miles from Beltsy. The upcoming journey was not a subject for discussion. In the culture where David grew up, it was assumed that parents made the decisions that were in the best interest of their child, and the child was supposed to carry out unconditionally what his parents were expecting from him. The question of whether David wanted to become a dentist did not exist; a Jewish student applied for admission to the university or college where there was a chance of being admitted and subsequently entering a profession that would provide a livelihood for him or her and his or her future family for the rest of his or her life.

David's visit to Kharkov supposed to be short. Ilana prepared a small piece of luggage for him with some food for the trip and the necessary changes of clothes. She gave him a generous amount of money that was very important for her son to return home.

On board the railroad car, David opened his luggage and carefully hid the money in a secret pocket. Not wasting time in preparation for the admission exams, he took couple of textbooks with him. Lying on the berth, he plunged into the study of the laws of physics. He felt secure in the company of a mature adult. He did not need to worry; the woman would take care of all accommodations and important decisions.

At the end of the uneventful trip, in the late morning of the next day, David, to his amazement, found out that he was not in the city of Kharkov but in the city of Dneprodzerzhinsk (now *Каменское*). From his school geography course, David knew of the existence of that city, known for its metallurgic industry, but he never thought he would ever visit it.

"My mother told me we were going straight to Kharkov. Why are we here?" David asked his supposed guide.

Raisa Nakhumovna appeared nonchalant. She gave David an indifferent look and explained only after a long pause. "Before we go to Kharkov," she said in her colorless monotonous voice, not apologizing for the change in the original plan, "I need to take care of some business in Dneprodzerzhinsk. We'll go to Kharkov tomorrow."

David did not protest because he was not experienced in arguing with adults and because he knew he could not change anything with his chaperone, who lived in her own world and did not have any desire to let anybody in it. By this time, David already knew that his older companion was not of high mental capacities. Forget about a book: during the entire trip, this woman hardly opened her mouth and was not interested in anything except looking out the window.

From the railroad station, they went to Raisa Nakhumovna's apartment. Her husband, Aron Michailovich, was much more hospitable than his wife. The room where David spent the night was nice, with clean bedding, which put David's mind at ease: overall, it appeared that he was among decent people.

The next day was Sunday. In the morning, after a good breakfast, for a reason unexplained to David, he joined his hosts when they walked to the city's downtown. There, friends, another married couple, were waiting for them. Before a walk, the couples exchanged news. It was a beautiful day in July: the sun was pleasantly warming, the birds were caroling, and green trees were decorating the clean city streets. David looked up at the sky and was surprised. High above the city of Dneprodzerzhinsk, he saw floating clouds of a poisonous reddish-brown color. He had never before seen such a "natural phenomenon" and asked Aron Michailovich what it meant.

"Oh, don't pay attention to it at all," he answered. "You see, our city is the center of Ukraine's metallurgy and chemical industries. These industries are responsible for the high levels of pollutants that their high chimneys send into the atmosphere. In the end, these pollutants fall into the water. Theoretically, these clouds are supposed to be blown away by air currents, but the city is located in a valley, and this doesn't happen. So we constantly have these pollutant-filled clouds above our city."

"But even if the clouds were blown away, sooner or later, the pollutants would settle on the ground. Pollution still remains," David remarked.

"You're right, but cleaning the smoke of the pollutants requires money, which the industry claims it doesn't have. This is our Soviet economy: those who are above us do whatever they want and are not too interested in the public's opinion. It's no wonder that many people in our city suffer from respiratory problems. This is an insoluble problem, believe me."

He was right. Sixty years later, the problem with pollution in Dneprodzerzhinsk, now *Каменское*, remains unresolved.

David thought they would leave Dneprodzerzhinsk the next day. To his dismay, Raisa Nakhumovna was not in a hurry. David reminded her at every opportunity that his parents expected him to come back soon and that they would be very concerned about his absence. His family did not have a home phone, and the only way David could communicate with his parents was by sending them letters, which might arrive later than he did. Raisa Nakhumovna got rid of his remarks with silence; she was able to keep her mouth shut.

The fourth day after their arrival, very early in the morning, David and his would-be benefactor took the train to Kharkov, arriving there at noon. Straight from the railroad station, they went to the person who was supposed to help David get into dental school. During their trip on the city tram, Raisa Nakhumovna remained as silent as a stone.

After the trip by tram and walking three city blocks, they finally found themselves in front of a typical three-story city building. The building was dilapidated, with peeling green plaster and balconies in emergency condition.

When the visitors entered the building and approached the door of the apartment they were looking for, David realized that his possible "influential" sponsor lived in a communal apartment with many neighbors. The woman who supposed to help David, Nelly Issakovna Frank, was sick and lay in bed under the blankets. At the sight of the guests, she revived. Apologizing for her cold, she invited the guests to sit down on the chairs next to her bed.

Five minutes of conversation between two women were enough for David to understand that these women not only hardly knew each other, but also hardly knew what they were talking about.

"Nelly Isaakovna, this is the boy I told you about a month ago when we met at the city market. His name is David. He came all the way from Moldova with me to hear from you how we can help him be admitted to Kharkov Dental School," Raisa Nakhumovna said in her monotonous voice.

"Welcome, David," Nelly Isaakovna said in artificially excited tone, presenting herself as a person who knows what she's talking about. "I'll be honest with you. You are smart enough to understand that I can't promise you one hundred percent success, but I know a professor at the dental school who likes money and who might help us. Unfortunately, I don't know yet if he'll be on the admission committee this year. If that happens, we're in luck. If not, we're not.

"You see, I work as a deputy accountant at the dental school, and this professor comes to my office to get his salary twice a month. We always have a small talk. After many years, we know each other well, and we can be open with each other. I think if he becomes a member of the admission committee, then we might have a good chance of enrolling you in the dental school. The problem with you is that you are Jewish . . ."

As if I didn't know it, David thought.

". . . and they try to admit a minimal number of Jews. I don't need to explain to you why. I can't tell you the name of this professor, but he always compliments me. Believe me, he is not the only one who compliments me. I'll soon recover and return to work. I'm in charge of the entire payroll department, and they depend on me there. At work every day, I hear words of praise and appreciation. But back to our sheep. If the professor I told you about is on the admission committee, I'm sure we'll be successful. He likes money, as I told you."

"But Nelly Isaakovna, I didn't know we had such an uncertain situation. When you met me in the market, while we stood in line for meat, you told me you didn't have any doubt that you could arrange for a Jewish person to be admitted to the dental school. Can you make us a more certain commitment? You see, this young man came all the way from Moldova with me, and we should be more assertive with him. He's a nice boy," David's advocate said.

"I repeat, I don't make promises, but I'll do my best," the answer followed. "You should understand that the dental school is very limited in accepting our tribesmen. You know they have their quotas;

one of the administrators told me recently that the quota is less than the previous year. Last year, they admitted only four Jews. Hopefully, this year we'll break the wall and achieve our goal."

Lost time, lost efforts, David thought to himself when he and Raisa Nakhumovna left the apartment. Notwithstanding Nelly Isaakovna, Raisa Nakhumovna was equally incompetent: she had wasted his time, and now he needed to go back to his parents.

David did not know what was going to happen next when he walked on the sidewalk of a wide city street with Raisa Nakhumovna, carrying his small piece of luggage. As always, Raisa Nakhumovna remained silent and did not say a word about the today's visit, allowing David to draw his own conclusions. Eventually, she stopped in front of a large building, and the unexpected happened: she began to talk.

"That's it," she said. "I did for you all I could. Tell your parents I'll look for other opportunities, but I doubt I'll find them. You go home. Tell you parents that right now nothing can be done for you in Kharkov.

"The building in front of you is Kharkov Central Railroad Station. Go inside, buy a train ticket to Beltsy, and you'll be home tomorrow. Your mother told me she gave you enough money for travel, so you're in good shape," she said, not looking at David.

"But I've never been to this railroad station, and I don't have any idea where I can buy a ticket." David tried to object.

"Don't worry, boy. You're grown up enough to figure out how to buy a ticket. I'm in a hurry. Say hello to your parents." With these words, and without additional explanation, Raisa Nakhumovna turned around and, big purse in hand, went about her business. In the middle of a big city unknown to him, David stood confused, surprised that a woman to whom his parents had entrusted his security had left him alone. Only now, did he realize that he did not have a single ID on him: he was too young for a passport, and he had left his birth certificate at home. After a brief reflection, David decided not to panic: the main thing was that he had enough money for even the most expensive ticket. Decisively, he entered the enormous hall of Kharkov's railway station. Now all that was left for him to do was to find the ticket window and buy a ticket. Tomorrow he would be back at home.

The huge railway station building was noisy, crowded, and smoky. People with luggage and without it were walking and running in different directions. To his satisfaction, before each of the four open ticket windows, David did not see many passengers.

"I need a ticket to the city of Beltsy in Moldova," David said to the cashier politely. "If possible, not an expensive one, please."

"Where are you coming from?" asked the cashier.

"Here, from Kharkov," David answered.

"In that case, I can't sell you a ticket," answered the woman in a dry tone. "I have a limited number of tickets for local residents, and they are only for transitory passengers. Next."

"But I came from Dneprodzerzhinsk this morning."

"Show me your ticket from there."

"I didn't know I'd need it, so I threw it away."

"That doesn't help. You're not a transit passenger. Come tomorrow morning. For today, there are no more trains in your direction. Don't even hope."

However, David did not want to give up; he thought he might reach home taking a trip with a transfer. For the rest of the day, he visited different ticket cashiers' windows, each time with a negative result. Eventually, an agent in a railway uniform, responsible for order on the floor of the station, noticed David and forbade him to approach cashiers' windows any longer.

All day long, David was on the floor of the railway station, unsuccessfully trying to obtain a ticket from Kharkov. Not able to get in touch with his parents, all he could rely on were his own efforts. With his little suitcase, he walked back and forth in the hall, trying to figure out how to solve the situation he was in, but he could not come to any decision.

When night fell, he realized that he should find a place to sleep. From traveling with his parents, David knew that railway stations had travelers' lodges available for passengers, something akin to cheap inns. Somebody told him that, indeed, on the second floor, there was a travelers' lodge. In anticipation of failure—without a ticket, he probably wasn't entitled to use the services of the railway station—he went up to the second floor and entered the travelers' lodge vestibule. There, at a large table, he saw an administrator on duty, a woman who was about forty years old. On her nose were glasses with black rims. Her unremarkable face was concentrated on some kind of document, in which she periodically made notes. She was dressed in a blue dress and a sweater of the same color. On the table where she sat stood a carafe of water and a faceted glass. On the other side of the table lay a half-knitted scarf and knitting needles.

Hesitantly, in anticipation of refusal, David approached her. Today, no one wanted to hear his story, so directly, without explanation, he asked the woman if he could spend the night in the travelers' lounge. The administrator, Maria Kirillovna, looked at David appraisingly and asked him what he was doing at the railway station without parents or guardians. To the first adult who was interested in the previously invisible teenager, David—trying to be as concise as possible in order not to lose her attention—explained what had happened to him. Maria Kirillovna listened with undivided attention, sometimes interrupting David for more details. David was touched by her interest, and for the first time, against his will, his eyes welled with tears and signs of anguish appeared in his voice.

When David finished his explanation, Maria Kirillovna said something that was very special for him at that moment: she told him not to worry because "Everything will be OK."

"I don't know where to go," David said. "I don't have a ticket, but will you let me sleep in one of your travelers' rooms?"

"Do you have any ID?"

"No. I'm too young for a passport, and I didn't know that I needed to bring my birth certificate with me."

Maria Kirillovna looked David at with compassion in her face. "I understand. Don't worry. I have a daughter your age, and I know how uncomfortable she'd be if she were in your position. Any mother would help you. Just pay me, and I'll take you to the room where you can spend the night."

The general rules in any railway station were that people were allowed to sit—not to lie—on the benches. A railway patrol person would periodically wake up anybody who was asleep in order not to create a refuge for homeless people in the waiting area. Without Maria Kirillovna, David would have been awakened many times during the night. If a railway patrol person had referred him to the militia, he could have been be arrested as a homeless individual. As for rooms in the hotels and inns, they were in chronic shortage; to get them, it was necessary to have a reservation or to give a bribe. And even if he had found a vacancy, he would not be allowed to stay without an ID, which he did not have.

The room where Maria Kirillovna brought David was clean and large. It accommodated eight beds for passengers, some of which were already occupied. David's bed was in the corner of the room. A gray blanket and snow-white sheets covered his bed. After the noise and chaos of the main hall of the railway station where David had spent the day, he was finally in the peace and quiet of a civilized human residence. The passengers did not know each other. They silently took off their clothes and went to bed. Gradually, more passengers filled the room.

David woke up in the middle of the night from a deep sleep. On this night, David experienced an unforgettable feeling of real happiness: he thought how lucky he was to sleep in a clean and warm bed instead of, as he had seen himself in his imagination, sitting on the bench in the noisy, busy, and dusty hall of the railway station. Outside the cozy and romantic window, he could hear the sounds of moving trains and hooters. David fell asleep again and woke up early in the morning, when many of the passengers had already gone. He washed up, dressed, and left the bedroom. Maria Kirillovna was still on duty; she sat at her desk talking with a passenger, and when, on his way back to the railway station, David thanked her for her hospitality, she gave him a friendly wave.

After breakfast in a dining hall, David was back to the main hall of the railroad station. Time after time, he stubbornly took his place in another cashier's line, only to hear repeatedly that, as he was not "a transitory passenger," he was not entitled to a ticket on the next train. The familiar railroad agent asked him to leave the line, but David did not give up: in the search for a compassionate cashier, he continued his futile attempts to obtain a hoped-for pass to his home. At the end of the day, when it got dark, David returned to the travelers' lodge and to his joy saw Maria Kirillovna, who gave him a precious maternal smile and allowed him to spend another night in the "earthly paradise."

Early in the morning, after another royal night in his bed with clean linens, David returned to his battlefield, hunting for a precious ticket back home. In the vain hope of finding an exit from the trap he was in, he stubbornly stood in cashiers' lines, each time receiving a resolute refusal of his request. He was patiently waiting his turn in one of the lines when a young man who smelled of alcohol accused him of cutting the line. As David stood his ground and did not move, the accuser approached him and began to drag him out of the queue. In vain, David tried to prove that he was in the line. His accuser, who grabbed him by his jacket, threw David to the floor.

David, who had not let his luggage slip from his hand, stood up and was ready to leave the line when, out of nowhere, a young man in his early twenties appeared . Dressed in the simple clothes of a worker, he was of average height and well built. His oval-shaped face expressed righteous anger at David's accuser.

"Why did you hit this guy?" he asked the attacker in a stern tone, piercing him with his eyes. "What wrong did he do to you?"

David's attacker looked back at him, appreciated his physical qualities, and stepped aside. The defender asked David to take his original place in the line and disappeared into the crowd as fast as he had appeared. David safely waited his turn and, reaching the ticket agent, received the same negative response he had heard many times before. Stepping aside, David took a seat on a bench in anticipation of a new opportunity.

Having nothing else to do, he picked up a newspaper that was lying on the floor and began to read it. When he had finished reading, he went to a trash can to throw the newspaper out. Returning to his seat, he noticed not too far away the young defender who had stood up for him. David approached him and thanked him for his support. In response, his defender smiled and extended his hand, introducing himself as Andrey. In return, David said his name. After three days of loneliness, David was happy to converse with somebody who was friendly to him.

Andrey was from Mogilev-Podolsk, a city in Vinnitskaya Oblast. His family was poor, and two years before, after graduating high school, he had gone to the city of Komsomolsk-on-Amur in the Far East to work as a construction worker. Now, after he had earned enough money there, he was returning home, which happened to be in the same direction as David's destination. Andrey was all attention when David told him his story. It was hard for David to believe how friendly this stranger was to him, but the secret was that his new friend belonged to "the salt of the earth," the rare category of people for whom being kind, supportive, and pleasant was as natural as for somebody else to be violent. To be good and moral is written in the genes of such people.

David shared his predicament with Andrey. He told him that now he was ready to return home by any complicated route and asked Andrey if he knows how to do it. Andrey disagreed, telling David that this might be to too long and expensive and that David should continue his efforts to reach home using the direct connection and avoiding transfers. Then he said words of human kindness that David never forgot. Andrey assured him that he would leave Kharkov only with him.

"Don't worry, " he continued. "I told you I'm coming from the Far East. They gave me a privilege ticket, which allows me to travel as long as necessary. Our destination is in the same direction, so a day or two more doesn't make too much difference to me. I'm not going to leave Kharkov until you have a ticket. Meanwhile, I'll see more of Kharkov, and if worse comes to worst—which I hope won't happen—if they keep refusing you to sell you a ticket, you can take mine, and I'll travel on the roof of the railway car. I have experience at it, and it's warm outside, so don't worry. We'll manage."

While David continued his hunt for a ticket, his precious friend periodically appeared next to him, never forgetting to encourage him.

When the day came to its end, David offered to let Andrey spend night with him at the travelers' lodge. After refusals and hesitation, Andrey, who had spent the night before on benches at the city park, eventually agreed. When both of them appeared before Maria Kirillovna, she looked at them over her glasses, told them that it was probably against the rules of the lodge, and then she waved her hand, smiled, and allowed them both to stay.

In the morning, the new friends left the travelers' lodge and went to the main railroad station hall. David took his place in the line at the ticket counter while Andrey went about his business. Fortunately, a different railroad agent was on duty today, and nobody kicked David out of line. At noon, David went to a buffet, bought a sandwich, and quickly returned to another line, trying his luck again.

"Hey, David, look how many companions you have now." David heard Andrey's familiar voice. He turned his head and saw next to Andrey three teenagers unknown to him, about his age, smiling and looking at him with a carefree air.

Andrey had met his new friends at the station. He never explained to David why these new acquaintances—according to Andrey—had volunteered to help him get home. With new support came success. This time, when David reached the ticket agent and heard from her that he was not a transitory passenger, David told her that he was ready to buy any ticket she might offer him. Not persuaded, the cashier hesitated. Using the short pause, David told her that he was a teenager without parents who had already spent four days at the station. The cashier looked attentively at David and decided to comply with his request, though it was against the rules.

"OK, boy, I can sell you a ticket in the luxury [soft] railroad car," she said. "But I'm sure you don't have enough money to pay for it."

Money is a very useful thing, especially when it can buy freedom.

"Oh yes," yelled David. "I do have enough money to buy it! My parents gave it to me."

As quickly as he could—before the cashier changed her mind—he opened his luggage, pulled the money out of its secret compartment, and handed it to the cashier.

David returned from the ticket office as excited and happy as if he had just received a pass to heaven. He held the precious ticket high above his head while his "bodyguards" all looked at him, grinning widely.

The train was departing in an hour, and Andrey left to register his ticket. When he got back, the new friend gang was on the platform waiting for the train. David and Andrey were traveling in different cars on the same train. After several hours of travel, they changed trains in the famous hub railway station in Zhmerynka. There they would part. As for the rest of the new company, these teenagers lived in a small town two hours from Kharkov and traveled for free on the roofs of the railway car. Traveling "stowaway class" and visiting Kharkov or other cities close to them was their regular entertainment. Traveling in a group had an advantage for them: this way, they could climb on each other's backs to reach the roof. When one of them was on the roof, he could pull his friends up.

When the train arrived, each member of the group took his assigned or not assigned place, but before parting, the boys agreed that during the trip, they would meet in David's car. When David found his place in the luxury car, the compartment was not yet occupied. David had never traveled in a luxury railway car and admired the comfort and good looks of the place. Soon two young women in their early twenties entered in his compartment . Beautiful and nicely dressed, these passengers from the upper social class ignored David's presence, except when they spoke about him in the third person.

An hour into the trip, there was a knock at the mirrored door. David opened the door and to his satisfaction saw all his gang. All his friends were in excellent spirits. In the compartment, the group exchanged their impression of the trip. David's female companions could not hide their resentment of the guests.

After an hour of brisk conversation, Andrey and David said farewell to the stowaway team, who were approaching their own town. Andrey also left David in his car after they agreed to meet at the Zhmerynka station.

The train came to the hub station on time at noon, and soon David met Andrey. As both of them had approximately three hours before their connecting trains, Andrey offered to buy David food from an outdoor food stall.

"Forget it, Andrey," David said. "I still have some money left; they have a famous restaurant at this station. I was there once when I traveled with my parents. I'm sure you'll like it."

Andrey reluctantly agreed, and soon they were in the restaurant. Before they took their seats, David, as a "seasoned man," showed Andrey all the outstanding features of the hall, especially the beautiful ceiling. Andrey was impressed, but it was obvious that he was not at ease. When the server came, Andrey asked David to order the same thing for him that he ordered for himself. Satisfying their young healthy appetites, both friends concluded that the food was delicious. They left the restaurant, found a convenient bench, and had a short chat.

"Excuse me, David, for not saying much when we were in the restaurant," Andrey said. He was visibly embarrassed. "I behaved like a jerk because I was visiting a restaurant for the first time in my life."

David once again understood that between himself and Andrey there was a social abyss. They lived in the same country, spoke the same language, went to similar schools, but their life experiences were utterly different. Nevertheless, Andrey's innate feeling of compassion and understanding kept them close.

There was still time left before the trains' departure, and the friends decided to visit an electronic merchandise store not far from the station square. The store was of medium size and all the goods—as was the rule at that time—were displayed on the shelves behind the counter. With Andrey next to him, David asked one of the sellers to show him one of the transistor radios. David and Andrey admired the electronic products as yet unknown to their generation—the harbinger of the electronic era of immediate news and uninterrupted and unlimited music. Having admired enough merchandise they couldn't afford, David left the radio on the counter and suggested to Andrey that they leave the store. Then he realized once again how different his life experience was from Andrey, who was a simple worker from a social level lower than his.

"Are you crazy, David?" his friend asked agitated. "I see you don't know real life. Never, ever leave merchandise on the counter and leave the store. Bring the transistor to the seller and hand it to him. Otherwise, they could accuse you of trying to steal it from the store."

There was nothing for David to do but to take the transistor radio and hand it to the service staff.

After an hour, it was time for the friends to part forever. They exchanged addresses and promised to write to each other.

Andrey's train departed later than David's. The friends waved to each other—David on the platform of the station and Andrey at the door of the railroad car—until the train separated them.

After more than a week of absence from home, David received a hearty welcome from his parents. They asked David about his trip, and he briefly explained to them what had happened. Not to worry them unnecessary—they had enough troubles—he never let them know all the unpleasant things that had happened to him. David had hardly ever complained since his childhood; it was not only because of the way he was, but also because he grew up in a culture where children complained to their parents only on special occasions. He told his parents that nothing good might come out of his trip to Kharkov: the woman who was allegedly supposed to help him get into the dental school was nothing but a fraud.

His parents told David he should forget about an opportunity in Kharkov.

"Don't worry, David," Ilana continued. "While you were gone, we found another, much more promising opportunity. This time a much more reliable person will help us. His name is Gersh Iosifovich Axelrod. He's a former winemaker. He knows people who'll help you become a student at Kishinev Medical School. So guess what? You're going to be a doctor."

That is how David learned for first time that his destiny was to take care of people's health.

David exchanged couple of letters with Andrey. He never again met his guardian angel, a simple young man who not only supported him in a difficult time but, more importantly, taught him that there are people in this world for whom being compassionate is the same as it is for the sun to send its revitalizing rays of light to the planet of human beings.

CPSIA information can be obtained
at www.ICGtesting.com
Printed in the USA
LVHW050851281121
704654LV00008B/631

9 781641 112895